# A2
LEVEL

# PHYSICS
## FOR CCEA A2 LEVEL

## 2nd EDITION

COLOURPOINT
EDUCATIONAL

**Pat Carson and Roy White**

ISBN: 978-1-78073-098-1

Second Edition
First Impression

Layout and design: April Sky Design, Newtownards
Printed by: GPS Colour Graphics Ltd, Belfast

## The Authors

**Roy White** taught Physics to A level for over 30 years in Belfast. He works for an examining body as Chair of Examiners for Double Award Science, Principal Examiner for GCSE Physics and Principal Examiner for A level Life and Health Sciences. In addition to this text, he has been the author or co-author of three successful books supporting the work of science teachers in Northern Ireland.

**Pat Carson** has been teaching Physics to A level for over 30 years in Belfast and Londonderry. He works for an examining body as Chief Examiner for GCSE Physics. In addition to this text, he has been co-author on a number of books supporting the work of Physics teachers at AS and A2 level.

**Colourpoint Educational**
*An imprint of Colourpoint Creative Ltd*
Colourpoint House
Jubilee Business Park
21 Jubilee Road
Newtownards
County Down
Northern Ireland
BT23 4YH

Tel:  028 9182 6339
Fax: 028 9182 1900
E-mail: sales@colourpoint.co.uk
Web site: www.colourpoint.co.uk

This book has been written to help students preparing for the A2 Level Physics specification from CCEA. While Colourpoint Educational and the authors have taken every care in its production, we are not able to guarantee that the book is completely error-free. Additionally, while the book has been written to closely match the CCEA specification, it the responsibility of each candidate to satisfy themselves that they have fully met the requirements of the CCEA specification prior to sitting an exam set by that body. For this reason, and because specifications change with time, we strongly advise every candidate to avail of a qualified teacher and to check the contents of the most recent specification for themselves prior to the exam. Colourpoint Educational therefore cannot be held responsible for any errors or omissions in this book or any consequences thereof.

Every effort has been made to ensure that practical work suggested in this book can be safely carried out in a school or college laboratory. However, it is the responsibility of teachers and lecturers to carry out an appropriate risk assessment when planning any practical activity. Where it is appropriate, they should consider reference to CLEAPPS guidance.

# CONTENTS

# Unit 4 (A2 1)

**Deformation of Solids, Thermal Physics, Circular Motion, Oscillations and Atomic and Nuclear Physics**

# 4.1 Deformation of Solids

**Students should be able to:**

4.1.1    State Hooke's law and use $F = kx$ to solve simple problems;

4.1.2    Demonstrate an understanding of the terms elastic and plastic deformation and elastic limit;

4.1.3    Distinguish between limit of proportionality and elastic limit;

4.1.4    Define stress, strain and the Young modulus;

4.1.5    Perform and describe an experiment to determine the Young modulus;

4.1.6    Use the equation for strain energy, $E = \frac{1}{2}Fx = \frac{1}{2}kx^2$;

4.1.7    Demonstrate an understanding of the importance of the stress, strain and the Young modulus of a material when making design and economic decisions about materials use;

## Hooke's Law

You will be familiar with Hooke's Law from your studies at GCSE. **At GCSE the 'elastic limit' and the 'limit of proportionality' were treated as meaning the same thing. In fact, this is not so and at A2 level we must make the distinction clear.** Hooke's Law, for any elastic material, states that:

**Up to a maximum load, known as the limit of proportionality, the extension of an elastic material is proportional to the applied load.**

For many materials, the limit of proportionality and the elastic limit are the same. This is why the form of Hooke's Law you may have learned for GCSE was accepted even if was in terms of elastic limit (which is wrong) rather than the limit of proportionality (which is correct).

Hooke's Law may be written as an equation:

$F = kx$     where  $F$ = applied load in N
$k$ = the Hooke's Law constant (N m$^{-1}$ or N cm$^{-1}$ or N mm$^{-1}$)
    Sometimes called the spring constant.
$x$ = the extension of the specimen under test (m, or cm or mm)

The graph opposite illustrates how the load and extension are related for a typical metal wire. From (0,0) up to the **limit of proportionality** the line is straight. This is the region where the wire obeys Hooke's Law. Beyond the limit of proportionality, the line curves: there is no longer direct proportion between load and extension.

A point is then reached where any further load will cause the wire to become permanently stretched. This is the **elastic limit**.

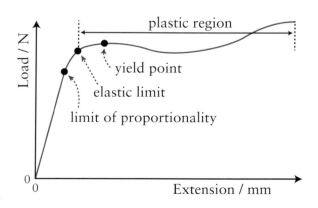

The elastic limit is therefore the maximum load a specimen can experience and still return to its original length when the deforming force is removed. Up to the elastic limit the material is undergoing **elastic deformation**. Beyond the elastic limit the wire reaches a 'yield point'. From this point onwards, the internal molecular structure is being permanently changed as crystal planes slide across each other. **A wire stretched beyond its elastic limit is said to be 'plastic', ie it is undergoing plastic deformation.** The shape of the material is being permanently changed and will not return to its original shape even when the force is removed. It may stretch enormously before it finally breaks.

## Stress, Strain and Young modulus

The definition of stress, strain and Young modulus are given below. All of them can be expressed as equations.

**Note:** You need to memorise these definitions and equations.

**Stress** ($\sigma$) is defined as the applied force per unit area of cross section.

$$\sigma = \frac{F}{A}$$

where: $\sigma$ = the stress (N m$^{-2}$ or Pa)
$F$ = the applied force (N)
$A$ = the cross section area (m$^2$)

**Strain** ($\varepsilon$) is defined as the ratio of the change in the length of a specimen to its original length.

$$\varepsilon = \frac{\Delta L}{L_o}$$

where: $\varepsilon$ = the strain (no units)
$\Delta L$ = the change in the length (m)
$L_o$ = the original length in (m)

Generally the application of a tensile stress to a material produces a corresponding strain. Provided the stress is not too large, the strain is directly proportional to the stress. Within the limit of proportionality, the ratio of stress to strain is defined as the **Young modulus** (E):

$$E = \frac{\sigma}{\varepsilon}$$

where: $E$ = the Young modulus (N m$^{-2}$ or Pa)
$\sigma$ = the stress (N m$^{-2}$ or Pa)
$\varepsilon$ = the strain (no units)

During your A2 course you should get the experience of determining the Young modulus of the material of a metal wire. This is a prescribed experiment which you may be required to describe in the examination.

## Measuring the Young modulus of a metal

The method below uses two long wires suspended from a common support in the ceiling. One wire is called the reference wire because the extension of the wire under test is measured with respect to it.

Both the reference wire and the wire under test should be made of the same material, have the same cross-section area and be approximately the same length. This ensures that errors arising from thermal expansion as a result of temperature changes in the wires are minimised. The wires should be as long as possible (at least 2 m) so as to obtain the greatest possible extension of the test wire. Even so, a Vernier gauge is necessary to measure the small extension with respect to the reference wire.

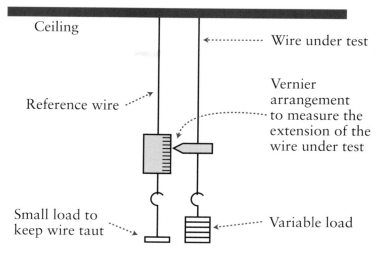

At the outset the **length, L, of the test wire is measured** in mm using a metre stick. The measurement should be taken from the point of suspension to the Vernier scale.

**Using a micrometer screw gauge, the diameter, d, of the test wire is measured at about six places spread out along its length.** It is necessary to measure the diameter in this way to avoid the possibility of small kinks in the wire giving rise to erroneous results. The cross section area, A, can then be found from the equation $A = \pi <d>^2 \div 4$ where $<d>$ is the average diameter of the wire from the measurements made.

The reference wire is loaded with about 5 N to keep it taught. The test wire is loaded in steps of 10 N from 10 N to about 100 N. For each load on the extension wire, the extension is found from the Vernier and the stress, $\sigma$, ($\sigma = F \div A$) and strain, $\varepsilon$, ($\varepsilon = \Delta L \div L_o$) calculated and recorded in a suitable table. Typical results are shown below.

| Typical Results for Young modulus experiment on a metal | | | |
|---|---|---|---|
| Length of test wire in metres: | 2.055 | | |
| Diameter of test wire in mm: | 1.38, 1.38, 1.37, 1.39, 1.38, 1.38 | | |
| Average diameter of test wire in mm: | 1.38 | | |
| Area of cross section in m²: | $1.496 \times 10^{-6}$ | | |

| Force / N | Extension / mm | Stress / MPa | Strain ($\times 10^{-4}$) no units |
|---|---|---|---|
| 10 | 0.07 | 6.68 | 0.341 |
| 20 | 0.14 | 13.37 | 0.681 |
| 30 | 0.21 | 20.05 | 1.022 |
| 40 | 0.27 | 26.74 | 1.314 |
| 50 | 0.34 | 33.42 | 1.655 |
| 60 | 0.41 | 40.11 | 1.995 |
| 70 | 0.48 | 46.79 | 2.336 |
| 80 | 0.55 | 53.48 | 2.676 |
| 90 | 0.62 | 60.16 | 3.017 |
| 100 | 0.69 | 66.84 | 3.358 |

It is left as an exercise for the reader to plot a graph of stress (y-axis) against strain (x-axis) and draw the straight line of best fit. The gradient of this **straight line** gives the Young modulus. For the results above, your graph should give you a value for the Young modulus of:

$$E = \frac{\sigma}{\varepsilon} = 60 \times 10^6 \div 3 \times 10^{-4} = 2 \times 10^{11} \text{ Pa.}$$

If we continue to measure stress and strain for increasing loads on a wire, we would eventually be able to plot a graph like the one shown.

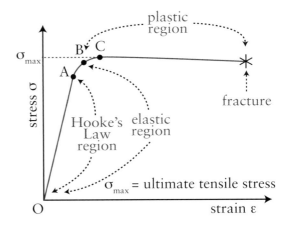

The gradient of the straight line region (OA) is the Young modulus. Point A represents the limit of proportionality beyond which the wire will not obey Hooke's Law. Point B represents the elastic limit beyond which the wire is plastic and will not return to its original length when the stretching force is removed. Point C marks the position of **ultimate tensile stress**.

The ultimate tensile stress (UTS) is defined as the maximum stress which can be applied to a wire without it breaking.

## Strain energy

The upper graph on the right shows how the extension of a material varies as the stretching force is increased. Up to the limit of proportionality the extension $x$ is proportional to the stretching force $F$.

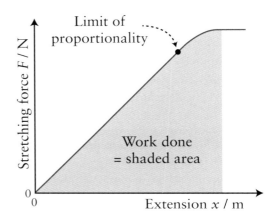

All the work done in stretching the material is stored as potential energy, sometimes known as **elastic strain energy**, $E$ (not to be confused with Young Modulus, usually also denoted by the letter $E$). This strain energy equals the work done in stretching the material.

The force varies with the extension, as shown in the graph, and the work done can be determined by calculating the area between the line of the graph and the extension axis.

If the stretching of the material obeys Hooke's Law, and it is not stretched beyond the limit of proportionality, the strain energy can also be calculated as the area under the straight-line graph as shown in the lower graph on the right.

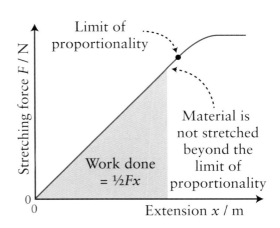

This is the area of a triangle
= ½(base × perpendicular height) = $\frac{1}{2}Fx$

Therefore the strain energy $E = \frac{1}{2}Fx$

Since Hooke's law is obeyed, $F = kx$ (where $k$ is the Hooke's Law constant measured in N m$^{-1}$):

**Strain energy, $E = \frac{1}{2}kx \times x = \frac{1}{2}kx^2$**

## Choice of materials

Many factors affect the choice of a material to be used for a particular purpose. These factors include:

- **Stiffness,** which is a measure of how much something stretches when a load is applied, and is represented by the Young modulus. It is a constant of the material and is not affected by the shape or size of an object. Many real-world applications require a stiff material, such as a metal. Examples include car subframes and railway tracks.

- **Lightness,** which is a measure of the density of the material. Some applications require light materials, eg packaging foams.

- **Cost,** another important factor when choosing a material for a particular application. For example, concrete is both cheap and stiff and is ideal for structures such as buildings, while cast iron is ideal for the base of a machine tool bed since it also provides high stiffness at low cost.

Selecting the best material for a particular purpose can be a difficult task and in most cases the use of appropriate computer software is an important part of the decision process. A useful graphical tool is to display two properties of many materials on a scattergram. These scattergrams can be used to compare the ratio of, for example, strength/cost or stiffness/lightness.

In the left scattergram below, stiffness is displayed against density and in the right diagram stiffness is displayed against cost. Note that the axes are not linear but use a **logarithmic** scale, increasing by factors of ten.

Some applications require materials that are **both** stiff and lightweight, for example rowing oars. Materials with both these properties are not very common but composites offer a good compromise. Their main disadvantage is that they can be quite expensive. Wood is often used for basic rowing oars since it provides

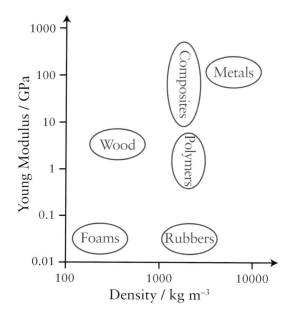
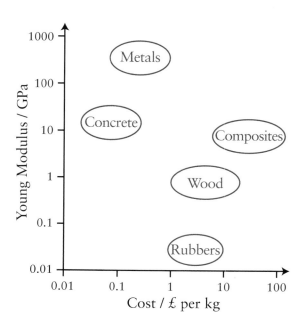

stiffness with a relatively low weight. Composite oars are both stronger and lighter than wood, but they are only used by professional rowing teams because they are much more expensive.

Aluminium frames are used for many applications where a combination of low weight, low cost and high strength is required, for example crutches and zimmer frames, or hang gliders. The covering of a hang glider is usually made from nylon or a similar strong, lightweight material.

## Exercise 4.1

1   Two identical springs are joined in series. One has a spring constant of 12 N cm$^{-1}$ and the other has a spring constant of 18 N cm$^{-1}$. One free end is connected to a fixed point and from the other a weight of 36 N is applied. Calculate

    (a) the extension in the combination caused by the 36 N load and

    (b) the spring (Hooke's Law) constant of the combination.

    (c) State the tension in each spring.

    (d) Show that if two springs having Hooke's Law constants, $k_1$ and $k_2$ are joined end-to-end, then their combined spring constant is $\dfrac{k_1.k_2}{(k_1 + k_2)}$.

2   Two springs are joined together in parallel with each other as shown in the diagram. One spring has a spring constant of 15 N cm$^{-1}$ and the other 25 N cm$^{-1}$. The lengths of the springs are such that a metal bar weighing 100 N suspended as shown rests horizontally. Calculate the tension and extension of each spring.

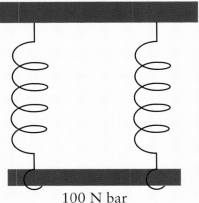

100 N bar

Show that if two springs having Hooke's Law constants $k_1$ and $k_2$ are joined in parallel, then their combined spring constant is: $k_1 + k_2$.

3   A nylon guitar string is in tune when it is under 32.0 N tension. The length of the string from the fixed point to the tension key is 850 mm. On average, each turn of the tension key increases the length of the string by 40.0 mm and the key must be turned exactly ten times to bring the string into tune. Assuming the string obeys Hooke's Law when in tune, calculate

    (a) the Hooke's Law constant and

    (b) the total length of the stretched string.

4   A metal cube of side 200 mm is held in a vice. Each turn of the handle of the vice moves the jaws 0.500 mm closer together. The vice is tightened up by a quarter turn. A strain gauge attached to the metal shows the compressive force to be 600 kN. Assuming the metal obeys Hooke's Law at this compression, calculate the reduction in the length of the metal and its spring constant.

5   When carrying out an experiment to see if a steel wire obeyed Hooke's Law, a teacher insisted on (a) all students wearing safety spectacles and (b) measurements of length being taken both when the wire was being loaded and unloaded. Why were these requirements of the teacher good experimental practice?

6  A lift and its occupants have a combined mass of 2500 kg. The lift is supported by a steel safety cable which the manufacturers say is safe up to a maximum stress of 100 MPa. The lift manufacturers require the lift to be able to accelerate up and down the lift shaft at a maximum rate of 0.500 m s$^{-2}$. Calculate:

(a) the minimum cross section area and

(b) the diameter of the safety cable.

7  In the showroom of an Irish crystal manufacturer, a chandelier of mass 11.0 kg hangs from the ceiling, supported only by a solid aluminium rod of diameter 2 mm and length 2 m.

What is the (a) stress (b) strain and (c) extension of the aluminium rod if the Young modulus for aluminium is 70 GPa?

8  A copper wire of length 900 mm and cross section area 0.9 mm$^2$ is welded to an iron wire of length 1400 mm and cross section area 1.3 mm$^2$. The compound wire is stretched so that its length increases by 10.0 mm. The Young modulus for copper is 130 GPa and that for iron is 210 GPa.

(a) Write down the length and cross section area of each wire in m and m$^2$ respectively.

(b) Show that the extension of each wire is given by the formula: $\Delta L = (FL_o) \div (AE)$ where the symbols have their usual meanings.

(c) Given that the force in each wire is the same, calculate (i) the ratio of the extensions of the wires, using the formula given in part (b), (ii) the extension of each wire and (iii) the tension in each wire.

9  A nylon rope of length 10.0 m and diameter 10.0 mm is used by a tow truck to tow a car which has broken down. The rope obeys Hooke's Law while being used for this purpose. The Young modulus for nylon is 3.00 GPa. While towing at a constant speed on level ground the extension of the tow rope is 25.0 mm Calculate:

(a) the strain in the tow rope,

(b) the stress in the tow rope,

(c) the tension in the tow rope,

(d) the sum of the forces which oppose the motion of the car.

(e) In what way, if at all, would the tension and the extension of the tow rope change if it has a larger cross section area? Assume the other factors remain as before.

The ultimate tensile stress of the rope is 21.8 MPa and the combined mass of the car and its driver is 750 kg.

(f) Calculate the acceleration of the car which is just enough to break the rope, assuming that the friction forces are unchanged.

# 4.2 Thermal Physics

4.2.1    Describe simple experiments on the behaviour of gases to show that $pV = constant$ for a fixed mass of gas at constant temperature, $\frac{p}{T} = constant$ for a fixed mass of gas at constant volume, and $\frac{V}{T} = constant$ for a fixed mass of gas at constant pressure, leading to the equation $\frac{pV}{T} = constant$;

4.2.2    Recall and use the ideal gas equation $pV = nRT$;

4.2.3    Recall and use the ideal gas equation in the form $pV = NkT$;

4.2.4    Demonstrate an understanding of the concept of internal energy as the random distribution of potential and kinetic energy among molecules;

4.2.5    Use the equation $pV = \frac{1}{3}Nm<c^2>$;

4.2.6    Use the equation for average molecular kinetic energy, $\frac{1}{2}m<c^2> = \frac{3}{2}kT$;

4.2.7    Demonstrate an understanding of the concept of absolute zero of temperature;

4.2.8    Perform and describe an electrical method for determining specific heat capacity;

4.2.9    Use the equation $Q = mc\Delta\theta$

## The behaviour of gases

Volume, pressure and temperature are the **macroscopic** (large-scale) properties of a gas that you can observe in the laboratory. These three properties are inter-related – if you change one, at least one of the others changes. They also depend on the amount of gas present, so if you want to find out the connections between the macroscopic properties of a gas, you need to carry out experiments with a **fixed** amount of gas.

In addition, changing one of these properties can affect **both** of the others. For example, a sealed balloon contains a fixed amount of gas. If we place it in warm water, the temperature rises. However, the volume and pressure also change.

When investigating the behaviour of a gas, we seek to investigate how any two properties depend on each other. Therefore, as well as keeping the amount of gas constant, we also need to keep one of the other properties constant (either the volume, pressure or temperature) and investigate the relationship between the remaining two properties. In the next three experiments we will examine each pair of properties by keeping the third property constant.

## Volume and pressure – leading to Boyle's Law

In this experiment we are investigating the relationship between volume and pressure by keeping the temperature constant.

In the diagram opposite, the oil in the closed tube traps a **fixed mass** of air above it. If the column of air has a constant cross-section, **its length is proportional to**

**its volume**. This experiment involves measuring the length of this column and recording the corresponding pressure on the Bourdon gauge. The oil used must have a low vapour pressure, otherwise we are compressing an oil vapour and air mixture, whose oil content will change with pressure. This in turn would cause the mass of the material being compressed to change.

Using the hand pump (some types of apparatus incorporate a foot pump) we very slowly increase the pressure acting on the trapped air. Compressing the gas warms it slightly, so after every compression we need to wait a few moments for the temperature of the trapped air to return to room temperature. Then we record the new volume and pressure readings in a table.

We can repeat this for several more values of pressure and then plot a graph of pressure against volume. The graph is called an **isothermal**, because it shows how pressure changes with volume at constant temperature ("iso" means "the same" and "thermal" means "temperature"). An example of a plot from a real experiment is shown on the right.

If you join the points together you will see that a graph of pressure against volume is a hyperbolic curve showing that volume decreases as pressure increases, as shown on the line graph on the right. This tells us that there is some kind of inverse relationship between pressure and volume.

To determine the nature of this relationship, we plot a graph of volume against 1/pressure as shown on the lower right. This graph is a straight line through the origin, confirming that volume is directly proportional to the inverse of the pressure. More succinctly, the volume is inversely proportional to the pressure.

This is formally expressed as **Boyle's Law** which states:

**For a fixed mass of gas at constant temperature, the volume (V) is inversely proportional to the applied pressure (p).**

**Boyle's Law** can be expressed as an equation:

**pressure × volume = constant**

or

$pV$ **= a constant**  where  $p$ = gas pressure (Pa)
$V$ = gas volume (m³)

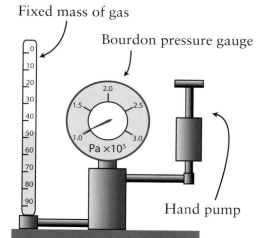

Fixed mass of gas

Bourdon pressure gauge

Pa ×10⁵

Hand pump

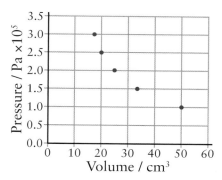

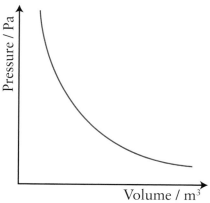

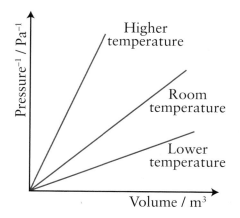

Higher temperature

Room temperature

Lower temperature

Boyle's Law can be demonstrated graphically in a number of different ways. We have already seen how the graph of pressure against volume is a hyperbolic curve as shown above. If we plot a graph of the product $pV$ against $V$ (or $P$) we will find that it is a horizontal straight line as shown on the right. The reader is encouraged to attempt question 3 in Exercise 4.2A to demonstrate these graphical relationships.

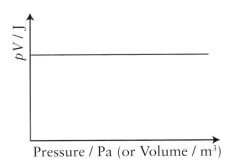

### About Robert Byole

Robert Boyle (1627-1691) was born in Lismore Castle, Ireland, the seventh son of the Earl of Cork. He could speak French and Latin fluently as a child and was sent to Eton at the age of eight. He spent his early life at Gresham College in London where he joined a group called *The Invisible Society*, which had the purpose of promoting scientific study and thinking. Later it was to become *The Royal Society* and Boyle was elected as its President in 1680. However, Boyle spent much of his life in Oxford carrying out scientific research, some of it with an assistant called Robert Hooke (of Hooke's Law fame). He published a book with the (abbreviated) title *The Spring of Air* and gave us the modern meaning of the word "elastic". Boyle's studies took him into many different fields. He was interested in bioluminescence, hydrometers, electricity, colour, combustion and theology (he learned Greek, Hebrew and Syriac).

Boyle is called **The Father of Chemistry**, because he was the main agent responsible for changing its outlook from alchemy (which was primarily interested in being able to change base metals like lead into precious metals like gold) to modern chemistry.

## Volume and temperature – leading to Charles' Law

This traditional experiment involves investigating how the volume of a fixed mass of air at constant pressure varies as the temperature changes.

In the usual apparatus, the air is held inside a glass capillary tube by a short length of concentrated sulphuric acid (the concentrated acid traps and **dries** the air to give better results). The length $y$ of the trapped air is a measure of the volume of the air **because the area of cross section of the capillary tube is constant.**

The glass tube is attached to a ruler with rubber bands. The position of the tube is adjusted until the bottom of the trapped air is opposite the zero mark of the ruler.

The experiment is carried out at constant

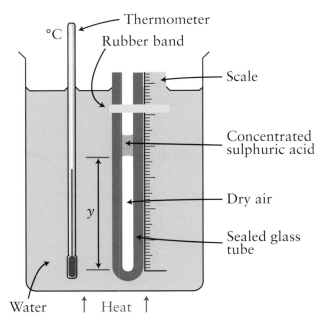

pressure: the pressure being exerted on the gas is that of atmospheric pressure and the thread of concentrated sulphuric acid.

The apparatus is then placed in a tall beaker of cold water with a thermometer. Throughout the experiment the water is stirred regularly so that the trapped air is at the same temperature as the water. The volume of the trapped air and the temperature are then recorded in a results table.

The water is then heated until it is about 10°C hotter and another pair of readings of volume and temperature recorded. This process is repeated, increasing the temperature of the water until it boils. A graph is then plotted of volume (on the $y$-axis) against temperature in degrees Celsius ($x$-axis).

Below is a typical set of results from such an experiment (the meaning of the third row, temperature in Kelvin, will be explained below). Note that, although air is used in school laboratory experiments, other gases give similar results.

| Length of trapped air thread / mm | 65 | 67 | 69 | 72 | 74 | 76 | 78 | 81 | 83 |
|---|---|---|---|---|---|---|---|---|---|
| Temperature / °C | 20 | 30 | 40 | 50 | 60 | 70 | 80 | 90 | 100 |
| Temperature in Kelvin / K | 293 | 303 | 313 | 323 | 333 | 343 | 353 | 363 | 373 |

The reader is encouraged to use the above data to plot (a) a graph of length of air thread in mm (proportional to volume) against temperature in degrees Celsius and (b) a graph of length of air thread in mm against temperature in Kelvin.

A sketch of a graph, typical of the type obtained in this experiment, is shown on the right. The graph of volume against the **Celsius** temperature is a straight line of positive slope. This shows that **the volume of a fixed mass of gas at constant pressure increases uniformly with temperature.** However as the graph does not pass through the origin, it does not illustrate proportionality.

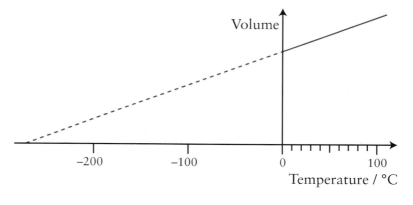

However, if the graph is extended backwards we find that it touches the horizontal axis at –273°C. Suppose now we define a new scale of temperature, the **Kelvin** scale, $T$, by the equation:

$T = \theta + 273$ 　　　where 　　$T$ = the temperature (Kelvin)
　　　　　　　　　　　　　　　　$\theta$ = the temperature (°C)

The Kelvin scale begins at zero Kelvin (0 K) and increases just like the Celsius scale. This means that **0°C is equal to 273 Kelvin (273 K)** and **100°C is equal to 373 K** and so on. In science, we often measure temperature on the Kelvin scale.

The third row in the table above shows the temperature in Kelvin. A graph of temperature against volume is a straight line **through the origin** when the temperature is measured on the Kelvin scale. This is shown in the graph on the right. The dotted vertical line shows the previous axis when temperature was measured on the Celsius scale.

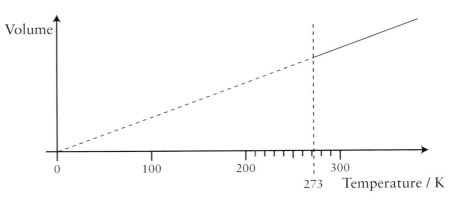

Now that the graph is a straight line passing through the origin, it does demonstrate proportionality. It tells us that:

**For a fixed mass of gas at constant pressure the volume (V) is directly proportional to the Kelvin (or absolute) temperature (T).**

This is called **Charles' Law.** Charles' Law can be expressed as an equation:

**volume = temperature** (in K) × **constant**

or

$\dfrac{V}{T}$ **= a constant**        where        $V$ = gas volume (m³)
$T$ = gas temperature (K)

### Absolute zero of temperature

The graph suggests that 0 K is the temperature at which the gas volume **would become zero.** But in fact this is not so. Every gas would liquefy before reaching this temperature. However the graph also suggests that **there is a limit to how cold objects can be.** This temperature, 0 K, is called the **absolute zero** of temperature. Absolute zero is the temperature at which all molecular motion stops and is approximately –273.16°C, although for purposes of calculations, it is sufficient to use –273°C. The temperature has never been reached because even the methods of measuring such temperatures change the temperature of the system. However, physicists are confident that they have come within about one millionth of a degree of absolute zero.

## Pressure and temperature – leading to the Pressure Law

This traditional experiment involves investigating how the pressure of a fixed mass of air at constant volume varies as the temperature changes.

The apparatus is set up as shown in the diagram opposite. A large glass flask is placed in a tall beaker of cold water with a thermometer. The pressure of the air in the flask is measured using a Bourdon pressure gauge. Throughout the experiment the water is stirred regularly to ensure that the trapped air is the same temperature as the water. The initial temperature and pressure of the trapped air are then recorded in a results table.

The water is then heated until it is about 10°C hotter and another pair of readings of pressure and temperature is recorded. This process is repeated, increasing the temperature of the water until it boils. A graph is then plotted of pressure (y-axis) against temperature in degrees Celsius (x-axis).

The table below shows a typical set of results from such an experiment.

The reader is encouraged to use the below data to plot (a) a graph of pressure against temperature in degrees Celsius and (b) a graph of pressure against temperature in Kelvin.

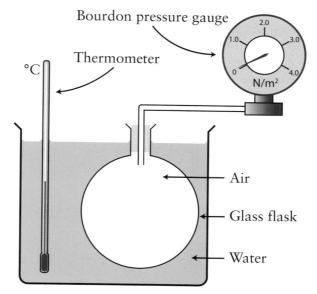

| Pressure / MPa | 2.00 | 2.07 | 2.14 | 2.20 | 2.27 | 2.34 | 2.41 | 2.48 | 2.55 |
|---|---|---|---|---|---|---|---|---|---|
| Temperature / °C | 20 | 30 | 40 | 50 | 60 | 70 | 80 | 90 | 100 |
| Temperature in Kelvin / K | 293 | 303 | 313 | 323 | 333 | 343 | 353 | 363 | 373 |

On the right is a *sketch* of the graph of pressure against temperature in Kelvin. Since it is a straight line through the (0,0) origin, it shows direct proportion.

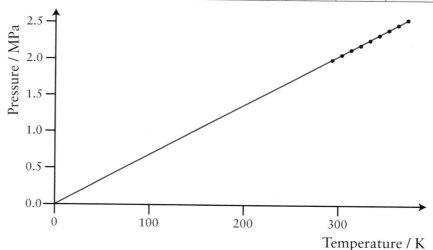

This tells us that:

**For a fixed mass of gas, at constant volume, the pressure ($p$) is directly proportional to the Kelvin (or absolute) temperature ($T$).**

This is known as the **Pressure Law**. It can be expressed as an equation:

**pressure = constant × temperature (in K)**

or

$\dfrac{p}{T}$ **= a constant**   where   $p$ = gas pressure (Pa)
$T$ = gas temperature (K)

Note that, because of the Pressure Law, this apparatus can also be used as a thermometer, called a **constant volume gas thermometer**. The dial of the pressure gauge can be marked out in °C.

## The ideal gas equation

From these three experiments, we have the equations:

$pV$ = a constant     (Boyle's Law, for a fixed mass of gas at constant temperature)

$\dfrac{V}{T}$ = a constant     (Charles' Law, for a fixed mass of gas at constant pressure)

$\dfrac{p}{T}$ = a constant     (Pressure Law, for a fixed mass of gas at constant volume)

These three equations can be combined into one, called the **ideal gas equation**:

$\dfrac{pV}{T}$ = a constant

Because the value of $\dfrac{pV}{T}$ remains constant, if a fixed mass of gas has values $p_1$, $V_1$ and $T_1$, and then some time later has values $p_2$, $V_2$ and $T_2$, then the equation becomes:

$$\dfrac{p_1 V_1}{T_1} = \dfrac{p_2 V_2}{T_2}$$

## The Mole

The experimental gas laws show that for a fixed mass of gas, $\dfrac{pV}{T}$ = a constant.

It turns out that the constant depends **only** on the **number of molecules** in the sample of gas being considered. But the number of molecules present in a given sample of gas is enormous, so a much more convenient way to express this idea is to talk in terms of the number of **moles** of gas in the sample.

You will recall that **amount of substance** is measured in moles and that the mole (abbreviated to **mol**) is one of the six SI base units introduced in your AS course. But what exactly is a mole? In 1960 physicists and chemists agreed to assign the value 12, **exactly**, to the relative atomic mass of the isotope of carbon with mass number 12 (carbon 12, $^{12}C$). The unit of 'amount of substance' is fixed in terms of the number of atoms in exactly 0.012 kg of carbon 12. This number of atoms is called Avogadro's Number ($N_A$).

**The mole is the amount of substance which contains as many particles as there are atoms in 0.012 kilogram of carbon 12.**

So, a mole of gas molecules is simply Avogadro's number of those molecules; a mole of electrons is Avogadro's number of electrons and so on. **Avogadro's number is the number of particles per mole.** Its numerical value is $6.02 \times 10^{23}$ mol$^{-1}$.

## Worked Examples

1 A sample of hydrogen gas, $H_2$, has a mass of 12 g (0.012 kg). If the relative atomic mass of hydrogen is 1, calculate (a) the number of moles in the sample of gas and (b) the number of hydrogen molecules in the sample.

Solution

(a) Hydrogen has 2 atoms in its molecule. If the relative atomic mass of hydrogen is 1, then 1 mole of hydrogen molecules has a mass of 2 g. So 12 g of hydrogen contains $12 \div 2 = 6$ moles.

(b) 6 moles of hydrogen molecules contain $6 \times N_A$ molecules, or $6 \times 6.02 \times 10^{23} = 3.612 \times 10^{24}$ molecules

2 A nitrogen gas sample contains $2.107 \times 10^{24}$ molecules and has a mass of 0.098 kg. Find (a) the number of moles of nitrogen and (b) the relative molecular mass of nitrogen.

Solution

(a) Number of moles $= \dfrac{\text{number of particles}}{\text{Avogadro's number}} = \dfrac{2.107 \times 10^{24}}{6.02 \times 10^{23}} = 3.5$ mol

(b) Relative molecular mass = mass of 1 mole in grams

$= \dfrac{\text{mass of gas sample in grams}}{\text{number of moles}} = \dfrac{(0.098 \times 1000)}{3.5} = \dfrac{98}{3.5} = 28$ grams $mol^{-1}$

## Kinetic theory and ideal gases

The **kinetic theory** attempts to explain the macroscopic behaviour of a gas by examining its microscopic properties, ie the behaviour of the molecules. In particular, the theory states that it is the collisions of the molecules with the walls of the container that produce an outward force or **pressure**.

To apply the kinetic theory we have to make some **assumptions**. These assumptions define the characteristics of what physicists call **an ideal gas** and are as follows:

- There are no intermolecular forces – the only time the molecules exert a force on each other is when they collide.
- The molecules themselves have a volume which is negligible compared to the volume of the gas.
- The collisions between molecules and between molecules and the walls of the container are elastic, so both kinetic energy and momentum are conserved.
- The duration of a collision is negligible compared with the time between collisions.
- Between collisions the molecules move with constant velocity.

### Kinetic theory and the behaviour of gases

Having made the above assumptions, we can use the kinetic theory to explain the different macroscopic features of a gas.

1  **The pressure exerted by a gas on the walls of the container.**

Molecules collide elastically with the walls of the container. Each collision results in a momentum change for the molecules.

Velocity of molecule before collision with wall = +$v$
Momentum of molecule before collision with wall = +$mv$

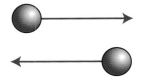

Velocity of molecule after collision with wall = −$v$
Momentum of molecule after collision with wall = −$mv$

**Change in momentum** as a result of collision = −$mv$ − $mv$ = −$2mv$

A momentum change (by Newton's second law) implies that a **force** was exerted on the molecules by the wall and of course by the molecule on the wall (according to Newton's third law). The **total** force on the wall is the sum of the forces exerted by **all** the colliding molecules. The pressure on the wall is the ratio of this total force to the area of the wall, ie the force per unit area.

2  **Boyle's Law: for a fixed mass of gas at constant temperature, the volume is inversely proportional to the applied pressure.**

A reduced volume means that the molecules have a shorter distance to travel to the walls of the container. The momentum change per collision is the same but the shorter distance between each collision means that **more** collisions occur each second, therefore the pressure **increases**.

3  **Charles' Law: For a fixed mass of gas at constant pressure the volume is directly proportional to the Kelvin (or absolute) temperature.**

An increase in temperature means that the kinetic energy, the momentum and velocity of the molecules all increase. This means that the momentum change per collision increases. To maintain the same pressure the number of collisions per second must decrease. Expansion ensures that the molecules have a greater distance to travel before they collide with the container. A greater distance means a longer time interval and so the number of collisions per second is reduced. This increase in one factor coupled with a decrease in the other ensures that the pressure remains **constant**.

4  **Pressure Law: for a fixed mass of gas, at constant volume, the pressure is directly proportional to the Kelvin (or absolute) temperature.**

An increase in temperature means that the kinetic energy, the momentum and velocity of the molecules all increase. This means that both the momentum change per collision, and the number of collisions per second, **increase**. Both of these result in an **increase** in pressure.

### The Ideal Gas Equation

We can now write down a new equation for **an ideal gas**.

$pV = nRT$  where  $p$ = gas pressure (Pa)
$V$ = gas volume (m³)
$n$ = number of moles of gas (mol)
$T$ = gas temperature (K)
$R$ = a constant (J mol⁻¹ K⁻¹)

The constant $R$ is known as the **universal gas constant** and has a value of $8.31$ J mol$^{-1}$ K$^{-1}$. $R$ is a **universal** constant because **it applies to all gases** – provided their behaviour is 'ideal'.

**Note:** This equation is not supplied in the CCEA formula sheet and must be remembered.

### The Boltzmann constant

Another important constant is the **Boltzmann constant**, $k$, which is defined by the equation:

$k = \dfrac{R}{N_A}$     where   $R$ = the universal gas constant (J mol$^{-1}$ K$^{-1}$)

                         $N_A$ = Avogadro's number (mol$^{-1}$)

The Boltzmann constant is therefore $8.31$ J mol$^{-1}$ K$^{-1}$ ÷ $6.02 \times 10^{23}$ mol$^{-1}$ and has a value of $1.38 \times 10^{-23}$ J K$^{-1}$.

Now consider a gas containing $N$ molecules.

The number of moles in this gas, $n$ is given by: $n = \dfrac{N}{N_A}$

Rearranging the equation for the Boltzmann constant gives: $R = kN_A$

Combining the previous two equations shows that: $nR = \dfrac{N}{N_A} \times kN_A = Nk$

Hence, the ideal gas equation, $pV = nRT$, can also be written:

$pV = NkT$     where   $p$ = gas pressure (Pa)

                         $V$ = gas volume (m$^3$)

                         $N$ = number of molecules of gas

                         $k$ = the Boltzmann constant (J K$^{-1}$)

                         $T$ = gas temperature (K)

**This equation is important** because it links the number of molecules in the gas, $N$, with its macroscopic properties of pressure volume and temperature. It also tells us that equal volumes of all gases under the same conditions of temperature and pressure contain the same number of molecules, $N$. This is sometimes called **Avogadro's Law.**

**Note:** This equation is not supplied in the CCEA formula sheet and must be remembered.

The equation is important for another reason. It is the first where the product $pV$ has been directly linked with the number of molecules in the gas. By beginning with the macroscopic observations of the gas laws, we are starting to obtain information about the **microscopic** properties of gas molecules.

## Linking the ideal gas equation to the molecular speeds of gases

Heating a gas generally causes its molecules to move faster, collide more frequently and with greater force on the walls of the container and so increase the gas pressure. There is therefore some statistical relationship between the pressure, volume, temperature and kinetic energy of the molecules.

Before stating that relationship, it is necessary to define some new statistical terms. If the speeds of the $N$ molecules in a sample of gas are $c_1, c_2, c_3, ...., c_N$, then the mean speed, $<c>$, is defined by:

$$<c> = \frac{c_1 + c_2 + c_3 + ... c_N}{N}$$

The mean square speed $<c^2>$ is defined by:

$$<c^2> = \frac{c_1^2 + c_2^2 + c_3^2 + ... c_N^2}{N}$$

And the root mean square speed $c_{rms}$ is defined by:

$$c_{rms} = \sqrt{<c^2>}$$

---

**Worked Example**

1   Five particles have speeds (in $ms^{-1}$) of 2, 4, 5, 5 and 7. Find (a) the mean speed $<c>$ (b) the mean square speed $<c^2>$ (c) the root mean square speed $c_{rms}$.

Solution

(a) Mean speed $<c> = \dfrac{2 + 4 + 5 + 5 + 7}{5} = 4.60$ m s$^{-1}$

(b) Mean square speed $<c^2> = \dfrac{2^2 + 4^2 + 5^2 + 5^2 + 7^2}{5} = \dfrac{119}{5} = 23.8$ m$^2$ s$^{-2}$ (note the unit)

(c) Root mean square speed $c_{rms} = \sqrt{\dfrac{2^2 + 4^2 + 5^2 + 5^2 + 7^2}{5}} = 4.88$ m s$^{-1}$

---

It can be shown that the mathematical link between the speeds of the molecules and the gas pressure, $p$, is given by:

$$pV = \frac{1}{3}Nm<c^2>$$

where    $N$ = number of molecules present in the gas
$m$ = mass of a single molecule (kg)
$<c^2>$ = mean square speed (m$^2$ s$^{-2}$)
and the other symbols have their usual meaning

**Note:** There is no need for A2 students to derive this equation. Candidates only need to know how to use it – the equation itself is reproduced on the CCEA formula sheet. However, candidates who are interested in learning more may wish to research the derivation themselves.

## Gas density

The density of the gas, $\rho$, is defined by the equation:

$$\rho = \frac{M}{V}$$

where    $M$ = mass of the gas (kg)
$V$ = volume of the gas (m$^3$)

Since the mass of gas, $M$, is the product of the total number of molecules present, $N$, and the mass of each molecule, $m$, it follows that:

$$\rho = \frac{M}{V} = \frac{Nm}{V}$$

Combining this equation with the equation $pV = \frac{1}{3}Nm<c^2>$ gives:

$p = \frac{1}{3}\rho<c^2>$ where $p$ = gas pressure (Pa)

$\rho$ = density (kg m$^{-3}$)

$<c^2>$ = mean square speed (m$^2$ s$^{-2}$)

## Molecular speed and temperature

Since $pV = \frac{1}{3}Nm<c^2>$ and $pV = NkT$ it follows that:

$\frac{1}{3}Nm<c^2> = NkT$

Multiplying both sides by $\frac{3}{2N}$ gives:

$\frac{1}{2}m<c^2> = \frac{3}{2}kT$

This equation above is important because it links the average kinetic energy of a collection of gas molecules with the Kelvin temperature. Note in particular that the **average kinetic energy of the molecules is directly proportional to the Kelvin temperature.** The equation applies only to ideal gases, where the only energy possessed by the atoms is the kinetic energy of straight line motion, known as **translational** kinetic energy.

---

### Worked Example

1  Calculate (a) the mass of a hydrogen molecule and (b) the rms speed of hydrogen molecules at 300 K, given that the relative molecular mass of hydrogen is 2.

   **Solution**

   (a) mass of hydrogen molecule $= \dfrac{2\times10^{-3}}{6.02\times10^{23}}$ kg $= 3.332\times10^{-27}$ kg

   (b) Rearranging the equation: $\frac{1}{2}m<c^2> = \frac{3}{2}kT$ gives: $<c^2> = \dfrac{3kT}{m}$

   So: $c_{rms} = \sqrt{\dfrac{3kT}{m}} = \sqrt{\dfrac{3 \times 1.38\times10^{-23} \times 300}{3.332\times10^{-27}}} = 1931$ ms$^{-1}$

2  A gas contains a mixture of oxygen and hydrogen molecules. Oxygen has a relative molecular mass of 32 and hydrogen has a relative molecular mass of 2. The rms speed of the oxygen molecules in the mixture is 220 m s$^{-1}$. Calculate the rms speed of the hydrogen molecules.

   **Solution**

   Using $\frac{1}{2}m<c^2> = \frac{3}{2}kT$ we can write: $\frac{1}{2}m_{H_2}<c_{H_2}^2> = \frac{3}{2}kT$ and $\frac{1}{2}m_{O_2}<c_{O_2}^2> = \frac{3}{2}kT$

   Since the temperature is the same for both, then: $\frac{1}{2}m_{H_2}<c_{H_2}^2> = \frac{1}{2}m_{O_2}<c_{O_2}^2>$

   Cancelling the $\frac{1}{2}$ factors and rearranging gives: $<c_{H_2}^2> = \dfrac{m_{O_2}}{m_{H_2}}<c_{O_2}^2>$

   Substituting values for $m_{H_2}$ and $m_{O_2}$: $<c_{H_2}^2> = \dfrac{32}{2}<c_{O_2}^2> = 16<c_{O_2}^2>$

   Taking square root of each side: $c_{H_2}^{rms} = 4c_{O_2}^{rms} = 4 \times 220 = 880$ m s$^{-1}$

## The internal energy of a gas

The internal energy of a **real** gas is the sum of the potential and kinetic energy of its molecules. All gas molecules in motion possess **translational kinetic energy**. In a monatomic gas (in which atoms are not bound to each other) such as helium, this is the **only** energy possessed by the atoms. However, a gas made of polyatomic molecules (consisting of two or more atoms) may also possess **rotational** kinetic energy and **vibrational** kinetic energy. Polyatomic molecules may also possess potential energy if the inter-atomic **bonds are compressed or stretched**. In general, the internal energy of a **real** gas is **randomly distributed as kinetic and potential energy.**

However, **ideal** gases are **monatomic** and for ideal gases it is assumed that there are **no forces of attraction between the atoms**. So, **ideal gases possess no potential energy.** The internal energy of the molecules of an ideal gas is therefore entirely kinetic.

### Exercise 4.2A

1  One form of Boyle's Law is $PV$ = a constant. Show that the unit for the constant is the Joule.

2  A fixed mass of gas at constant temperature has a volume of 24.0 litres when the pressure is 100 kPa.
   (a) Calculate the volume when the pressure is
       (i) 50 kPa (ii) 150 kPa.
   (b) Calculate its pressure when its volume is
       (i) 4.8 litres (ii) 8 litres (iii) 12 litres

3  The data in the table below were obtained in a Boyle's Law investigation. Copy and complete the table adding appropriate units.
   (a) Process the data so that a linear graph can be obtained.
   (b) Determine the gradient of the graph and give the units of the gradient.

| Pressure, $P$ / MPa | 0.25 | 0.4 | 0.6 | 0.75 | 1.0 | 1.5 |
|---|---|---|---|---|---|---|
| Volume, $V$ / cm³ | 45.0 | 28.0 | 19.0 | 15.0 | 11.3 | 7.5 |

4  Why can we be confident that the volume of a gas is not directly proportional to the Celsius temperature?

5  A fixed mass of gas at 27°C has a volume of 12.0 litres. Find its volume when its temperature rises to 127°C at constant pressure.

6  The volume of a fixed mass of gas rises from 25 litres to 40 litres when it is heated at constant pressure. The initial temperature is 77°C. Find the final temperature in °C.

7  A fixed mass of gas at constant pressure has a volume of 12.0 litres and has a temperature of 100°C. To what temperature must the gas be cooled to reduce its volume to 1.2 litres?

8  A deep-sea diver is working at a depth where the pressure is 3.0 atmospheres. The diver is breathing out air bubbles. The volume of each bubble is 2 cm³. At the surface the pressure is 1.0 atmosphere. What is the volume of each bubble when it reaches the surface, assuming the temperature remains constant?

9  A cycle pump contains 70 cm³ of air at a pressure of 1.0 atmosphere and a temperature of 7°C. The air is compressed to 30 cm³ at a temperature of 27°C. The situation before and after compression is shown in the diagram.

Calculate the final pressure.

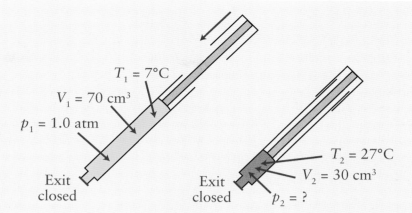

$T_1 = 7°C$
$V_1 = 70$ cm³
$p_1 = 1.0$ atm

Exit closed

$T_2 = 27°C$
$V_2 = 30$ cm³
$p_2 = ?$

Exit closed

10  Oxygen gas consists of diatomic molecules. The mass of an oxygen molecule is $5.35 \times 10^{-26}$ kg.

(a) Calculate the number of moles that are required to obtain 10 g of molecular oxygen.

(b) The gas is contained in a vessel of volume 100 cm³ at a temperature of 50°C. Calculate the pressure exerted by the gas.

(c) Calculate the average kinetic energy of an oxygen molecule.

11 A student gives the following statement:

"The pressure exerted by an ideal gas is directly proportional to the volume of the gas."

(a) State what is wrong with this statement and write down the correct version of the statement.

(b) Hydrogen gas behaves approximately as an ideal gas. In an experiment the pressure exerted by a sample of this gas is $1.5 \times 10^5$ Pa when the temperature is 80°C. Draw a graph to show how the pressure of the gas varies with the temperature measured in K.

(c) Indicate the values of pressure and temperature of your graph.

(d) Calculate the gradient of the graph, stating the unit of the gradient.

12 A tyre contains a gas at a pressure of 150 kPa. If the gas has a density of 2.0 kg m⁻³, find the root mean square speed of the molecules.

13 A cylinder contains gas at a temperature of 300 K and at atmospheric pressure. More gas at the same temperature is pumped into the cylinder until the pressure rises to 200 kPa above atmospheric pressure. If the volume of the cylinder is 0.015 m³ calculate, in moles, the amount of extra gas pumped in. Take R = 8.31 J mol⁻¹ K⁻¹

14 Helium is monatomic with a relative atomic mass of 4.0. Calculate

(a) the density of helium gas at a temperature of 0°C and a pressure of 101 kPa and

(b) the rms speed of the helium atoms under these conditions.

15 The root mean square speed of five molecules (in m s⁻¹) is 306 m s⁻¹. Four of the molecules have speeds (in m s⁻¹) of 301, 301, 305 and 310. Find the speed of the fifth molecule.

16 (a) Calculate the root mean square speed of carbon dioxide molecules at 30°C. The mass of a carbon dioxide molecule is $7.3 \times 10^{-26}$ kg.

(b) Sketch a graph to show how the mean square speed $<c^2>$ of carbon dioxide molecules depends on the Kelvin temperature.

17 How does the Kinetic Theory explain each of the following?

   (a) The pressure exerted by a gas on the walls of the container.

   (b) For a fixed mass of gas at constant temperature Boyle's law tells us that as the volume of a gas is reduced the pressure increases.

   (c) For a fixed mass of gas at constant volume the Pressure Law tells us that as the temperature is increased the pressure increases.

   (d) For a fixed mass of gas at constant pressure Charles' Law tells us that as the temperature is increased the volume increases.

18 A student writes: "*Charles' Law states that the volume of a gas at constant pressure is directly proportional to its temperature.*"

   (a) What two omissions has the student made?

   (b) In a Charles' Law investigation the gas is trapped by a short length of concentrated sulfuric acid. Why is this acid used?

   (c) The student claims that the length of the air trapped in the capillary tube is a measure of its volume. What does this mean?

   (d) Charles' Law leads to the concept of absolute zero temperature. What happens at absolute zero temperature?

19 (a) The temperature of the gas in a room decreases. Describe and explain how the pressure exerted by the gas molecules on the walls of the room changes.

   (b) One of the cylinders in a car engine has a volume of 500 cm$^3$ and contains a fixed mass of gas at a pressure of $1.2 \times 10^5$ Pa and a temperature of 27°C.

     (i) How many moles of gas are trapped in the cylinder?

     (ii) How many molecules of gas are trapped in the cylinder?

     (iii) In what way, if at all, will the number of molecules in the cylinder change if the temperature of the gas rises to 127°C?

## Specific heat capacity

When heat is supplied to an object the temperature of the object generally rises. The rise in temperature $\Delta\theta$ of the object depends on the quantity of heat supplied, the mass of the object and the material from which it is made. These ideas are expressed in the following equation:

$Q = mc\Delta\theta$       where     $Q$ = the quantity of heat energy supplied (J)

                              $m$ = the mass of the object (kg)

                              $c$ = the specific heat capacity of the object (described below)

                              $\Delta\theta$ = the rise in temperature (°C or K)

The specific heat capacity, $c$, of a material is the quantity of heat energy needed to raise the temperature of 1 kg of the material by 1 K.

The units of specific heat capacity are J kg$^{-1}$ K$^{-1}$ (or J kg$^{-1}$ °C$^{-1}$).

There is a wide range of values for specific heat capacity – the table lists the specific heat capacities of some common substances.

In general the specific heat capacity of gases is higher than that of liquids, and the specific heat capacity of liquids is higher than that of solids. The high specific heat capacity of hydrogen makes it suitable as a coolant in large electrical turbines, in spite of the dangers associated with this explosive gas.

| Substance | $c$ / J kg$^{-1}$ K$^{-1}$ |
| --- | --- |
| Hydrogen | 14 300 |
| Water | 4 200 |
| Ethanol | 2 400 |
| Ice | 2 100 |
| Stainless Steel | 510 |
| Copper | 385 |
| Mercury | 140 |

## Electrical methods of measuring specific heat capacity

These methods involve supplying a measured quantity of heat to an object of known mass and then measuring the temperature increase produced.

### Metal solid

The apparatus is set up as shown in the diagram. A metal cylinder has two holes in it, one to hold an electrical heater and other to hold a thermometer. A small amount of oil or glycerine in the hole containing the thermometer is used to improve the thermal contact between the thermometer and the metal.

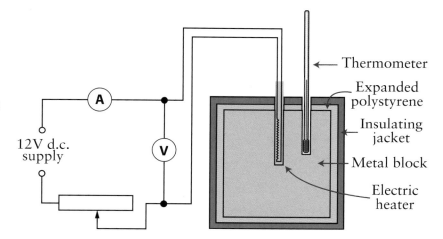

To reduce heat loss and improve accuracy the metal block is wrapped in an insulator, such as expanded polystyrene, to **reduce heat loss by conduction**. The expanded polystyrene is then covered with shiny aluminium foil to **reduce heat loss by radiation**, and an outer insulating jacket to **reduce heat loss by convection**.

The mass of the metal cylinder is measured using a balance and the **initial temperature** of the metal is measured with the thermometer. The amount of energy can be found using a voltmeter, ammeter and stop clock. The heater is switched on and the stop clock activated.

The **power** of the heater = current × voltage = $I \times V$

The stop clock is used to determine the time, $t$, since the heater was switched on.

Therefore the energy supplied = $I \times V \times t$ (time in seconds).

The experimentalist must go on reading the temperature of the metal block for several minutes after the heater is switched off. This is because the temperature of the heater is higher than that of the block and it takes some time for equilibrium between them to be established. The final temperature is taken to be the **highest temperature** reached by the block **after the heater is switched off**.

A set of typical results is given below:

| | |
|---|---|
| Mass of metal cylinder, $m$: | 0.9 kg |
| Voltage across heater, $V$: | 12.0 V |
| Current in heater, $I$: | 5.0 A |
| Power of heater, $P = I \times V$: | 60 W |
| Length of time heater switched on, $t$: | 300 s |
| Heat supplied, $Q = P \times t$: | 18 000 J |
| Initial temperature, $\theta_i$: | 19.5 °C |
| Final (highest) temperature $\theta_f$: | 59.5 °C |
| Temperature rise, $\Delta\theta = \theta_f - \theta_i$: | 40.0 °C |

$$\text{Specific heat capacity, } c = \frac{Q}{m\Delta\theta} = \frac{18\ 000}{(0.9 \times 40)} = 500 \text{ J kg}^{-1}\text{ °C}^{-1}$$

## Liquids

The method used here is much the same as that employed for solids. However the liquid obviously has to be placed in a container, as shown in the diagram, which will also heat up as energy is supplied to the liquid. To minimise this, a container made from a material with a low specific heat capacity should be chosen. The container, called a **calorimeter**, should also be insulated, as with the experiment with the metal block. In addition, in this experiment an **insulating lid** is added to **reduce heat lost due to convection and evaporation**.

The heat supplied, $Q$, is used to raise the temperature of the liquid **and the container**. The relevant equation is:

$$Q = (m_L \times c_L \times \Delta\theta) + (m_C \times c_C \times \Delta\theta)$$

where  $m_L$ = mass of the liquid (kg)
  $m_C$ = mass of the calorimeter (kg)
  $\Delta\theta$ = the rise in temperature in the liquid (°C)
  $c_L$ = specific heat capacity of the liquid (J kg$^{-1}$ °C$^{-1}$)
  $c_C$ = specific heat capacity of the calorimeter (J kg$^{-1}$ °C$^{-1}$)

Provided the liquid is stirred well during the experiment, the temperature of the liquid and that of the calorimeter will be the same. The temperature **rise** in the liquid, $\Delta\theta$, will therefore be the same as the temperature rise in the calorimeter.

As with the metal block experiment, the energy supplied can be determined using the ammeter, voltmeter and stop clock method.

It is common in this procedure for the experimental value for specific heat capacity to be larger than the generally accepted value. This is

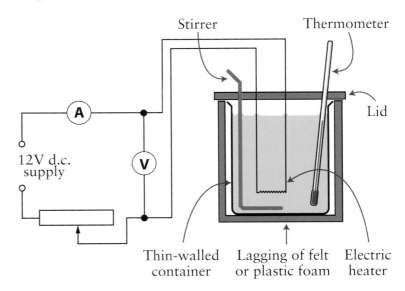

because heat is **always** lost to the environment, resulting in a lower rise in temperature than would otherwise be expected. Since in the calculation of specific heat capacity the rise in temperature is part of the denominator, the calculated value for $c$ is larger than the true value.

One way to reduce the error in this experiment is to cool the liquid in a refrigerator to a temperature of around 5°C. When poured into the calorimeter the liquid temperature quickly rises until both calorimeter and liquid are in thermal equilibrium. Heating begins when the liquid and calorimeter are both about 5°C **below** room temperature and continues until the liquid temperature is about 5°C **above** room temperature. During the time when the calorimeter and its contents are below room temperature the liquid and the container both absorb heat from the environment. When the calorimeter and contents are above room temperature the liquid and the container both lose heat to the environment. By doing this it is expected that the heat lost to the environment will cancel the heat gained from the environment, and results in a value for the specific heat capacity closer to that which is generally accepted.

A set of typical results for water are given below (note that the starting and finishing temperatures are below and above room temperature respectively):

Mass of water, $m$:     0.41 kg
Voltage across heater, $V$:     12.0 V
Current in heater, $I$:     5.0 A
Power of heater, $P = I \times V$:     60 W
Length of time heater switched on, $t$:     300 s
Heat supplied, $Q = P \times t$:     18 000 J
Initial temperature, $\theta_i$:     13.5 °C
Final (highest) temperature, $\theta_f$:     23.5 °C
Temperature rise $\Delta\theta = \theta_f - \theta_i$:     10.0 °C
Mass of calorimeter, $m_C$:     0.160 kg
Specific heat capacity of calorimeter, $c_C$:     385 J kg$^{-1}$ °C$^{-1}$

Heat gained by calorimeter, $Q_C = (m_C \times c_C \times \Delta\theta) = 0.160 \times 385 \times 10.0 = 616$ J

So heat supplied to water, $Q_L = Q - 616 = 18\ 000 - 616 = 17\ 384$ J

Specific heat capacity of water, $c_L = \dfrac{Q_L}{m\Delta\theta} = \dfrac{17\ 384}{(0.41 \times 10)} = 4240$ J kg$^{-1}$ °C$^{-1}$

## Exercise 4.2B

1 Express the units of specific heat capacity in terms of SI base units.

2 A block of metal having mass 4 kg and temperature 25°C is heated to a temperature of 80°C. How much heat energy is required to do this? Assume no heat is lost to the surroundings and that the specific heat capacity of the metal is 385 J kg$^{-1}$ K$^{-1}$.

3 A 12 V electric heater draws 2.0 A for 12 minutes to raise the temperature of a 3.0 kg block of metal. If the initial temperature is 20°C, what would the final temperature be? Assume no heat is lost to the surroundings. The specific heat capacity of the metal = 500 J kg$^{-1}$ K$^{-1}$.

4  A car of mass 1400 kg is travelling at 30 ms$^{-1}$. The driver applies the brakes which have a total mass of 104 kg. Calculate the increase in the temperature of the brakes. What assumption have you made? The specific heat capacity of brake material = 600 J kg$^{-1}$ K$^{-1}$.

5  The diesel engine of a ferry uses water as a coolant. Every minute 35 kg of water enters the engine at 285 K and leaves again at 375 K. How much heat energy is transferred to the water every minute? The specific heat capacity of water is 4200 J kg$^{-1}$ K$^{-1}$.

6  The temperature of a block of copper of mass 250 g is raised to 100°C. It is then placed into an insulated aluminium can of mass 20 g which contains 150 g of alcohol at an initial temperature of 15°C. Calculate the final temperature of the alcohol. Assume no energy losses to the surroundings. The specific heat capacity of copper = 400 J kg$^{-1}$ K$^{-1}$, aluminium = 900 J kg$^{-1}$K$^{-1}$ and alcohol = 2400 J kg$^{-1}$ K$^{-1}$.

7  The diagram shows a long glass tube filled with 100 g of lead shot. The initial temperature of the lead shot is 12°C. The tube is inverted so that the lead shot falls a distance of 50 cm. The tube is inverted 150 times and the final temperature of the lead shot is found to be 15°C.

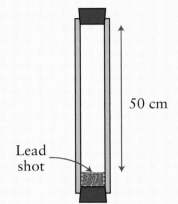

50 cm

Lead shot

(a) Calculate the specific heat capacity of lead.

(b) The accepted value for the specific heat capacity of lead is 130 J kg$^{-1}$ K$^{-1}$. Explain the difference between your calculated value and the accepted value.

8  The diagram on the right shows some of the apparatus used to find, by an electrical method, the specific heat capacity of the 350 g of liquid contained within a metal calorimeter.

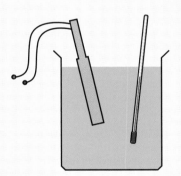

The calorimeter has a mass of 0.05 kg and the metal from which it is made has a specific heat capacity of 400 J kg$^{-1}$ °C$^{-1}$.

(a) What additional apparatus does the student need to carry out this experiment?

(b) The results obtained by the student are shown below:

| Temperature of liquid and calorimeter before heating | = 20.0°C |
| Temperature of liquid and calorimeter after heating | = 45.0°C |
| Voltage applied to heater | = 12.0 V |
| Current through heater | = 5.0 A |
| Time for which heater is on | = 800 s |

(i) Use the data above to calculate the specific heat capacity of the liquid, taking into account the information given about the calorimeter.

(ii) Explain why, even taking into account the calorimeter, the experimental specific heat capacity of the liquid is likely to be less than the true value.

(iii) Suggest one thing the student could do to obtain a value closer to the true value of specific heat capacity for this liquid.

# 4.3 Uniform Circular Motion

CD players, satellites, spin-dryers, the hammer thrower in the photograph and fairground rides all involve **circular** motion. But what makes an object move in a circle? Newton's first law tells us that an object continues to move in a **straight** line unless a resultant force acts on it. So to make something move in a circle **we need a force.**

The hammer thrower in the photograph makes the hammer move in a circle using the tension in the wire. In which direction does this force act?

Your own experiences of circular motion may lead you to the wrong conclusion here. Imagine yourself sitting on the ride in the lower photograph. What force do you feel as you swing round in a circle? It **feels** as if you are being pushed outwards. For this reason people often talk, **wrongly,** about an outwards or 'centrifugal' force. Centrifugal forces **do not exist.**

In fact, the chair exerts an **inward** force on you. Therefore, by Newton's third law, you exert an equal **outward** force on the chair.

Credit: foxypar4 (via Flickr)

Credit: iStockPhoto

## Angular velocity

In Physics we use **angular velocity** to measure how quickly something rotates. One way to measure rotational speed is revolutions per minute (rpm). For example, the typical spin speed of a washing machine is 1000 rpm, and the maximum rotational speed of a car engine is typically 6500 rpm.

We can also measure rotational speed in terms of the angle turned through per second. One complete circle is equivalent to 360°. However, we can also measure angles in **radians**.

In radian measure, the angle $\theta$, as shown in the diagram on the right, is defined as the ratio of the arc length, $s$, to the radius of the circle, $r$, ie:

$\theta = \dfrac{s}{r}$    where  $\theta$ = angle turned through (radians, abbreviated to rad)
   $s$ = the arc length (m)
   $r$ = the radius (m)

If the arc length, $s$, is the **same** as the radius, $r$, then the angle between the two radii is equal to **1 radian**.

One complete circle (360°) is equivalent to $2\pi$ radians, as shown in the diagram on the right. Angular velocity can be measured in degrees per second but the preferred unit is **radians per second**.

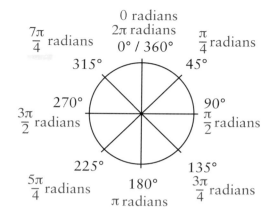

Measured this way, the typical spin speed of a washing machine is $2000\pi$ radians per second, and the maximum rotational speed of a car engine is typically $13000\pi$ radians per second.

**Angular velocity, ω,** is the rate of change of angular displacement (the angle turned through in one second). It is defined as follows:

Angular velocity = $\dfrac{\text{angle turned through}}{\text{time taken}}$, or

$$\omega = \frac{\theta}{t}$$

where  $\omega$ = angular velocity (rad s$^{-1}$)
$\theta$ = angle turned through (°)
$t$ = time taken (s)

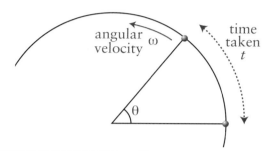

### Worked Examples

1   What is the angular velocity of the seconds hand of a clock?

   Solution

   In 60 seconds the hand sweeps through $2\pi$ radians, so $\omega = \dfrac{\theta}{t} = \dfrac{2\pi}{60} = \dfrac{\pi}{30}$ radians per second.

2   What is the angular velocity of the Earth as it rotates about its axis?

   Solution

   It takes the Earth 23 hours, 56 minutes and 4 seconds, to complete one revolution relative to the stars = 86 164 s.

   So $\omega = \dfrac{\theta}{t} = \dfrac{2\pi}{86\ 164} = 7.29\times10^{-5}$ radians per second, or rad s$^{-1}$.

## Angular displacement

Now suppose a particle moves from point P to point P' at a constant speed, $v$, along a circular arc of length $s$ in a time, $t$, as shown in the diagram on the right.

The angle $\theta$ swept out by the particle moving from P to P' is called the **angular displacement**. By rearranging the definition of the radian we can write:

$s = r\theta$       where  $s$ = the arc length (m)
$r$ = the radius (m)
$\theta$ = angular displacement (rad)

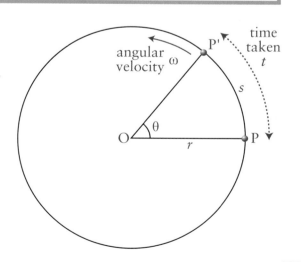

## Angular velocity

The **angular velocity** of the particle, $\omega$, is defined as the **rate of change of angular displacement**. Since the particle is moving at a steady speed, $v$, the angular velocity, $\omega$, is constant and therefore we can write:

$$\omega = \frac{\theta}{t}$$

where   $\omega$ = angular velocity (rad s$^{-1}$)
$\theta$ = angular displacement (rad)
$t$ = time taken (s)

Since speed is the rate of change of distance with time, then combining the equations for angular displacement and angular velocity enables us to write:

$$v = \frac{s}{t} = \frac{r\theta}{t} = r\omega$$

where   $v$ = speed (ms$^{-1}$)
$r$ = the radius (m)
$\omega$ = angular velocity (rad s$^{-1}$)

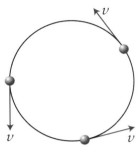

An object moving in a circle with a constant angular velocity has a constant linear (or tangential) **speed**. However its linear **velocity** is not constant. This is because the **direction** the particle is moving is **changing** from one moment to the next. Since the direction is continually changing, the particle's velocity must be continually changing also, as shown in the diagram on the right. The particle is therefore **accelerating**.

## Periodic time and frequency

The **periodic time** of the motion, $T$, is defined as the time taken for the particle to travel once round the circle. Since the radius vector sweeps out 360° or $2\pi$ radians as the particle moves once round the circle, then:

$$T = \frac{s}{v} = \frac{2\pi r}{r\omega} = \frac{2\pi}{\omega}$$

where   $T$ = periodic time, or period (s)
$\omega$ = angular velocity (rad s$^{-1}$)

The **frequency**, $f$, of the motion is the number of revolutions made per second. Since the particle takes $T$ seconds to make one revolution, we can write:

$$f = \frac{1}{T} = \frac{\omega}{2\pi}$$

where   $f$ = frequency (Hertz, or Hz)

---

### Worked Examples

1   The seconds hand of a clock is 15.0 cm long. (a) Write down its period and frequency, and (b) calculate the mean speed of its tip. Take the tip to be the point at maximum distance from the centre of the clock.

   Solution

   (a) Period $T$ = time to make 1 revolution = 60.0 s

   Frequency, $f = \dfrac{1}{T} = \dfrac{1}{60.0}$ Hz = 0.0167 Hz

   (b) $f = \dfrac{\omega}{2\pi}$, so angular velocity $\omega = 2\pi f = \dfrac{2\pi}{60.0} = 0.105$ rad s$^{-1}$

   Speed of tip, $v = r\omega = 0.150 \times 0.105 = 0.0158$ m s$^{-1}$

2  An astronaut in training is rotated at the end of a horizontal rotating arm of length 5 m. The arm makes 42 revolutions per minute. Calculate (a) the frequency (b) the period and (c) angular velocity of the rotating arm, and (d) the speed of the astronaut.

**Solution**

(a)  Frequency, $f$ = number of revolutions per second = $\dfrac{42}{60}$ = 0.70 Hz

(b)  Period, $T = \dfrac{1}{f} = \dfrac{1}{0.70}$ = 1.43 s

(c)  Angular velocity, $\omega = 2\pi f = 2\pi \times 0.70 = 1.4\pi = 4.4$ rad s$^{-1}$

(d)  Speed of astronaut, $v = r\omega = 5 \times 4.4 = 22$ m s$^{-1}$

3  An electron in a hydrogen atom moves in a circular path of radius 50 pm with a constant speed of 2.2 Mm s$^{-1}$. Calculate (a) its angular velocity and (b) its frequency.

**Solution**

(a)  Angular velocity, $\omega = \dfrac{v}{r} = \dfrac{2.2 \times 10^{6}}{50 \times 10^{-12}} = 4.4 \times 10^{16}$ rad s$^{-1}$

(b)  Frequency, $f = \dfrac{\omega}{2\pi} = \dfrac{4.4 \times 10^{16}}{2\pi} = 7.0 \times 10^{15}$ Hz

4  The planet Venus orbits the Sun in a roughly circular orbit of mean radius of 108 million kilometres every 224 days. Calculate (a) the angular velocity and (b) the speed of Venus.

**Solution**

(a)  224 days = 224 days × 24 hours × 60 minutes × 60 seconds = $1.94 \times 10^{7}$ s

Angular velocity, $\omega = \dfrac{2\pi}{T} = \dfrac{2\pi}{19.4 \times 10^{6}} = 3.24 \times 10^{-7}$ rad s$^{-1}$

(b)  Speed of Venus, $v = r\omega = 1.08 \times 10^{11} \times 3.24 \times 10^{-7} = 3.51 \times 10^{4}$ m s$^{-1}$

5  The United States Air Force uses a centrifuge with an arm of 5 m radius to train pilots. This centrifuge has period of 3.0 s. The pilot is positioned at the end of the rotating arm. Calculate (a) the pilot's angular velocity and (b) the pilot's linear or tangential speed.

**Solution**

(a)  Angular velocity $\omega = \dfrac{2\pi}{T} = \dfrac{2\pi}{3} = 2.094$ rad s$^{-1}$

(b)  Speed of pilot, $v = r\omega = 5 \times 2.094 = 10.47$ m s$^{-1}$

6  Calculate the tangential velocity of a point on the Earth's equator. Assume that the radius of the Earth is 6400 km and that it takes the Earth 1 day to complete one revolution.

**Solution**

$v = \dfrac{2\pi r}{T} = \dfrac{2\pi \times 6.4 \times 10^{6}}{24 \times 60 \times 60} = 465.4$ m s$^{-1}$

## Centripetal acceleration

As already discussed, any particle moving in a circular path at a constant speed must be accelerating because the direction of its motion, and hence its velocity, is constantly changing.

However the speed of the particle is neither increasing nor decreasing. This shows us that the acceleration must have no component **parallel** to the direction of the velocity. It follows therefore that at any instant the acceleration must be **perpendicular** to the velocity.

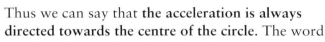
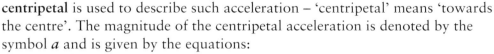

Thus we can say that **the acceleration is always directed towards the centre of the circle**. The word centripetal is used to describe such acceleration – 'centripetal' means 'towards the centre'. The magnitude of the centripetal acceleration is denoted by the symbol $a$ and is given by the equations:

$$a = v\omega = \frac{v^2}{r} = r\omega^2 \quad \text{where} \quad \omega = \text{angular velocity (rad s}^{-1})$$
$$v = \text{tangential speed (m s}^{-1})$$
$$r = \text{the radius (m)}$$

Since the particle is being accelerated there must also be an accelerating **force** in accordance with Newton's second law. This force, $F$, is given by the equation:

$$F = ma = mv\omega = \frac{mv^2}{r} = mr\omega^2$$
$$\text{where} \quad m = \text{mass of the particle (kg)}$$
$$\text{and the other symbols have their usual meanings}$$

Since the force and the acceleration are always in the same direction, **the force acts towards the centre of the circle** and is known as the **centripetal force**.

> **Note:** The CCEA specification does not require candidates to derive the equations for centripetal acceleration and centripetal force. However, the ability to recall and use the equations is almost invariably examined.

---

### Worked Examples

1 A disc spins at 45 revolutions per second. A speck of dust on the disc has a mass of 1 mg and is 5 cm from the centre. Calculate the centripetal force on the speck of dust.

**Solution**

Angular velocity, $\omega = 2\pi f = 2\pi \times 45 = 90\pi$ rad s$^{-1}$

Centripetal force, $F = ma = mr\omega^2 = 1\times10^{-6} \times 0.05 \times (90\pi)^2 = 0.004$ N

2 At what angular velocity must a centrifuge spin so that a particle placed 20 cm from the centre experiences a centripetal acceleration equal to the acceleration due to gravity at the Earth's surface?

**Solution**

$$\omega = \sqrt{\frac{a}{r}} = \sqrt{\frac{9.81}{0.2}} = \sqrt{49.05} = 7.00 \text{ rad s}^{-1}$$

## Causes of the centripetal force

The centripetal force is caused by some physical phenomenon. It is important to understand that the **circular motion does not produce the force.** Rather, **the force is needed for circular motion to take place.** Without this force the object would travel in a straight line along the tangent to the curve. There is no outward centrifugal force on the particle.

Suppose an object was moving in a circular path at the end of a string. If the string were to break, the centripetal force would disappear and the object would fly off along the tangent to the circle.

The table below identifies the cause of the centripetal force in four different situations.

| Physical situation | Cause of the centripetal force |
|---|---|
| A planet orbiting the Sun | The **gravitational force** between the Sun and the planet |
| Electrons orbiting the nucleus of an atom | The **electrical force** between the positively charged nucleus and the negatively charged electron |
| A 'conker' being whirled in a circle at the end of a string | The **tension** in the string |
| A racing car going round a circular track | The **friction force** between the tyres and the track |

## Worked Examples

1  Calculate the centripetal force on the Earth as it orbits the Sun. You may assume the mass of the Earth is $6{\times}10^{24}$ kg and that its mean orbital radius is $1.5{\times}10^{11}$ m. Take 1 year as $3.2{\times}10^{7}$ seconds.

   Solution

   $$\omega = \frac{2\pi}{T} = \frac{2\pi}{3.2{\times}10^{7}} = 1.964{\times}10^{-7} \text{ rad s}^{-1}$$

   $$F = mr\omega^{2} = 6{\times}10^{24} \times 1.5{\times}10^{11} \times (1.964{\times}10^{-7})^{2} = 3.47{\times}10^{22} \text{ N}$$

2  At what minimum speed must a motorcyclist ride over a hump-back bridge of radius 12 m if they just lose contact with the road? Take $g$ as 9.81 m s$^{-2}$.

   Solution

   If contact is just lost, then:
   - reaction = 0
   - centripetal force = weight of motorcycle and rider

   So: $\dfrac{mv^{2}}{r} = mg$

   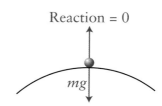

   Cancelling $m$ and rearranging gives:

   $v^{2} = rg = 12 \times 9.81 = 117.72$

   $v = 10.8$ m s$^{-1}$

3   The breaking force in a length of string is 5 N. What is the maximum number of revolutions per minute which can be made with a conker of mass 60 g at one end of an 80 cm length of this string? Ignore gravitational effects.

Solution

$F = mr\omega^2 = mr(2\pi f)^2 = 4\pi^2 mrf^2$

$f^2 = \dfrac{F}{(4\pi^2 mr)} = \dfrac{5}{(4\pi^2 \times 0.06 \times 0.8)} = 2.639$

So $f = 1.624$ revolutions per second

Therefore number of revolutions per minute $= 60f = 60 \times 1.624 = 97.5$

## Motion in a vertical circle

The diagram below represents an object of mass $m$ being whirled clockwise at a constant speed $v$ in a **vertical** circle at the end of a piece of string of length $L$. When we take the force of gravity into account, the resultant force on the object is **not** constant.

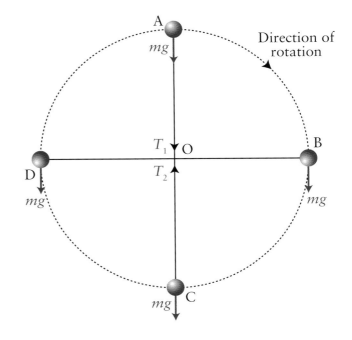

At point A, the tension $T_1$ in the string is given by:

$$T_1 + mg = \frac{mv^2}{L}$$

So: $T_1 = \dfrac{mv^2}{L} - mg$

At point C, the tension $T_2$ in the string is given by:

$$T_2 - mg = \frac{mv^2}{L}$$

So: $T_2 = \dfrac{mv^2}{L} + mg$

At points B and D, the tension in the string provides the centripetal force $\dfrac{mv^2}{L}$. The weight, acting at right angles to the string, does not contribute to the centripetal force at these points.

As the object moves from A to B to C, the tension increases sinusoidally (meaning, like a sine wave), reaching a maximum at C. As it moves from C to D to A the tension decreases sinusoidally, reaching a minimum at A.

We can calculate the forces acting on the object at **any** point in its orbit by resolving vectors.

The diagram on the next page shows the forces acting on the object as it moves around in a vertical circle. The weight of the object, $mg$, can be resolved into two components. One component, $mg \cos \theta$, acts either in the same direction as the tension, $T$, or in the opposite direction. The other component, $mg \sin \theta$, is always perpendicular to the tension. Thus:

At points P and S we have:

$$T_P = T_S = m\omega^2 L - mg \cos \theta$$

At Q and at R we have:

$$T_Q = T_R = m\omega^2 L + mg \cos \theta$$

The graph below shows how the tension varies sinusoidally over one complete rotation.

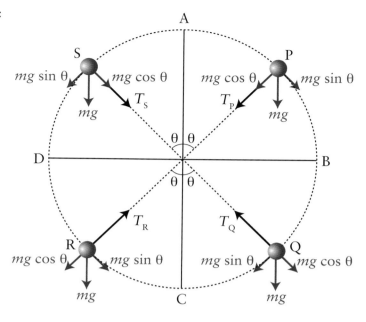

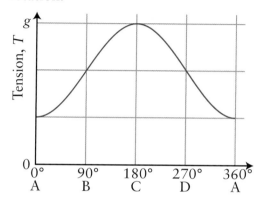

## Circular motion at an angle

The diagram on the right shows a conical pendulum. The tension in the string is $T$ and the angle between the string and the horizontal is $\theta$. The radius of the circle is $R$. The vertical component of the tension in the string, $T \sin \theta$, must balance the weight of the orbiting mass, $mg$. Meanwhile, the horizontal component of the tension, $T \cos \theta$, provides the centripetal force. Therefore we can write:

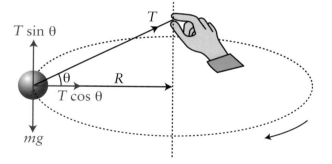

$$T \cos \theta = \frac{mv^2}{R} + mg \quad \text{and} \quad T \sin \theta = mg$$

Dividing the second equation by the first gives:

$$\frac{T \sin \theta}{T \cos \theta} = \tan \theta = \frac{mg}{mv^2 \div R} = \frac{gR}{v^2}$$

We can use this equation to show that it is not possible for the string to be horizontal. To be horizontal the angle $\theta$ must be zero. This would mean that $\tan \theta = 0$. To achieve this, the value of $v^2$ must be infinite, which is not possible. Therefore the angle $\theta$ can never be zero, meaning that the string can never be horizontal.

**Exercise 4.3**

1   A ball of mass 0.5 kg is rotated in a horizontal plane as shown in the diagram on the right. The length of the string 0.8 m. Calculate the number of revolutions per second that the object must have so that the angle θ is 20°.

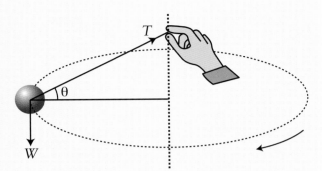

2   A motor car travels with uniform speed along a straight, level road. The diameter of each wheel of the car is 65 cm, and the angular velocity of the wheel about the axle is 59.6 rad s⁻¹.

   (a) Calculate the angular velocity of a point on the wheel midway between the axle and the outer edge of the tyre.

   (b) As the car in proceeds at a constant speed of 72 kilometres per hour, it passes over a hump-back bridge. The bridge may be considered to be the arc of a circle in a horizontal plane. The car travels over the bridge, just without losing contact with the road. Calculate the radius of curvature of the bridge, r.

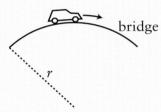

3   A metal sphere M of mass 1.35 kg is suspended from a rigid support by a light string of length 1.50 m. The sphere is made to move with uniform speed in a horizontal circle of radius 0.90 m, as shown in the diagram on the right. The tension in the string is T and the weight of the sphere is W. The angle between the string and the vertical is θ.

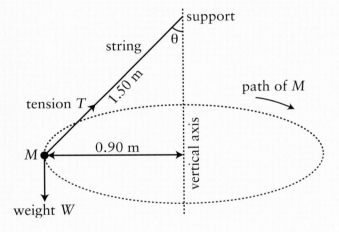

   (a) Write down expressions for the vertical and horizontal components of the tension.

   (b) One of the components of the tension effectively supports the weight of the sphere, and the other provides the centripetal force to move it in a horizontal circle. Identify the component responsible for supporting the weight of the sphere. Hence find the magnitude of the tension in the string.

   (c) Calculate the linear speed of the sphere as it moves in the horizontal plane.

   (d) Calculate the time required for the sphere to make one complete revolution of its horizontal motion.

4   The drum of a spin dryer rotates a 720 rpm, the diameter of the drum is 0.5 m.

   (a) Calculate the number of revolutions the drum makes in 1 second.

   (b) Calculate the angular velocity of the drum.

## Velocity

The **velocity**, $v$, at any instant is equal to the gradient of the displacement-time graph at that instant. The general equation for $v$ is:

$v = -\omega A \sin \omega t$

> **Note:** The CCEA specification does not require candidates to recall this equation.

The velocity has a maximum value of $\omega A$ at the instant the object passes through the centre of oscillation.

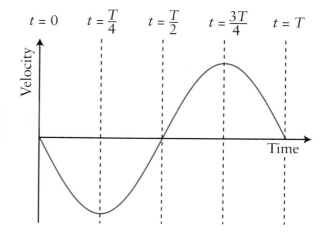

## Acceleration

The **acceleration, $a$**, at any instant is equal to the gradient of the velocity-time graph at that instant. The general equation for $a$ is:

$a = -\omega^2 x = -\omega^2 A \cos \omega t$

The acceleration has a maximum value of $-\omega^2 A$ at the instant the object reaches the extremities of its oscillation. The acceleration is zero when the object reaches the centre of the oscillation.

The minus sign tells us that the acceleration is always in the opposite direction to the displacement from O.

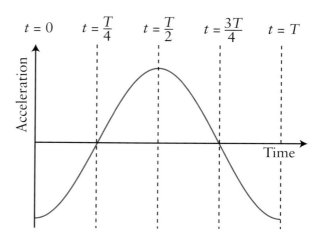

### Relationship between velocity and displacement

We have seen how the velocity varies with time. But how does the velocity vary with the **displacement** from the centre of the oscillation?

> **Note:** The CCEA specification does not require candidates to know the derivation below. However, the equation linking velocity and displacement is so useful that it is presented here for completeness.

If we take the previous equations, which show how the displacement and velocity vary with time, and square them, we have:

$x = A \cos \omega t$ $\qquad\qquad$ $v = -\omega A \sin \omega t$

$x^2 = A^2 \cos^2 \omega t$ $\qquad\qquad$ $v^2 = \omega^2 A^2 \sin^2 \omega t$

From trigonometry, we know that sine and cosine are linked by the relationship:

$\sin^2 \theta + \cos^2 \theta = 1$

Using this relationship, we can write:

$\sin^2 \omega t + \cos^2 \omega t = 1$

Multiplying both sides by $\omega^2 A^2$ gives:

$\omega^2 A^2 \sin^2 \omega t + \omega^2 A^2 \cos^2 \omega t = \omega^2 A^2$

Substituting for $x$ and $v$ into this equation gives:

$v^2 + \omega^2 x^2 = \omega^2 A^2$

which can be rearranged to give:

$v^2 = \omega^2 A^2 - \omega^2 x^2$

Therefore:

$v = \pm\omega\sqrt{(A^2 - x^2)}$

The $\pm$ indicates that the value of the velocity can be positive or negative, ie to left or to the right or up or down. In other words, the sign indicates the direction of movement.

**Summary of equations for displacement, velocity and acceleration**

|  | Displacement | Velocity | Acceleration |
|---|---|---|---|
| Variation with time | $x = A \cos \omega t$ | $v = -\omega A \sin \omega t$ | $a = -\omega^2 A \cos \omega t$ |
| Maximum value | Amplitude = $A$ | At fixed point, maximum velocity = $\pm\omega A$ | At extreme displacement, maximum acceleration = $\omega^2 A$ |
| Minimum value | At fixed point, displacement = 0 | At extreme displacement, minimum velocity = 0 | At fixed point, minimum acceleration = 0 |
| Variation with displacement |  | $v = \pm\omega\sqrt{(A^2 - x^2)}$ | $a = -\omega^2 x$ |

## Energy during SHM

An object moving with SHM experiences a constant interchange between kinetic energy and potential energy. In the case of the simple pendulum as the bob moves down from its highest position the gravitational potential energy is converted to kinetic energy, and as it moves upwards again the kinetic energy is converted back to gravitational potential energy. In the case of an oscillating mass on the end of a spring, the kinetic energy that exists when it is moving is converted to the potential energy (strain energy) as the spring is compressed, and back to kinetic energy again when it is stretched. It is important to remember that **the total energy remains constant with time**.

We know that the velocity at any given instant, $v = -\omega A \sin \omega t$. (The velocity can also be found by calculating the gradient of the displacement-time graph, ie the derivative of the displacement with respect to time, $v = \dfrac{\Delta x}{\Delta t}$.)

Therefore kinetic energy,

$\begin{aligned} E_k &= \tfrac{1}{2}mv^2 = \tfrac{1}{2}m(-\omega A \sin \omega t)^2 \\ &= \tfrac{1}{2}m\omega^2 A^2 \sin^2 \omega t \end{aligned}$

The graph on the right shows how the kinetic energy varies with time over one complete cycle of an oscillation.

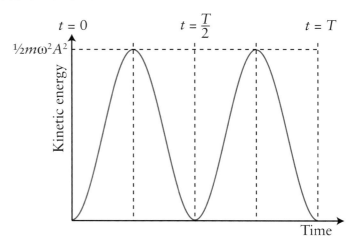

## Motion of a simple pendulum and loaded spiral spring

### Simple pendulum

The motion of the bob of a simple pendulum is an example of simple harmonic motion. To prove this, let us first look at the forces acting on the bob at the moment it is released from its highest position, as shown in the diagram on the right.

The only forces are the tension, $T$, in the string and the weight of the pendulum bob $W = mg$. Resolving the weight along the direction of the string gives $mg \cos \theta$. Because there is equilibrium in this direction we can say: $T = mg \cos \theta$

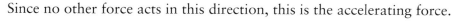

The component of the weight acting perpendicular to the string, $F$, is given by: $F = mg \sin \theta$

Since no other force acts in this direction, this is the accelerating force.

The displacement from the centre O is $x$, which is the arc of a circle. Using the equation for angular displacement, $s = r\theta$:

$x = l\theta$      where $\theta$ = angle (rad)
                $l$ = length of the string (m)

This can be rearranged to give: $\theta = \dfrac{x}{l}$

For small angles (10° or under), we can use the approximation: $\sin \theta = \theta$, and so we can write:

$$F = mg \sin \theta = mg\theta = \frac{mgx}{l}$$

Since $F = ma$, we can write: $a = \dfrac{gx}{l}$

As we have seen, the **general** equation for acceleration during SHM, $a = -\omega^2 x$

This can be rearranged to give: $-\omega^2 = \dfrac{a}{x}$

Substituting in the value $a = \dfrac{gx}{l}$ gives us: $-\omega^2 = \dfrac{g}{l}$

The minus sign just indicates that the direction of the acceleration is in the opposite direction to that of the force, so we can omit it and write: $\omega = \sqrt{\dfrac{g}{l}}$

This equation demonstrates that the motion of a simple pendulum meets both criteria for simple harmonic motion:
1  the acceleration is proportional to its displacement, $x$, from the centre, and
2  the direction of the acceleration is towards the centre point.

Since the general equation for period, $T = \dfrac{2\pi}{\omega}$, for a simple pendulum:

$$T = 2\pi\sqrt{\frac{l}{g}}$$    where   $T$ = period (s)
                     $l$ = length of the string (m)
                     $g$ = acceleration due to gravity (m s$^{-2}$)

### Loaded spiral spring

When a weight, $W = mg$ is attached to a spring it produces an extension, $e$, as shown on the right. When it comes to rest at the equilibrium position, O, the tension, $T$, is equal to the weight, so we can say that $T = mg$. Hooke's Law states:

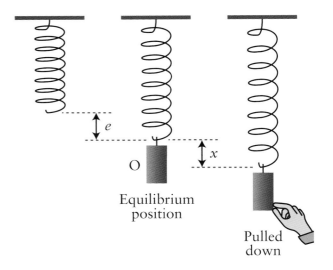

$T = ke$     where
         $k$ = the spring constant (N m⁻¹)
         $e$ = extension (m)

Equilibrium position

Pulled down

Consequently, we can write: $ke = mg$

Suppose that the spring is then pulled down a distance $x$ and released. At the instant of release:

Upward force = $k(e + x) = ke + kx$
Downward force = $mg$
So the resultant force, $F = ke + kx - mg$
But we know that $ke = mg$, therefore: $F = kx$

The direction is important, because both displacement, $x$, and force, $F$, are vectors. Since the force acts in the opposite direction to the direction of the displacement, we add a minus sign to indicate this. Therefore, for a spring:

Resultant force at the moment of release, $F = -kx$

Using $F = ma$, the acceleration of the mass at the moment if release is:

$$a = \frac{F}{m} = -\frac{kx}{m}$$

This equation demonstrates that the motion of a loaded spiral spring meets both criteria for simple harmonic motion:
1   the acceleration is proportional to its displacement, $x$, from the equilibrium position, O and
2   the direction of the acceleration is towards the equilibrium position.

As we have seen, the **general** equation for acceleration during SHM, $a = -\omega^2 x$

This can be rearranged to give: $-\omega^2 = \dfrac{a}{x}$

Substituting in the value $a = -\dfrac{kx}{m}$ gives us: $\omega^2 = \dfrac{k}{m}$

Therefore: $\omega = \sqrt{\dfrac{k}{m}}$

Since the general equation for period, $T = \dfrac{2\pi}{\omega}$, for a loaded spiral spring:

$T = 2\pi\sqrt{\dfrac{m}{k}}$    where   $T$ = period (s)
                 $m$ = mass of the spring (kg)
                 $k$ = the spring constant (N m⁻¹)

## Experimental and graphical investigation of SHM

### Simple pendulum

Set up the apparatus as shown in the diagram on the right. The pendulum bob is to be displaced from its equilibrium position – when doing so, ensure the angle between the thread and the vertical is less than 10°. When the bob is released it will oscillate with simple harmonic motion. As shown in the previous section, the periodic time (A to O to B and back to A) depends on the length of the string and the acceleration of free fall.

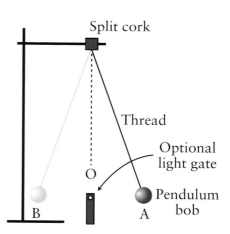

The length of the pendulum is measured from the just below the suspension point to the centre of the pendulum bob. To determine the period $T$ it is necessary to time at least 10 complete oscillations and calculate an average. It is also possible to use a light gate and computer software to take sufficient and appropriate measurements to determine the periodic time $T$.

Carry out the experiment for different lengths of thread and tabulate the results in a table like the one below:

| Length of the pendulum, $l$ / m | Time for 10 oscillations / s | Period, $T$ / s |
| --- | --- | --- |
| 0.2 | | |
| 0.4 | | |
| 0.6 | | |
| 0.8 | | |
| 1.0 | | |
| 1.2 | | |

We can now draw a graph from these data. A simple plot of $T$ against $l$ will yield a curve as shown in the example on the right.

However we know that the periodic time, $T$, of the pendulum is given by the equation:

$$T = 2\pi\sqrt{\frac{l}{g}}$$

So, to obtain a **linear** plot, graphs of $T$ against $\sqrt{l}$ or $T^2$ against $l$ are needed. The gradient of the linear graphs will provide a value for the acceleration of free fall, $g$. Examples of such graphs are shown on the next page.

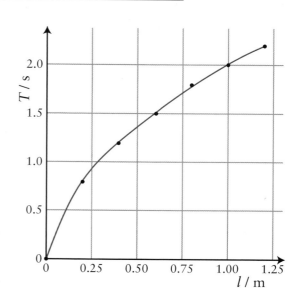

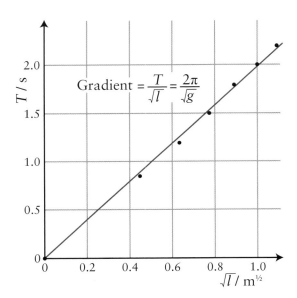

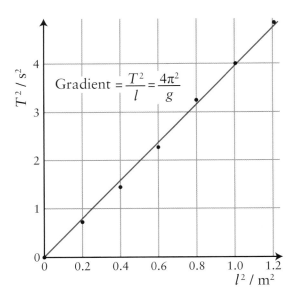

Since $T = 2\pi\sqrt{\dfrac{l}{g}}$, we can write this as:

$T = bl^n$      where $b$ = a constant equal to $\dfrac{2\pi}{\sqrt{g}}$

               $n = \frac{1}{2}$ (meaning square root)

Taking logs of both sides gives:

$\log T = \log b + n \log l$

Comparing this to the equation of a straight line, $y = mx + c$, shows that we can plot a linear graph of $\log T$ against $\log l$, which will intersect the $y$-axis at $\log b$, and have a gradient of $n$. An example of such a graph is shown on the right. Calculating the gradient from this graph will yield a value of $n = \frac{1}{2}$, confirming that $T = b\sqrt{l}$.

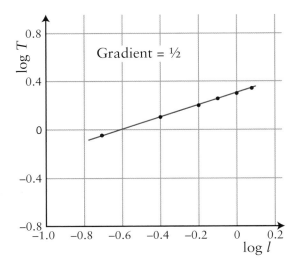

### Loaded spiral spring

Set up the apparatus as shown in the diagram on the right. When the mass is pulled down by a small distance and released the mass will oscillate vertically with simple harmonic motion. The distance the mass is displaced vertically should be small – 5 cm is enough to produce easily-observable oscillations.

The approach to measuring the periodic time is similar to that used for the simple pendulum. To determine the period, $T$, it is necessary to time at least 10 complete oscillations and take an average. It is also possible to use a light gate and computer software, as shown in the diagram, to take sufficient and appropriate measurements to determine the period.

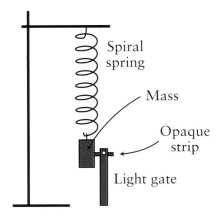

Carry out the experiment for different masses, varying it in steps of 100 g, and tabulate the results in a table like the following:

| Mass attached, $m$ / kg | Time for 10 oscillations / s | Period, $T$ / s |
|---|---|---|
| 0.1 | | |
| 0.2 | | |
| 0.3 | | |
| 0.4 | | |
| 0.5 | | |
| 0.6 | | |

We can now draw a graph from these data. A simple plot of $T$ against $m$ will yield a curve as shown in the example on the right.

However we know that the periodic time, $T$, of the pendulum is given by the equation:

$$T = 2\pi\sqrt{\frac{m}{k}}$$

So, to obtain a **linear** plot, graphs of $T$ against $\sqrt{m}$ or $T^2$ against $m$ are needed. The gradient of the linear graphs will provide a value for the spring constant, $k$. Examples of such graphs are shown below.

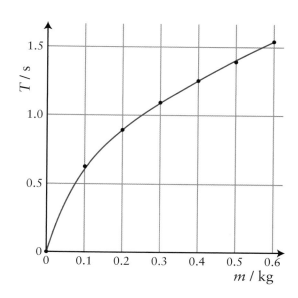

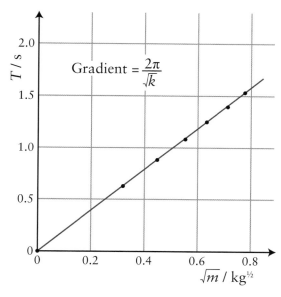

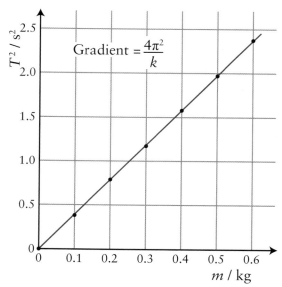

Since $T = 2\pi\sqrt{\frac{m}{k}}$, we can write this as:

$T = am^n$    where $a$ = a constant equal to $\dfrac{2\pi}{\sqrt{k}}$

$n = \frac{1}{2}$ (meaning square root)

Taking logs of both sides gives:

$\log T = \log a + n \log m$

Comparing this to the equation of a straight line, $y = mx + c$, shows that we can plot a linear graph of $\log T$ against $\log m$, which will intersect the $y$-axis at $\log a$, and have a gradient of $n$. An example of such a graph is shown on the right. Calculating the gradient from this graph will yield a value of $n = \frac{1}{2}$, confirming that $T = a\sqrt{m}$.

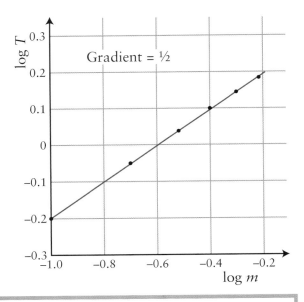

**Worked Examples**

1  A steel strip is clamped at one end and made to vibrate at a frequency of 5 Hz and with an amplitude of 50 mm.
   (a) (i) Calculate the period, $T$ and the angular velocity, $\omega$.
       (ii) Calculate the acceleration at maximum displacement.
   (b) At time $t = 0$, the displacement is +50 mm.
       (i) Calculate the displacement at time $t = 0.04$ s.
       (ii) Calculate the times during the first period at which the distance from the fixed point is 33 mm.

   **Solution**

   (a) (i) $T = \dfrac{1}{f} = \dfrac{1}{5} = 0.2$ s          $\omega = 2\pi f = 2\pi \times 5 = 10\pi = 31.4$ rad s$^{-1}$

       (ii) $a = \omega^2 x = (10\pi)^2 \times 5\times10^{-2} = 5\pi^2 = 49.3$ mm s$^{-2}$

   (b) (i) $x = A \cos \omega t = 50 \cos (10\pi \times 0.04) = 15.5$ mm

       (ii) In the first quarter cycle:

       $x = A \cos \omega t$

       $33 = 50 \cos 10\pi t$

       $\cos 10\pi t = 33 \div 50 = 0.660$

       $10\pi t = \cos^{-1} 0.660 = 0.850$ rad

       $t = 0.850 \div 10\pi = 0.027$ s

       In the second quarter cycle:

       $x = A \cos \omega t$

       $-33 = 50 \cos 10\pi t$

       $\cos 10\pi t = -33 \div 50 = -0.660$

       $10\pi t = \cos^{-1} -0.660 = 2.292$ rad

       $t = 0.850 \div 10\pi = 0.073$ s

   **Note:** Ensure that your calculator is set to 'radian' mode when calculating the cosines and inverse cosines in this question.

       In the third quarter cycle, the displacement is −33 mm exactly half a period (0.1 s) after the time in the first quarter cycle. So $t = 0.027 + 0.1 = 0.127$ s

       In the fourth quarter cycle, the displacement is 33 mm exactly half a period (0.1 s) after the time in the second quarter cycle. So $t = 0.073 + 0.1 = 0.173$ s

2. An object vibrates with simple harmonic motion. Its displacement varies with time as shown in the graph on the right. The displacement $x$ is given by the equation $x = A \cos \omega t$.

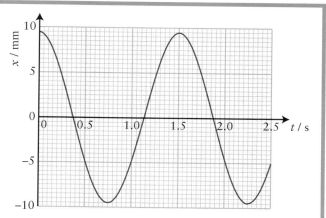

   (a) Making use of the graph determine the amplitude of the motion.
   (b) Determine the maximum acceleration of the object.

**Solution**

   (a) The amplitude is the maximum displacement. Amplitude is not a vector so the sign is not relevant. Amplitude $A = 9$ mm.

   (b) Maximum acceleration $a = \omega^2 A$. To find $\omega$ we need to find the periodic time, $T$. This is the time between two peaks, from 0 to 1.5 s, so $T = 1.5$ s.

   $T = \dfrac{2\pi}{\omega}$ giving $\omega = \dfrac{2\pi}{T} = 4.19$ rad s$^{-1}$

   Maximum acceleration, $a = \omega^2 A = 4.19^2 \times 9 \times 10^{-3} = 1.67$ m s$^{-2}$

3. The diagram shows a mass of 0.65 kg suspended from the end of spring. The graph shows how the tension, $F$, in the spring varies with the extension, $x$, of the spring.

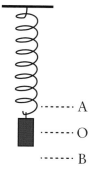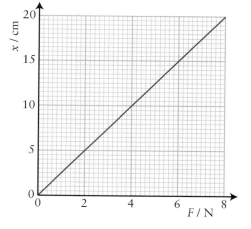

   (a) Use the graph to find the spring constant, $k$, of the spring (ie the force per unit extension).
   (b) The mass is then pulled down a little and released so that is oscillates vertically. Calculate the periodic time of oscillations of this mass.
   (c) Calculate the acceleration of the mass when it is 10 cm above point O and state the direction of the acceleration.

**Solution**

(a) Spring constant, $k$ = force ÷ extension = $F \div x = 4 \div 0.1 = 40$ N m$^{-1}$

(b) $T = 2\pi\sqrt{\dfrac{m}{k}} = 2\pi\sqrt{\dfrac{0.65}{40}} = 0.8$ s

(c) $T = \dfrac{2\pi}{\omega}$, so: $\omega = 2\pi \div 0.8 = 7.85$ rad s$^{-1}$

Acceleration, $a = -\omega^2 x = -(7.85^2) \times 0.1 = -6.16$ m s$^{-2}$

The minus sign indicates that the acceleration is in the opposite direction to the displacement, ie the acceleration is 6.16 m s$^{-2}$ towards O.

4. A simple pendulum is 1.25 m long. It is displaced to point P so that the string makes an angle of 10° with the vertical, as shown in the diagram. When released it is found to have a period of 2.2 s.
   (a) Calculate its acceleration at the moment of release.
   (b) Calculate its velocity as it passes O.
   (c) Calculate its displacement 0.8 s after release and state its position relative to O.

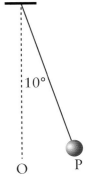

**Solution**

(a) Period, $T = \dfrac{2\pi}{\omega}$, so: $\omega = 2\pi \div 2.2 = 2.85$ rad s$^{-1}$

To find the amplitude, $A$:

$\sin 10° = \dfrac{A}{1.25}$ , so $A = 1.25 \sin 10° = 0.22$ m

Acceleration at P $= \omega^2 A = (2.85)^2 \times 0.22 = 1.79$ m s$^{-2}$

(b) Velocity $= \omega A = 2.85 \times 0.22 = 0.62$ m s$^{-1}$

(c) Displacement $= A \cos \omega t$
But $\omega t = 2.85 \times 0.8 = 2.28$ rad. Convert this to degrees $= 360 \times 2.28 \div 2\pi = 130.7°$.
So displacement $= A \cos 130.7° = -0.14$ m.
The minus sign indicates that the pendulum is to the left of O.

## Damping

A swinging pendulum involves a repeated conversion of energy from kinetic to potential and back to kinetic. In theory this process would continue forever. However, in reality, if a pendulum is allowed to oscillate, the amplitude gradually decreases until eventually it stops oscillating. Why does this happen?

In the real world, resistive forces due to the presence of air and friction between the string and the suspension point cause energy to be gradually converted to heat until all the kinetic energy is lost. Resistive forces, like these, that act on an oscillating system are known as **damping** forces. How an oscillating system behaves depends on the size of the damping forces. The graphs below show the effect of different sizes of damping forces.

**Undamped oscillations** are said to be **free vibrations** (ie perfect SHM). The displacement varies periodically as shown. However the amplitude remains constant with time.

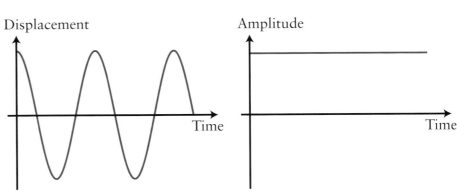

When a system is **lightly damped** the displacement will vary with time, as with free oscillations. However the amplitude of the oscillations will gradually get smaller until eventually the oscillations cease.

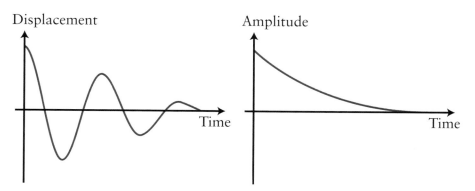

When a system is **over-damped** it does not oscillate when displaced from its equilibrium position. The system returns very slowly to the equilibrium position, as shown on the right.

When the damping forces are such that the system can return to its equilibrium position in the shortest possible time then we have **critical damping**.

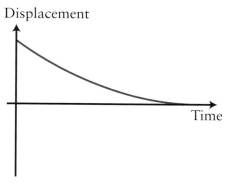

The shortest possible time for any oscillating system to return to its equilibrium position is ¼$T$ where $T$ is the periodic time, as shown in the graph on the right. Electrical meters, such as ammeters, are critically damped so that the pointer moves to the reading as quickly as possible without any oscillation.

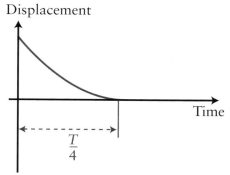

## Forced vibrations and resonance

A **forced vibration** occurs when any external force which varies with time is used to make an object oscillate. Example include pushing a child on a swing, or making a mass on a spring oscillate by holding it and moving your hand up and down.

Forced vibrations can be demonstrated using Barton's pendulums. This consists of a number of paper cone pendulums of various lengths, as shown in the diagram. A paper clip is placed inside each cone. All are suspended from the same string as a 'driver' pendulum which has a heavy bob. The length of this driver pendulum is the same as **one** of the paper cone pendulums.

The driver pendulum is pulled to one side and released. After a time all the pendulums will

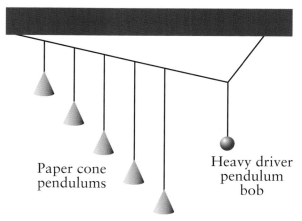

Paper cone pendulums

Heavy driver pendulum bob

oscillate with very nearly the same frequency as the driver, but with different amplitudes. However, the paper cone with the same length as the driver pendulum has the largest amplitude. This is called **resonance**.

The length of the pendulum determines its periodic time and hence its frequency. Resonance takes place when the frequency of the driving force is the **same** as the frequency of the oscillating system.

The graph on the right shows how the amplitude of a forced vibration depends on the frequency of the force causing it to vibrate (the driver frequency). The amplitude reaches a maximum when the frequency of the driving force equals that of the natural frequency of the oscillating system.

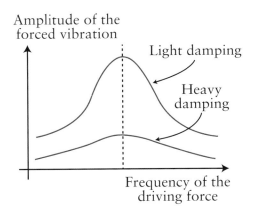

When the damping force is small (light damping) the peak is sharp. However when the frictional or damping forces are greater the peak is broader, and in fact the maximum occurs at a slightly lower frequency.

## Examples of resonance

Resonance can be a destructive phenomenon in **mechanical systems**. The photographs below show the destruction of a suspension bridge over the Tacoma Narrows in the USA in 1940. The speed of the wind blowing over the bridge on a particular day caused a forced vibration which matched the natural frequency of the bridge, eventually resulting in its collapse. Wind tunnels are now used to ensure such effects are avoided when designing structures, ranging from bridges to the wings of an aircraft.

Image ©1940 The Camera Shop, Tacoma. Used with permission.

Image ©1940 The Camera Shop, Tacoma. Used with permission.

**Musical instruments** rely on resonance to make their sound more audible. A guitar string has a number of frequencies at which it will naturally vibrate. These natural frequencies are known as the **harmonics** of the guitar string. Each of these harmonics is associated with a standing wave pattern. Plucking a string, so that it vibrates, produces a sound that is barely audible on its own. In a guitar it is the vibrations of the air inside the body of the guitar that produce the louder sound that we hear. The vibrations of the string cause the air inside the guitar to vibrate at the same frequency. This is resonance.

# 4.5 The Nucleus

**Students should be able to:**

4.5.1    Describe alpha-particle scattering as evidence of the existence of atomic nuclei;

4.5.2    Interpret the variation of nuclear radius with nucleon number;

4.5.3    Use the equation $r = r_0 A^{1/3}$ to estimate the density of nuclear matter;

## Atomic structure

By the end of the nineteenth century the notion that atoms were indivisible particles of matter was beginning to crumble. The study of cathode rays, positive rays and radioactivity had made it clear that atoms contained particles of positive and negative charge. However, how these charges were arranged inside the atom was still unknown.

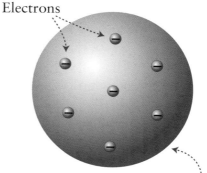

Electrons

Uniform, positively charged sphere

In 1902, Lord Kelvin expressed the opinion that an atom might consist of a sphere of positive charge with negative electrons dotted about inside it. This idea was taken up in 1903 by Sir JJ Thomson, who developed his 'Plum Pudding Model' in which the atom was regarded as a positively charged sphere in which the negatively charged electrons were distributed like currants in bun in sufficient numbers to make the atom as a whole electrically neutral, as shown in the diagram on the right.

In 1906, the New Zealand physicist Ernest Rutherford at McGill University in Canada noticed that α-particles (alpha particles) went easily through mica without making holes in it as a bullet might. This led him to suspect that the α-particles were passing right through the atoms themselves rather than pushing atoms out of the way.

Rutherford also noticed that some of the α-particles were deflected out of their straight-line paths as they went through the mica, and he thought that this was caused by electric repulsion between the positively charged part of the mica atoms and the positive α-particles. Shortly afterwards Rutherford left Canada to become Professor of Physics at Manchester where, with post-graduate students Hans Geiger and Ernest Marsden, he carried out a series of experiments on the scattering of α-particles by thin metal films.

The most celebrated of these experiments was carried out with thin gold foil. The diagram overleaf shows the apparatus. A source of α-particles was contained in an evacuated chamber (ie, in a vacuum). The α-particles were incident on a thin gold foil whose plane was perpendicular to their direction of motion. The α-particles were detected by the flashes of light (scintillations) they produced when they hit a glass screen coated with zinc sulphide. The experiment had to be carried out in a vacuum in order to prevent the α-particles being deflected by collisions with gas atoms.

Rutherford found that:
- most of the α-particles were undeflected,
- some were scattered by appreciable angles,
- about 1 in 8000 was 'back-scattered' through a very large angle indeed.

The back-scattering was so unexpected that Rutherford later wrote: *"It was quite the most incredible event that ever happened to me in my life. It was almost as incredible as if you fired a 15-inch shell at a piece of tissue paper and it came back and hit you."*

Based on these results, Rutherford correctly deduced (as shown in the diagram on the right):

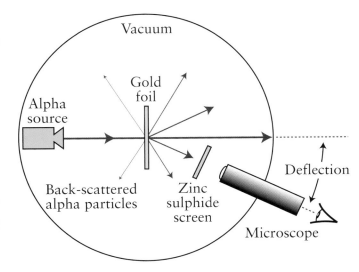

- The majority of the α-particles passed straight through the metal foil because they did not come close enough to any repulsive positive charge at all.
- All the positive charge and most of the mass of an atom formed an exceptionally small, dense core or nucleus.
- The negative charge consisted of a 'cloud of electrons' surrounding the positive nucleus.
- Only when a positive α-particle approached sufficiently close to the nucleus, was it repelled strongly enough to be 'back-scattered' through a large angle.
- The small size of the nucleus explains why only a small number of α-particles that were repelled in this way.
- Most of an atom is empty space.

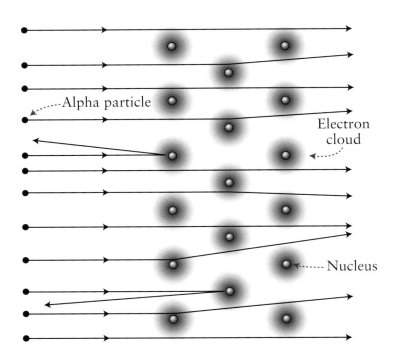

## Nuclear radius

It was a challenging exercise for physicists to determine the size of a nucleus by experiment. This is because the nucleus does not have a sharp edge; rather we should describe the edge of a nucleus as being 'fuzzy'. Nevertheless, physicists obtained an early indication of the size of a nucleus by firing α-particles at it. The physicists were able to measure the distance of closest approach which gave an approximate upper limit to the size of a nucleus. Early experiments suggested that the nucleus might be considered to be a sphere of radius $\approx 10^{-15}$ m.

Suppose we assume that the volume of a nucleon (ie, a proton or a neutron) in any nucleus is about the same. Then the volume of the nucleus would be directly proportional to the total number of nucleons contained within it (ie, the **mass number**, $A$). If we also suppose the nucleus to be spherical, then the radius of the nucleus is directly proportional to $A^{1/3}$. This allows us to write:

$r = r_0 A^{1/3}$     where   $r$ = radius of a given nucleus (m)
                               $r_0$ = the constant of proportionality (m)
                               $A$ = mass number (number of nucleons within the nucleus)

The constant of proportionality, $r_0$, in the equation above is the radius of the nucleus for which $A = 1$, ie it is the radius of a proton. The value of $r_0$ is found by experiment to be **approximately** $1.2 \times 10^{-15}$ m or 1.2 femtometres (sometimes written 1.2 fm or 1.2 fermi). However, it must be emphasised that the value of $r_0$ is not a well-defined constant and different values are obtained using different experimental techniques.

## Nuclear density

We can show that the density of nuclear matter is constant, ie that all atomic nuclei have the same density.

Volume, $V$, of a sphere of radius, $r$, is given by $V = \dfrac{4\pi r^3}{3}$

Mass, $M$, of a spherical nucleus of radius, $r$, is given by:

$M = \rho \dfrac{4\pi r^3}{3}$   where   $M$ = mass of nucleus (kg)
                            $\rho$ = density of nuclear matter (kg m$^{-3}$)

However, $r = r_0 A^{1/3}$, so therefore we can write:

$M = \rho \dfrac{4\pi r_0^3 A}{3}$

We can also write the mass, $M$, of a nucleus as:

$M = Am$     where   $A$ = mass number
                          $m$ = mass of a nucleon

This allows us to write:

$Am = \rho \dfrac{4\pi r_0^3 A}{3}$

Cancelling $A$ on both sides leaves us with:

$m = \rho \dfrac{4\pi r_0^3}{3}$

This can be rearranged to give an equation for the density of nuclear matter:

$\rho = \dfrac{3m}{4\pi r_0^3}$

Since $m$ and $r_0$ are both constant values, the density of nuclear matter, $\rho$, must therefore also be constant.

Using the values $r_0 = 1.2 \times 10^{-15}$ m and $m$, the mass of the proton, as $1.66 \times 10^{-27}$ kg, we can calculate the density of nuclear matter to be:

$$\rho = \frac{3m}{4\pi r_0^3} = \frac{3 \times 1.66 \times 10^{-27}}{4\pi \times (1.22 \times 10^{-15})^3} = 2.3 \times 10^{17} \text{ kg m}^{-3}$$

which is an amazing 230 000 000 000 000 times greater than the density of water! The enormous density of nuclear matter in comparison with everyday matter is a reflection of the fact that in ordinary matter there is a great deal of empty space between the nucleus and the orbiting electrons. There is no empty space between the particles inside the nucleus.

## Exercise 4.5

1 Experimental evidence for the existence of atomic nuclei was provided by the scattering of α-particles through a thin gold foil. The apparatus is shown in the diagram.
   (a) Name those parts indicated by the letters A to D.
   (b) Describe how Geiger and Marsden carried out their observations.
   (c) The observations led to three important conclusions about the nucleus. State what they are and how the observations supported the conclusions.
   (d) Why was it essential that the region containing the parts marked in the diagram was a vacuum?

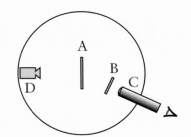

2 The nuclear radius of many elements were measured and their values, along with the mass number $A$ of the element, is shown in the table below.

| Mass number $A$ | 1 | 4 | 12 | 16 | 28 | 32 | 40 |
|---|---|---|---|---|---|---|---|
| Nuclear radius $r$ / fm | 1 | 2.08 | 3.04 | 3.41 | 3.92 | 4.02 | 4.54 |

   (a) The nuclear radii are measured in fm. What does fm stand for?
   (b) The relationship between the radius, $r$, and the mass number, $A$, is of the form $r = kA^n$. Plot a suitable linear graph and use it to find $k$ and $n$.

3 The relationship between nuclear radius and atomic mass number is shown below.

$r = r_0 A^{1/3}$

$r_0$ is the mean nucleon radius and equals 1.2 fm.

The relationship between volume of a sphere and its radius is given below.

$V = \dfrac{4\pi r^3}{3}$

The mean mass of a nucleon is $1.66 \times 10^{-27}$ kg.
   (a) Use these two relationships to determine the nuclear density of the $^{16}_{8}$O (oxygen-16) nucleus.
   (b) Oxygen has an atomic density of 1.4 kg m$^{-3}$. Explain the difference between the atomic density and the nuclear density.

4 (a) Calculate the volume of the nucleus of calcium with a mass number 40.
   (b) Calculate the nuclear density of the calcium-40 nucleus.

(c) The atomic density of calcium is approximately $1.6 \times 10^3$ kg m$^{-3}$. Estimate by how many orders of magnitude the nuclear density of calcium is bigger than the atomic density of calcium and account for the difference.

5 The nucleus of silver is described by the notation $^{107}_{47}$Ag. Calculate the density of the silver nucleus. Take $r_0$ to be equal to $1.2 \times 10^{-15}$ m, and the average mass of a nucleon to be $1.66 \times 10^{-27}$ kg.

6 A nucleus can be regarded as a sphere of radius $r$. The mass number of the element is $A$. The mass of each nucleon is $m$.
(a) Write down an expression for the volume of the nucleus.
(b) Write down an expression for the mass of the nucleus.
(c) Using the relationship between the nuclear radius and the mass number show that nuclear density is independent of mass number.

7 A nucleus has a volume of $4.1 \times 10^{-43}$ m$^3$.
(a) Calculate the radius of the nucleus.
(b) Calculate the mass number $A$ of the nucleus. (Take $r_0 = 1.2$ fm.)

# 4.6 Nuclear Decay

**Students should be able to:**

4.6.1    Demonstrate an understanding of how the nature of alpha particles, beta particles and gamma radiation determines their penetration and range;

4.6.2    Calculate changes to nucleon number and proton number as a result of emissions;

4.6.3    Demonstrate an understanding of the random and exponential nature of radioactive decay;

4.6.4    Use the equation $A = -\lambda N$, where $\lambda$ is defined as the fraction per second of the decaying atoms;

4.6.5    Use the equation $A = A_0 e^{-\lambda t}$, where $A$ is the activity;

4.6.6    Define half-life;

4.6.7    Use the equation $t_{\frac{1}{2}} = \dfrac{0.693}{\lambda}$;

4.6.8    Describe an experiment to measure half-life of a radioactive source.

## The nucleus

The diameter of an atom is around $10^{-10}$ m. Every atom has a central, positively charged nucleus with a diameter of around $10^{-15}$ m. Therefore an atom is typically 100 000 times larger than its nucleus. Over 99.9% of the mass of an atom is in its nucleus. Atomic nuclei are totally unaffected by chemical reactions.

Atomic nuclei contain **protons** and **neutrons**. These are collectively known as **nucleons**. Electrons are not normally found in the nucleus. The properties of nucleons are compared with those of the electron in the table below.

|  | Electron | Proton | Neutron |
|---|---|---|---|
| Relative Mass (relative to the proton) | $^1/_{1840}$ | 1 | 1 |
| Actual Mass ($m_e$ = mass of the electron) | $9.109 \times 10^{-31}$ kg ($= 1\ m_e$) | $1.673 \times 10^{-27}$ kg or $1836\ m_e$ | $1.675 \times 10^{-27}$ kg or $1839\ m_e$ |
| Relative Charge | $-1$ | $+1$ | 0 |
| Charge | $-1.60 \times 10^{-19}$ C | $+1.60 \times 10^{-19}$ C | Zero |

Nucleons are held together by one of the four fundamental forces of nature, the **strong interaction**. This nuclear force acts over very short distances and is much stronger than the electric force of repulsion that exists between protons within the nucleus.

### Isotopes

**Isotopes** are nuclei with the **same number of protons but differing numbers of neutrons**. An isotope is described using two numbers and the chemical symbol of the element:

$^{A}_{Z}$X     where  $A$ = Mass number, the total number of nucleons in
                                                          the nucleus

                  $Z$ = Atomic number, the total number of protons in
                                                          the nucleus

                  X = the chemical symbol of the element

So, for example, the isotope of uranium having 238 nucleons in its nucleus, of which 92 are protons, is given the symbol:

$^{238}_{92}$U

Hydrogen has three stable isotopes, hydrogen (1p), deuterium (1p, 1n) and tritium (1p, 2n). These are written as follows:

$^{1}_{1}$H   $^{2}_{1}$H   $^{3}_{1}$H

## Radioactivity

Some elements have unstable isotopes whose nuclei disintegrate randomly and spontaneously. This effect known as **radioactivity**. It was first noticed by Becquerel in 1896 when he observed that some photographic plates which had been stored close to a uranium compound had become fogged. In his honour, the name Becquerel (Bq) is given to the unit of activity.

**1 Bq = 1 disintegration per second**

### Types of radiation

### Alpha (α) radiation

- Alpha radiation is made up of a stream of α-particles emitted from large nuclei.
- An α-particle is a helium nucleus with two protons and two neutrons, and so has a mass number of 4. The symbol for an α-particle is $^{4}_{2}$α or $^{4}_{2}$He.
- α-particles are positively charged and so will be deflected in a magnetic field.
- α-particles have poor powers of penetration and can only travel through about 4 centimetres of air. They can easily be stopped by a sheet of paper.
- Since α-particles move relatively slowly (about 6% of the speed of light) and have a high momentum they **interact with matter producing intense ionisation** – a typical α-particle can produce about **100 000 ion-pairs per centimetre of air** through which it passes.

**Note:** Ionisation is the process by which electrically neutral atoms or molecules are converted to electrically charged atoms or molecules (ions). It happens when an α-particle, β-particle or gamma ray causes an electron to be ejected from the atom or molecule. An ion-pair is the positively charged particle (positive ion) and the negatively charged particle (negative ion) simultaneously produced by an α-particle, β-particle or gamma ray interacting with the molecule.

- Alpha decay is described by the equation below:

Decaying parent nucleus        Daughter nucleus remains        α-particle emitted

$^{A}_{Z}$X        $\longrightarrow$        $^{A-4}_{Z-2}$Y        +        $^{4}_{2}$He

67

Note that the number of nucleons (mass number) is conserved ($A$ to $A - 4 + 4$) and the charge (atomic number) is also conserved ($Z$ to $Z - 2 + 2$).

## Beta (β) radiation

- Beta radiation is emitted from nuclei where the number of neutrons is much larger than the number of protons.
- A β-particle is a very fast electron (up to 98% of the speed of light) and thus it has relative atomic mass of about $^1/_{1840}$. The symbol for a β-particle is therefore $^{4}_{2}\beta$ or $^{0}_{-1}e$.
- β-particles are emitted by nuclei that contain too many neutrons to be stable. One of the neutrons changes into a proton and an electron. The proton remains inside the nucleus but the electron is immediately emitted from the nucleus as a β-particle.
- As β-particles are negatively charged, they will be deflected in a magnetic field. This deflection will be greater than that of α-particles, as the β-particles have a much smaller mass to charge ratio.
- β-particles move much faster than α-particles and so they interact less with matter than β-particles and have a greater penetrating power.
- β-particles can travel several metres in air, but are stopped by 5 mm thick aluminium foil.
- Beta radiation has an ionising power between that of alpha and gamma radiation. Ionising power is the energy the particle has that is capable of knocking electrons off an atom.
- Beta emission is described by the equation below:

Decaying parent nucleus     Daughter nucleus remains     β-particle emitted

$$^{A}_{Z}X \longrightarrow {}^{A}_{Z+1}Y + {}^{0}_{-1}e$$

Note that the total number of nucleons (mass number) does not change, but the atomic number ($Z$) of the daughter nucleus ($Z + 1$) is greater than that of the parent ($Z$) by 1.

## Gamma (γ) radiation

- Unlike alpha and beta radiation, gamma radiation does not consist of particles but short wavelength, high energy electromagnetic waves known as gamma rays (γ-rays) which are emitted from unstable nuclei.
- The wavelength of γ-rays is characteristic of the nucleus that emits it. The wavelengths of γ-rays are typically in the region $10^{-10}$ to $10^{-12}$ m. (X-rays can also have wavelengths in this range, but it is the method of production that differentiates X-rays from γ-rays.)
- Like alpha and beta radiation, gamma radiation comes from a disintegrating unstable nucleus.
- As there are no particles, gamma radiation has no mass.
- As there are no charged particles, a magnetic field has no effect on gamma radiation.
- Gamma radiation has great penetrating power, travelling several metres in air.
- A thick block of lead or concrete is used to greatly reduce the effects of gamma radiation, but cannot stop it completely. A lead block about 5 cm

thick will absorb around 90% of the γ-rays.

- Gamma radiation has the weakest ionising power as it interacts least with matter.
- The decay equation for this is:

Nuclide in excited state      Nucleus remains      γ-radiation emitted

$$_{Z}^{A}X^* \longrightarrow \quad _{Z}^{A}X \quad + \quad \gamma$$

**Note:** You studied the concept of excitation in the AS course.

## The law of radioactive decay

Radioactive nuclei disintegrate **spontaneously and randomly**. This means that we can neither tell **which** particular nuclei in a given sample are going to decay nor can we tell **when** they are going to decay. However, if we have sufficiently large numbers of nuclei in our sample, the random decay of individual nuclei averages out in such a way as to be governed by empirical laws. The rate of disintegration cannot be speeded up or slowed down by any known means (temperature, pressure, particle size, chemical reactions etc).

The number of unstable nuclei (and hence the activity) decreases exponentially and is governed by the equation:

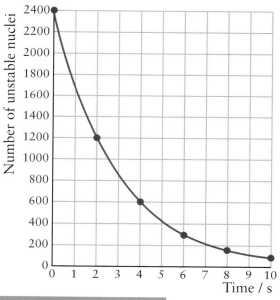

$N = N_0 e^{-\lambda t}$    where   $N$ = number of unstable nuclei present after a time, $t$

$N_0$ = number of unstable nuclei present at time $t = 0$

$t$ = time (s)

$\lambda$ = decay constant (s⁻¹) discussed below

The graph on the right shows an example of exponential decay.

**Note:** e is a mathematical constant that you will find on your calculator.

**The rate of decay of a particular radioactive element is directly proportional to the number of unstable nuclei of that nuclide present.**

If there are $N$ unstable nuclei present at time $t$, then the rate of disintegration with time of the unstable nuclei, $A$, is given by:

$A = -\lambda N$    where   $A$ = rate of disintegration of the unstable nuclei of the source, called the **activity** of the source (Bq)

$\lambda$ = decay constant (s⁻¹) discussed below

$N$ = number of unstable nuclei present

The minus sign is present because as $t$ increases $N$ decreases.

The decay constant λ

The decay constant, λ, is defined as **the fraction of the unstable nuclei that decay per second**, and is measured in units of $s^{-1}$.

One of the isotopes of Protactinium $^{234}_{91}$Pa has a decay constant of $1.01 \times 10^{-2}$ $s^{-1}$. A mass of 1 mg of this isotope contains $2.57 \times 10^{18}$ unstable nuclei. Therefore at this instant the number of nuclei that are decaying per second is given by:

$1.01 \times 10^{-2} \times 2.57 \times 10^{18} = 2.60 \times 10^{16}$ nuclei

As time passes there are few unstable nuclei so the number that decay each second gradually decreases. Therefore the **activity also decreases exponentially with time** since it is directly proportional to the number of unstable nuclei present. This means that we can also write:

$A = A_0 e^{-\lambda t}$    where  $A$ = activity at time, $t$ (Bq)
$A_0$ = initial activity at time $t = 0$ (Bq)
$t =$  time (s)
$\lambda$ = decay constant ($s^{-1}$)

# Half–life $t_{\frac{1}{2}}$

The half-life of a radioactive nuclide, $t_{\frac{1}{2}}$, is **the time taken for half of the radioactive nuclei present to disintegrate**. We know that:

$N = N_0 e^{-\lambda t}$

After one half-life has passed only half the unstable nuclei remain, so:

$\frac{N_0}{2} = N_0 e^{-\lambda t_{\frac{1}{2}}}$

Dividing both sides by $N_0$ gives:

$\frac{1}{2} = e^{-\lambda t_{\frac{1}{2}}}$

Taking natural logs of both sides gives:

$\log_e 1 - \log_e 2 = -\lambda t_{\frac{1}{2}}$

And since $\log_e 1 = 0$, on re-arranging we get:

$\log_e 2 = 0.693 = \lambda t_{\frac{1}{2}}$

Since $\log_e$ is more frequently written as ln, so we get:

$\ln 2 = 0.693 = \lambda t_{\frac{1}{2}}$

This can be rearranged to give the following equation for the half-life, $t_{\frac{1}{2}}$:

$t_{\frac{1}{2}} = \dfrac{0.693}{\lambda}$    where  $t_{\frac{1}{2}}$ = half-life (s)
$\lambda$ = decay constant ($s^{-1}$)

Half-life can also be defined in terms of the activity: **the half-life of a radioactive material is the time taken for the activity of that material to fall to half of its original value.**

## Worked Examples

1  A sample of radioactive phosphorous has an activity of 1000 Bq. Seven days later the activity was found to have decreased by 29%.
   (a) What is the decay constant for this isotope of phosphorous? Give your answer in days$^{-1}$.
   (b) Calculate the half-life of the isotope of phosphorous in days.
   (c) Calculate the number of atoms of phosphorous in the sample.

### Solution

(a) $A = A_0 e^{-\lambda t}$. Taking logs to base e of both sides gives:

   $\ln A = \ln A_0 - \lambda t$. We know that $A = 71\%$ of 1000 Bq, so:

   $$\lambda = \frac{(\ln A_0 - \ln A)}{t} = \frac{(\ln 1000 - \ln 710)}{7} = 0.0489 \text{ days}^{-1}$$

(b) $t_{\frac{1}{2}} = \dfrac{0.693}{\lambda} = \dfrac{0.693}{0.0489} = 14.2$ days

(c) Note that since activity is measured in Bq (disintegrations per second), $\lambda$ must first be converted from units of days$^{-1}$ to units of s$^{-1}$. Therefore:

   $$N = \frac{A}{\lambda} = \frac{1000}{0.0489 \div (24 \times 3600)} = 1.77 \times 10^9 \text{ atoms}$$

   Note: the minus sign is not needed when calculating the value of $N$ or $A$. The minus sign is there to indicate that the number of unstable nuclei decreases with time.

2  A small volume of a solution containing a radioactive isotope has an activity of $1.2 \times 10^4$ disintegrations per minute. This solution is injected into the bloodstream of a patient. After 30 hours a 1 cm$^3$ sample of the blood is found to have an activity of 0.5 disintegrations per minute. The half life of the isotope is 15 hours.
   (a) Estimate the volume of blood in the patient.
   (b) Another radioisotope of the same activity and emitting the same type of radiation of the same energy but with a half-life of 2.6 years is available. Give one advantage and one disadvantage of using this for estimating the volume of blood in the patient.

### Solution

(a) Total initial activity $A_0 = 1.2 \times 10^4$ disintegrations per minute

   Since $t_{\frac{1}{2}} = 15$ hours, then total final activity after 30 hours (2 half-lives) is:

   ½ × ½ × $1.2 \times 10^4$ = 3000 disintegrations per minute.

   The activity in 1 cm$^3$ sample of the blood is 0.5 disintegrations per minute, therefore the total volume of blood = 3000 ÷ 0.5 = 6000 cm$^3$ = 6 litres.

(b) Advantage: The very long half-life means that the activity of the sample is very low, which is therefore likely to cause least radiation damage to patient.

   Disadvantage: The time required to get the same activity from 1 cm$^3$ blood is two half-lives – but 5.2 years is an unacceptably long time for both medical staff and the patient. Moreover, exceptionally sensitive equipment would be required to measure the change in activity over a 30 hour period.

3  A certain isotope used in medical physics has a half-life of 3.0 minutes. It is taken from a locked cupboard and prepared for injecting into a patient's vein. The time taken to make up the required solution is exactly 2.0 minutes and at that time the isotope has an activity of 500 Bq. Calculate the activity at the time when the isotope was removed from the cupboard.

**Solution**

$$\lambda = \frac{0.693}{t_{\frac{1}{2}}} = \frac{0.693}{3} = 0.231 \text{ minutes}^{-1}$$

We must find the activity at time $t = -2.0$ minutes:

$$A = A_0 e^{-\lambda t} = 500 \times e^{-0.231 \times (-2.0)} = 500 \times e^{0.462} = 500 \times 1.5872 = 794 \text{ Bq}$$

**Note:** The same result is reached whether the calculation uses minutes or seconds. The important point is to ensure that if $\lambda$ is calculated in minutes$^{-1}$, then $t$ should be calculated in minutes, and if $\lambda$ is calculated in seconds$^{-1}$, then $t$ should be calculated in seconds.

## Measuring the half-life of a radioactive substance

Two common methods are used in schools and colleges to measure the half-life of a radioactive substance. One involves the use of an ionisation chamber and a source of radon gas ($^{220}$Rn). This isotope of radon emits $\alpha$-particles. The other method involves the use of a Geiger-Müller tube, a scaler or ratemeter and a source of protactinium ($^{234}$Pa). This isotope of protactinium emits $\beta$-particles.

### Finding the half-hife of radon–220 with an ionisation chamber

The apparatus for this experiment is shown in the diagram below. The ionisation chamber consists of an aluminium can about the size of one used for baked beans. A metal rod (the negative electrode) can be mounted centrally within the chamber. The metal can is insulated from its mounting but the whole chamber

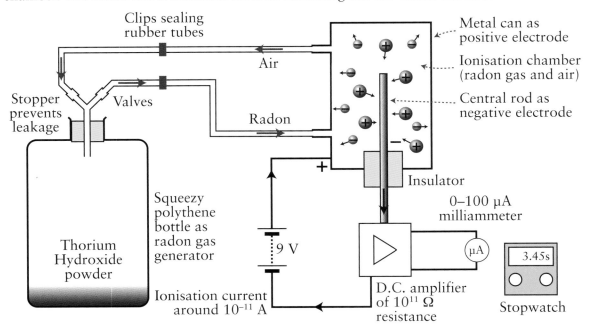

screws directly onto the input of the DC amplifier so that the connection between its central negative electrode and the amplifier is as short as possible.

When in operation, a voltage of about 9 V is maintained between the central electrode and the can itself. Suppose now there is a source of α-particles within the chamber. These α particles cause considerable ionisation of the air inside the chamber. The electron-ion pairs so formed will move apart under the influence of the electric field between the central electrode and the metal can. When these particles strike the appropriate electrode, they cause a tiny electric current, called the ionisation current, to flow. This small ionisation current is fed into a DC amplifier which amplifies it about 100 million times until it is large enough to work a moving-coil milliammeter.

The experiment is carried out the following sequence of steps:

**1. Adjust the DC amplifier**
- Set the input selector switch to the set-zero position so that the input of its amplifier is short-circuited and the input is zero.
- Adjust the set-zero control to give a zero output current on the milliammeter.
- Select the highest resistance input, usually $10^{11}$ Ω.

**2. Fill the ionisation chamber with radon gas**
- Connect the polythene bottle radon generator to the ionisation chamber with the two thin rubber tubes.
- Release both clips on the tubes.
- Squeeze the bottle two or three times until the reading on the milliammeter just goes past full-scale deflection.
- Refit both clips on the tubes.

**3. Take readings**
- Start the clock as the milliammeter current reading falls to full-scale deflection.
- Read and record the current every 10 seconds for about three minutes.

As the number of radon gas atoms in the chamber gets smaller and smaller they emit fewer and fewer α particles. These produce fewer and fewer ions and so as time passes a smaller ionisation current flows. **The ionisation current is directly proportional to the number of radon atoms remaining and hence to the activity of the gas within the chamber.** The time taken for the ionisation current to fall to half its initial value is therefore the half-life of radon.

### Using the results to find the half-life

There are **two** possible approaches to finding the half-life once the results have been recorded. One is to plot a graph of the readings of ionisation current, $I$, against time, $t$, and draw a **smooth curve** through the points. Then read from the graph three time intervals during which the current had fallen by 50%. These three times represent the half-life of radon–220 and, if the experiment has been carried out correctly, should all be around 52 seconds. Take the mean of these three values as the half-life of radon–220. An example of such a graph is shown overleaf (left hand side).

Another approach is to plot a **linear** graph. Since the ionisation current, $I$, is directly proportional to the activity of the gas within the chamber, then:

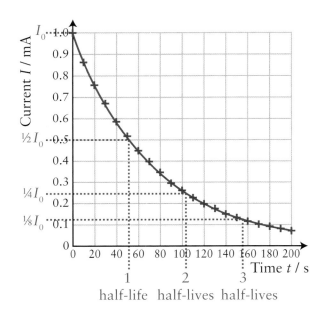

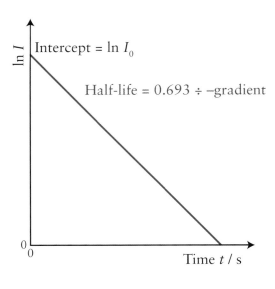

$I = I_0 e^{-\lambda t}$     where  $I_0$ = the current at time $t = 0$ (A)
$\lambda$ = the decay constant (s$^{-1}$)

Taking natural logs of both sides gives:

$\ln I = \ln I_0 - \lambda t$

Comparing this equation with that for a straight line, $y = mx + c$, we see that a graph of $\ln I$ ($y$-axis) against time, $t$ ($x$-axis) will be a straight line of gradient $-\lambda$ and $y$-axis intercept $\ln I_0$.

Therefore we can plot a graph of $\ln I$ ($y$-axis) against time ($x$-axis), draw the straight line of best fit. We then determine its gradient, which is $-\lambda$, and hence find $\lambda$. An example of such a graph is shown above (right hand side).

We can then find the half-life by calculating the value of $\dfrac{0.693}{\lambda}$.

### Measuring the half-life of protactinium-234 using a scaler (counter)

The apparatus for this experiment is shown in the diagram below. The experiment involves the use of a Geiger-Müller (GM) tube and a counter to measure the activity of a sample of protactinium. When alpha, beta or gamma

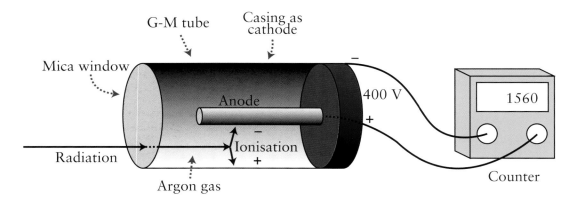

radiation enters the GM tube, it causes some of the argon gas inside to ionise and give an electrical discharge. This discharge is detected and counted by the counter. If the counter is connected to its internal speaker, you can hear the click when radiation enters the tube.

However, even in the absence of all known sources of radioactivity, the GM tube and counter still detects radiation. This is known as **background radiation** and it comes from the Sun, cosmic rays from space, hospital nuclear physics departments, nuclear power stations, granite rocks and so on.

Before we use a GM tube to carry out any quantitative work on radiation we must first measure the background radiation if we are to correct for it in our experiment.

The experiment is carried out the following sequence of steps:

### 1. Measure the background radiation
- Remove known sources of radiation from the laboratory, then set the GM counter to zero. Switch on the counter and start a stopwatch.
- After 30 minutes read the count on the counter. Divide the count by 30 to obtain the background count rate in counts per minute. A typical figure is around 15 counts per minute.
- This background count must **always** be subtracted from any other count when measuring the activity from a specific source.

### Setting up the protactinium source
- Protactinium-234 is one of the decay products of uranium-238 and any compound of uranium-238 will have within it traces of protactinium. These traces may be conveniently extracted from it by chemical means.
- The protactinium decays by β-emission into another long-lived isotope of uranium ($^{234}U$) which is itself α-emitting. The very long half-life of $^{234}U$ (246 000 years) indicates low radioactivity, and in any case, is not enough to interfere with this experiment. Moreover, the α particles which are emitted will not penetrate the polythene bottle containing the protactinium.
- The β-activity at any instant of the extracted solution can therefore be used as a measure of the quantity of protactinium still present in it.
- A simple practical arrangement is that shown on the right. A thin-walled polythene bottle is filled with equal volumes of an acid solution of uranyl nitrate and pentyl ethanoate.

### 3. Take readings
- When the liquids are shaken up together the organic ethanoate removes most of the protactinium present. The solutions are not miscible and the protactinium remains in the upper layer when the liquids have once more separated.
- The β-activity of the protactinium is observed with a GM tube and ratemeter, and the count-rate is recorded at 10 second intervals.
- Allowance is then made for the background count of the GM tube. If, say, the measured rate with the GM

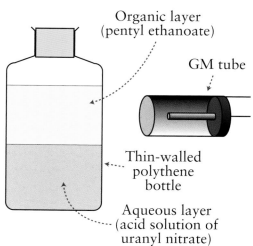

Organic layer
(pentyl ethanoate)

GM tube

Thin-walled
polythene
bottle

Aqueous layer
(acid solution of
uranyl nitrate)

tube and ratemeter is 32 counts per minute and the background rate is 15 counts per minute, then the corrected count rate is 32 – 15 = 17 counts per minute.

### Using the results to find the half-life

The corrected count rate of the protactinium is taken as a measure of its activity, $A$. By the law of radioactive decay:

$A = A_0 e^{-\lambda t}$    where   $A_0$ = the activity at time $t = 0$ (Bq)
$\lambda$ = the decay constant ($s^{-1}$)

Taking natural logs of both sides gives:

$\ln A = \ln A_0 - \lambda t$

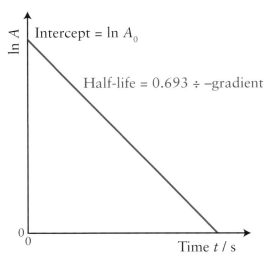

Intercept = $\ln A_0$

Half-life = 0.693 ÷ −gradient

Comparing this equation with that for a straight line, $y = mx + c$, we see that a graph of $\ln A$ ($y$-axis) against time, $t$ ($x$-axis) will be a straight line of gradient $-\lambda$ and $y$-axis intercept $\ln A_0$.

Therefore we can plot a graph of $\ln A$ ($y$-axis) against time ($x$-axis), draw the straight line of best fit. We then determine its gradient, which is $-\lambda$, and hence find $\lambda$. An example of such a graph is shown on the right.

We can then find the half-life by calculating the value of $\frac{0.693}{\lambda}$.

The generally accepted value for the half-life of protactinium-234 is 68 seconds.

**Safety notes for these experiments**

- Teachers must satisfy themselves before carrying out these demonstrations that they are fully compliant with the various regulations governing the use of ionising radiations in schools.
- In the first experiment, it is essential that the coupling between the can and the DC amplifier is absolutely air tight and that the rubber tubing connecting the radon gas generator to the ionisation chamber is neither worn nor cracked. While α-particles themselves have a short range in air, the radon gas which emits them presents a serious hazard if ingested and every precaution must be taken to prevent radioactive radon getting into the atmosphere.
- At the end of a practical session do not immediately dismantle the ionisation chamber. Leave it for half an hour until the remaining radioactivity has decayed to a very low level.

## Exercise 4.6

1  A radioactive decay series can be represented on a graph of mass number, $A$, ($y$-axis) against atomic number, $Z$. Part of a table for such a series is given below.
   (a) In what ways do mass number and atomic number change in:
      (i) $\alpha$-decay (ii) $\beta$-decay?
   (b) Copy and complete the table below.
   (c) Plot the points on a graph of mass number ($y$-axis) against atomic number ($x$-axis) to show the decay of each element. Join the points with arrows to show the decay.
   (d) Explain why the emission of a gamma ray cannot be shown on such a graph.
   (e) Identify two pairs of isotopes using the table.

| Element (symbol) | Atomic number | Mass number | Decays by emitting | Leaving element |
|---|---|---|---|---|
| U | 92 | 238 | $\alpha$ | Th |
| Th | 90 | 234 | $\beta$ | Pa |
| Pa | 91 | 234 | $\beta$ | |
| | 92 | 234 | $\alpha$ | |
| | 90 | 230 | | Ra |
| Ra | 88 | 226 | | Rn |
| Rn | 86 | | | Po |
| Po | | 218 | $\alpha$ | Pb |
| Pb | | | | Bi |
| Bi | 83 | | | Po |

2  Copy and complete the following decay equations:
   (a) $^{226}_{88}\text{Ra} \rightarrow\; ^{—}_{—}\text{Rn} + \;^{—}_{—}\text{He}$        (b) $^{238}_{—}\text{U} \rightarrow\; ^{—}_{90}\text{Th} + \alpha$        (c) $^{—}_{37}\text{Rb} \rightarrow\; ^{87}_{—}\text{Sr} + e$

3  The radioactive isotope calcium-49 has a half-life of 8.5 minutes.
   (a) Calculate the decay constant of this isotope.
   (b) How many nuclei of this isotope are needed to produce an activity of 200 Bq?

4  (a) Define the terms 'half-life' and 'decay constant'.
   (b) Derive the relationship between these two quantities.

5  To determine the amount of wear in a car engine, a piston ring was made from a radioactive metal. The mass of the piston ring was 0.20 kg. The radioactive substance used had a half-life of 49 days. When it was installed in the engine it had an activity of $3.0 \times 10^5$ Bq. The engine was run for 50 days. When the engine oil was tested it was found to have a total activity of 50 Bq. What mass of metal was removed from the piston ring and deposited in the engine oil?

6  A radioactive source was to be used in an experiment and the activity required at the start of the experiment was to be 4000 Bq. The half-life of the radioactive element used in the source was 38 days. The apparatus and the source were assembled 24 hours before the experiment was to begin. What would the activity be at the time the apparatus was assembled?

7  At time $t = 0$ two radioactive sources X and Y have equal numbers of atoms. Source X has a half-life of 30 s and source Y has a half life of 60 s. What is the ratio of the activity of X to that of Y after 120 s have passed?

8  Carbon-14 has a half-life of $1.81 \times 10^{11}$ s. A sample of wood is found to have an activity of $5.00 \times 10^6$ Bq. How many atoms of carbon-14 are contained in this sample of wood?

9  Trees absorb carbon dioxide from the atmosphere. One isotope of carbon, $^{14}_{6}$C is radioactive and when the tree dies the radioactivity of the wood of the tree decreases with time. Carbon dating is a method to determine the age of wood from an archaeological site. The half-life of carbon-14 is 5730 years. The activity of 0.2 kg of wood from an archaeological site has an activity of 1.5 disintegrations per minute. A modern sample of the same wood of mass 1 kg has an activity of 20 disintegrations per minute. Calculate the age of the wood from the archaeological site.

10 (a) What type of decay is represented by the arrows X and Y in the graph below?
   (b) What is the mass number and atomic number of the nucleus Z?

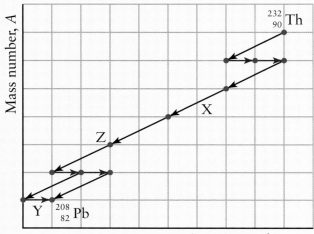

11 The emission of alpha particles from a radioactive nucleus can be used to kill cancer cells. The radioactive isotope used has a half-life of 11.4 days. The radioactive sample used has to matched to the mass of the patient. In a case the required activity is 80 kBq for every 1 kg of the patient's mass. The patient has a mass of 60 kg. Calculate the initial activity required if the sample is prepared 1 day in advance of the treatment.

12 Technetium-99m is used in nuclear medicine to study a range of functions in the human body. It emits gamma rays of energy 140 keV and has a half-life of 6 hours. A patient is injected with Tc-99 with activity $4 \times 10^6$ Bq. The gamma rays emitted from the patient are detected and used to diagnose any illness. Calculate the time it takes for the total gamma ray energy emitted by the patient to half to $1.0 \times 10^{-8}$ J.

13 Many dice can be used to model the radioactive decay process. 500 dice are thrown. Any that land as a '6' are removed from the pile before the next throw. In this model, the 'throw number' is equivalent to the 'time taken' in radioactive decay.
   (a) What does the number of dice removed after each throw represent?

   The table on the next page shows the results of carrying out this model.

| Throw number | 0 | 1 | 3 | 3 | 4 | 5 | 6 | 7 |
|---|---|---|---|---|---|---|---|---|
| Number of 6s | - | 83 | 70 | 58 | 48 | 40 | 34 | 28 |
| Number of dice remaining | 500 | 417 | 347 | 289 | 241 | 201 | 167 | 139 |

(b) Using the data in the table plot a graph of ln (number of dice remaining) against throw number.

(c) Use the graph to find the decay constant.

(d) Use your graph to find the theoretical half-life of the dice in units "number of throws".

# 4.7 Nuclear Energy

4.7.1    Demonstrate an understanding of the equivalence of mass and energy;

4.7.2    Recall and use the equation $E = \Delta mc^2$ and demonstrate an understanding that it applies to all energy changes;

4.7.3    Describe how the binding energy per nucleon varies with mass number;

4.7.4    Describe the principles of fission and fusion with reference to the binding energy per nucleon curve.

## Equivalence of mass and energy

In 1905 Albert Einstein published a remarkable paper which astonished the scientific community. It was called 'The Special Theory of Relativity', and it dealt with the speed of light for observers moving with a constant velocity relative to each other. The predictions made by Einstein's Special Theory have now all been shown to be true. However, for the purpose of this chapter, the important assertion made by Einstein was that **there is an equivalence to a mass, *m*, and energy, *E*,** given by the equation

$E = mc^2$    where  $E$ = energy (J)

$m$ = mass (kg)

$c$ = the speed of light in a vacuum (m s$^{-1}$) = $3 \times 10^8$ m s$^{-1}$

What does the notion that mass and energy are equivalent really mean? It tells us, for instance, that when 1 kg of uranium in a nuclear power station undergoes fission and releases $8 \times 10^{13}$ J of energy, there is a corresponding reduction in mass of $E \div c^2$, or $8 \times 10^{13} \div 9 \times 10^{16}$ kg, which is about $9 \times 10^{-4}$ kg. Of course, this is a tiny reduction in mass, but that mass reduction is measurable and actual measurements have confirmed Einstein's ideas. Equally, under certain circumstances, very high energy electromagnetic waves, called cosmic rays, can vanish, leaving behind two particles, an electron and a positron. And the remarkable thing is that the reduction in the energy due to the annihilation of the cosmic ray is exactly the same as the equivalent mass of the positron and the electron, according to Einstein's equation.

Chemical reactions release relatively little energy compared to nuclear reactions. Burning 1 kg of oil, for example, releases about $5 \times 10^7$ J of energy. According to Einstein's equation this results in a reduction in mass of about $5.5 \times 10^{-10}$ kg. It is now firmly established that **wherever** energy is released there will **always** be a reduction in mass. Raising the temperature of a beaker of water, striking a football so that it moves faster, causing an electric current to make a bulb shine all cause a mass reduction – but, of course, the energy involved is so tiny that the mass reduction **is extremely small**.

## The electron-volt (eV) and the unified atomic mass unit (u)

The values of 1 joule and 1 kilogram are much too large to be useful when dealing with atomic and nuclear processes. A much more appropriate unit for energy is the electron-volt (eV). The electron volt is defined as the kinetic energy possessed by an electron accelerated from rest through a voltage of one volt. However, for our purposes it is sufficient to know that:

$1 \text{ eV} = 1.6 \times 10^{-19} \text{ J}$

$1 \text{ MeV} = 1 \text{ million eV} = 1.6 \times 10^{-13} \text{ J}$

The masses of nucleons, electrons, nuclei and atoms are usually given in **unified atomic mass units (u)**, where:

$1 \text{ u} = \dfrac{1}{12}$ of the mass of the carbon-12 atom

$1 \text{ u} = 1.66 \times 10^{-27} \text{ kg}$

It is sometimes helpful to remember that $1 \text{ u} = 1.49 \times 10^{-10} \text{ J} = 931 \text{ MeV}$

## Nuclear binding energy

If you place 100 g on a top-pan balance and then add another 100 g you would expect the combined mass to be 200 g, and you would be correct. It will therefore be a surprise to learn that the mass of a nucleus is **always less** than the sum of the masses of its constituent nucleons. This difference in mass is called the **mass defect** of the nucleus where:

mass defect = total mass of the nucleons − mass of the nucleus

This reduction in mass arises due to the act of combining of the nucleons to form the nucleus. When the nucleons are combined to form a nucleus a tiny portion of their mass is converted to energy. This energy is called the **binding energy** of the nucleus. The binding energy is the amount of energy that has to be supplied to separate the nucleons completely, ie to an infinite distance apart.

Recall from Einstein's special theory of relativity that a change in mass $\Delta m$ is equivalent to an amount of energy, $E$:

$E = \Delta mc^2$      where   $E$ = energy (J)
                       $\Delta m$ = change in mass (kg)
                       $c$ = the speed of light in a vacuum (m s$^{-1}$)

The binding energy of a nucleus is therefore:

**binding energy = mass defect (kg) × $c^2$**

Binding energies can be given in joules (J), but are usually quoted in millions of electron volts (MeV).

**Worked Example**

1 The mass of a proton is 1.0078 u, and the mass of a neutron is 1.0087 u. Given that the mass of a Helium nucleus is 4.0026 u, calculate the binding energy of Helium in MeV.

Solution

The He nucleus contains 2 protons and 2 neutrons.
mass of protons = 2 × 1.0078 u = 2.0156 u
mass of neutrons = 2 × 1.0087 u = 2.0174 u
mass of constituent nucleons = 2.0156 + 2.0174 = 4.0330 u
mass defect = mass of nucleus − mass of constituent nucleons = 4.0026 − 4.0330 = 0.0304 u

To find the binding energy we must first convert the mass defect to kg.
Since 1 u = $1.66 \times 10^{-27}$ kg we have: $\Delta m = 0.0304 \times 1.66 \times 10^{-27}$ kg
binding energy = $\Delta mc^2 = 0.0304 \times 1.66 \times 10^{-27} \times (3 \times 10^8)^2 = 4.54 \times 10^{-12}$ J

Finally, convert this to MeV. Since 1 MeV = $1.6 \times 10^{-13}$ J:
binding energy = $4.54 \times 10^{-12} \div 1.6 \times 10^{-13} = 28.39$ MeV

A useful measure of the **stability** of a nucleus is the **binding energy per nucleon**:

average binding energy per nucleon = binding energy ÷ number of nucleons

For Helium the average binding energy per nucleon is therefore:

28.39 ÷ 4 = 7.1 MeV

The average binding energy per nucleon varies with nucleon number as shown below. Note that a graph of average binding energy per nucleon against atomic number has a similar shape.

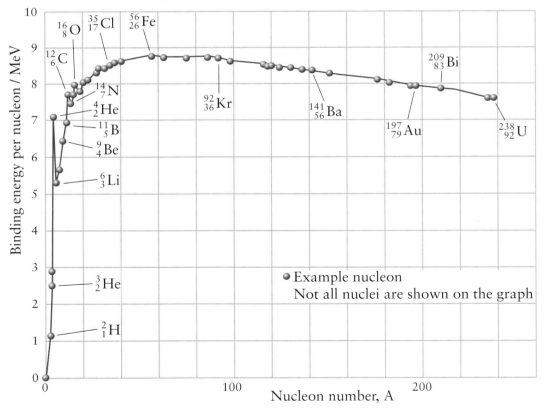

## Nuclear fission

In nuclear fission a massive nucleus is divided and breaks up into two less massive nuclei. The average binding energy of these fission fragments is **higher** than that of the original, heavy nucleus. Because of this increase in the total binding energy, some of the mass of the heavy nucleus is converted to kinetic energy of the fission fragments. The graph of average binding energy per nucleon, shown on the previous page, indicates why the release of energy via fission can only happen with heavier nuclei.

---

### Worked Example

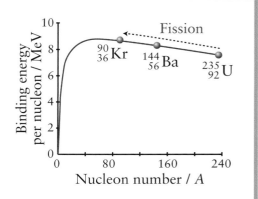

1  Uranium-235 undergoes fission when it absorbs a neutron. One possible fission reaction is:

$$^{235}_{92}U + ^{1}_{0}n \rightarrow ^{144}_{56}Ba + ^{90}_{36}Kr + 2^{1}_{0}n + Q \text{ (energy)}$$

This is illustrated in the diagram on the right. Given the masses below, calculate how much energy, $Q$, is released by this fission reaction, in MeV.

Mass of $^{235}_{92}U$ nucleus = 235.12 u

Mass of $^{144}_{56}Ba$ nucleus = 143.92 u

Mass of $^{90}_{36}Kr$ nucleus = 89.94 u

Mass of neutron $^{1}_{0}n$ = 1.0087 u

Solution

Mass on left hand side of reaction = 235.12 + 1.00087 = 236.1287 u

Mass on right hand side = 143.92 + 89.94 + (2 × 1.0087) = 235.8774 u

Mass reduction = 236.1287 − 235.8774 = 0.2513 u

Convert this to kg = 0.2513 × $1.66{\times}10^{-27}$ kg = $4.17158{\times}10^{-28}$ kg

Energy released, $Q = mc^2 = 4.17158{\times}10^{-28} \times (3{\times}10^8)^2$ J = $3.76442{\times}10^{-11}$ J

Convert this to MeV = $3.76442{\times}10^{-11} \div 1.6{\times}10^{-13}$ MeV

$Q$ = 234.7 MeV

---

## Nuclear fusion

Fusion is the joining of lighter nuclei to produce a heavier and more stable nucleus. The fusion process results in the release of energy since the average binding energy of these fusion products is **higher** than that of the lighter nuclei which join together. Because of this increase in the total binding energy, some of the mass of the lighter nuclei is converted to kinetic energy of the fusion product – ie, the mass of the heavier nucleus is less than the total masses of the two light nuclei that fuse. The graph of average binding energy per nucleon, shown on the previous page, indicates why the release of energy via fusion can only happen with lighter nuclei.

The reaction cannot take place at room temperature because of the repulsive electric force between the positively charged nuclei. Only when the speed of the colliding nuclei is great enough for the nuclei to overcome this repulsive force can they come close enough for the attractive, but very short-range, strong nuclear force to trigger fusion. For example, hydrogen nuclei can only fuse when their temperature is about 15 million degrees Celsius.

---

**Worked Example**

1  The formula below is the fusion reaction for two deuterium nuclei, as illustrated in the diagram on the right. When these two nuclei fuse they produce a nucleus of helium. The letter $Q$ represents the quantity of energy released in the reaction. Given the masses below, calculate the value of $Q$, in MeV.

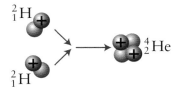

Before        After

$^2_1H + {}^2_1H \rightarrow {}^4_2He + Q$ (energy)

Mass of $^2_1H$ nucleus = 2.014102 u

Mass of $^4_2He$ nucleus = 4.002604 u

Solution

Mass on left hand side of reaction = 2.014102 + 2.014102 = 4.028204 u

Mass reduction = 4.028204 − 4.002604 = 0.0256 u

Convert this to kg = 0.0256 × 1.66×10⁻²⁷ kg = 4.2496×10⁻²⁹ kg

Energy released, $Q = mc^2$ = 4.2496×10⁻²⁹ × (3×10⁸)² J = 3.82464×10⁻¹² J

Convert this to MeV = 3.82464×10⁻¹² ÷ 1.6×10⁻¹³ MeV

$Q$ = 23.9 MeV

---

**Exercise 4.7**

1  According to Einstein's theory of special relativity, mass and energy were equivalent as shown in the equation $E = \Delta mc^2$.
(a) Explain what is meant by the mass defect, $\Delta m$, of an atomic nucleus.
(b) Explain what is meant by the binding energy, $E$, of a nucleus.

Using the data below, calculate the following, giving your answers in MeV:
(c) the binding energy of $^{16}_8O$,
(d) the average binding energy per nucleon in $^{16}_8O$.

*Data:*
Mass of $^{16}_8O$ nucleus = 15.9905 u          Mass of neutron = 1.0087 u
Mass of proton = 1.0078 u

2  Consider the following decay in which an isotope of thorium decays to radium by α-particle emission:

$^{228}_{90}Th \rightarrow {}^{224}_{88}Ra + {}^4_2\alpha$

*Data:*
Mass of $^{228}_{90}Th$ nucleus = 227.97929 u          Mass of $^{224}_{88}Ra$ nucleus = 223.97189 u
Mass of α-particle = 4.00151 u          1 u = 1.66×10⁻²⁷ kg

(a) Use the information given in the data box to calculate the mass difference in unified atomic mass units (u) between the LHS and the RHS of the equation.

(b) Express this mass difference in kg.

(c) Use Einstein's equation to convert this mass difference into (i) J and (ii) MeV.

(d) In what form does this energy appear?

3 An isotope of aluminium decays by beta emission to silicon:

$$^{29}_{13}\text{Al} \longrightarrow ^{29}_{13}\text{Si} + ^{0}_{-1}\beta$$

*Data:*

Mass of $^{29}_{13}\text{Al}$ nucleus = 28.97330 u

Mass of $^{29}_{13}\text{Si}$ nucleus = 28.96880 u

Mass of β-particle = 0.000549 u

Use the data above to calculate the energy released by this decay.

4 Use the data below to calculate the energy released when a uranium-236 nucleus undergoes fission according to:

$$^{236}_{92}\text{U} \longrightarrow ^{146}_{57}\text{La} + ^{87}_{35}\text{Br} + 3^{1}_{0}\text{n}$$

*Data:* Binding energy per nucleon of

uranium-236 = 7.59 MeV     lanthanum-146 = 8.41 MeV     bromine-87 = 8.59 MeV

5 A nuclear submarine has an average power requirement of 500 kW. It obtains this from the fission of uranium-235. The fuel is enriched uranium containing 3% uranium-235 and 97% uranium-238 by mass. The energy released in each fission is $3\times10^{-11}$ J.

(a) Calculate the number of uranium–235 atoms in 1 kg fuel.

(b) Estimate how long 1 kg of this fuel would last.

6 The mass of the isotope $^{7}_{3}\text{Li}$ is 7.018 u. Find the binding energy of the $^{7}_{3}\text{Li}$ nucleus given that the mass of the proton is 1.008 u and the mass of the neutron is 1.009 u. Take 1 u $\equiv$ 931 MeV.

7 The fusion of a lithium-6 nucleus and a deuterium nucleus produces 2 helium-4 nuclei.

(a) Show this fusion reaction as a nuclear equation.

The energy released in this reaction is approximately 3.6 pJ.

(b) (i) Convert this energy to MeV.

   (ii) Calculate the energy released per nucleon of fuel used. Give your answer in MeV.

   (iii) The energy released in the fission of one uranium-235 nucleus is approximately 32 pJ. Comment on your answer to (b) (ii) in comparison with the energy released per nucleon in this fission reaction.

(c) State two other advantages of fusion over fission.

8 One example of a fusion reaction involving hydrogen is:

$$^{6}_{3}\text{Li} + ^{1}_{0}\text{n} \longrightarrow ^{4}_{2}\text{He} + ^{3}_{1}\text{H}$$

Use the data below to calculate the energy released in this reaction. Give your answer in J. Show your working clearly.

*Data:* Nuclear masses:

$^{6}_{3}\text{Li}$ = 6.0151u     $^{3}_{1}\text{H}$ = 3.016030 u     $^{4}_{2}\text{He}$ = 4.002604 u     $^{1}_{0}\text{n}$ = 1.008665 u

9  A proton has a mass of 1.00728 u, a neutron has a mass of 1.00867 u and an electron has a mass of 0.00055 u. The mass of a neutral helium atom is 4.00260 u.

(a) (i) By how much is the mass of this helium atom less than the mass of its constituents? Give you answer in kg.

   (ii) What name do nuclear physicists give to this mass difference?

(b) A neutron of mass 1.00867 u is fired at the helium atom. Calculate the minimum speed of the neutron if its energy is just enough to break the atom up into separate protons, neutrons and electrons.

10 One example of a fusion reaction involving hydrogen is:

$$_1^2H + {_1^2}H \longrightarrow {_2^3}He + {_0^1}n$$

The energy released in this reaction is 3.28 MeV. Using the data below, calculate the mass of the neutron in kg.

*Data:* Nuclear masses:

$$_1^2H = 2.014102 \text{ u} \qquad _2^3He = 3.016030 \text{ u}$$

11 The fission of uranium-235 produces a number of different reactions. Three of these are shown below. Complete the reactions by stating the correct value for the letters W, X and Y.

$$_{54}^{142}Xe + {_{38}^{90}}Sr + W{_0^1}n + energy$$

$$_{92}^{235}U + {_0^1}n \longrightarrow {_X^{139}}Ba + {_{36}^{94}}Kr + 3{_0^1}n + energy$$

$$_{55}^{144}Cs + {_{37}^{Y}}Rb + 2{_0^1}n + energy$$

12 A common fission reaction involves $_{92}^{235}U$ absorbing a neutron and splitting with the release of energy. In one such reaction, the result is the nuclei $_{56}^{141}Ba$ and $_{36}^{92}Kr$ plus some neutrons result. The fission releases 173.2 MeV of energy.

(a) Write down the equation for the fission reaction described above.

(b) What form does this energy release take?

(c) Using the data below calculate the mass, in kg, of a single neutron.

*Data:*

Mass of $_{92}^{235}U$ nucleus = 235.0439 u

Mass of $_{36}^{92}Kr$ nucleus = 91.9265 u

Mass of $_{56}^{141}Ba$ nucleus = 140.9143 u

13 The mass of a carbon-14 ($_6^{14}C$) nucleus is 14.0032 u. The mass of a proton is 1.0073 u and the mass of a neutron is 1.0087 u. Calculate the binding energy, in MeV, for carbon-14.

14 The mass of a certain star in a distant galaxy is $2 \times 10^{30}$ kg and its surface temperature is 6000 K. It radiates energy at a constant rate of $3.8 \times 10^{26}$ W due to nuclear fusion. Calculate:

(a) how long it would take for 0.5% of its mass to be lost during this process.

(b) the root mean square speed of a hydrogen atom on the surface of this star.

You may assume that the mass of an atom of hydrogen is $1.67 \times 10^{-27}$ kg and that 1 year = $3.16 \times 10^7$ s.

15 Calculate the kinetic energy of the products when uranium-235 undergoes fission by the following reaction.

$$^{235}_{92}U + ^{1}_{0}n \longrightarrow ^{92}_{36}Kr + ^{141}_{56}Ba + 3^{1}_{0}n$$

Use the masses given below to calculate the total amount of energy released. Give your answer in MeV to 3 significant figures.

*Data:* Nuclear masses:

$^{235}_{92}U = 235.0439$ u          $^{92}_{36}Kr = 91.8976$ u          $^{141}_{56}Ba = 140.9136$ u          $^{1}_{0}n = 1.0087$ u

# 4.8 Nuclear Fission and Fusion

4.8.1　Demonstrate an understanding of the terms chain reaction, critical size, moderators, control rods, cooling system and reactor shielding, as used in describing a fission reactor;

4.8.2　Demonstrate an understanding of the social, environmental, security and economic issues surrounding the use of nuclear power as a solution to a future energy crisis;

4.8.3　Describe the ITER (tokamac concept) fusion reactor in terms of fuel, D-T reaction, temperature required, plasma, three methods of plasma heating, vacuum vessel, blanket, magnetic confinement of plasma, difficulties of achieving fusion on a practical terrestrial scale, and advantages and disadvantages of fusion;

4.8.4　Describe the following methods of plasma confinement: gravitational, inertial and magnetic.

## Nuclear fission

In the previous chapter we looked at the principles of nuclear fission. In this chapter we will examine in some detail how physicists bring about the conditions in which controlled nuclear fission can occur, so as to generate the heat needed to produce steam for electricity production. In that chapter we saw that one possible fission reaction process was:

$$^{235}_{92}U + ^{1}_{0}n \longrightarrow ^{144}_{56}Ba + ^{90}_{36}Kr + 2^{1}_{0}n + energy$$

But this is only one of several reactions which can occur. Another is:

$$^{235}_{92}U + ^{1}_{0}n \longrightarrow ^{141}_{56}Ba + ^{92}_{36}Kr + 3^{1}_{0}n + energy$$

This reaction is illustrated graphically below.

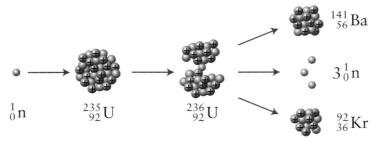

$^{1}_{0}n$　　$^{235}_{92}U$　　$^{236}_{92}U$　　$^{141}_{56}Ba$　$3^{1}_{0}n$　$^{92}_{36}Kr$

Regardless of which reaction occurs, the fission of uranium always has the following features:

- It always releases huge quantities of energy, about **80%** of which is carried away by the kinetic energy of the two major fission fragments. Burning one atom of carbon (eg, in the form of coal) typically releases 5 eV. By contrast, the fission of one uranium nucleus releases more than 200 million eV.
- The fission fragments are often radioactive and their subsequent decay accounts for approximately a further **10%** of the total energy released.
- Extremely penetrating and highly dangerous gamma rays are always produced along with the fission fragments. These gamma rays and the kinetic

energy of the sub-atomic particles produced account for the remaining **10%** energy released.

### Chain reactions

When a uranium atom undergoes fission, further neutrons are produced, on average around 2.5 per fission. There are three possible fates for the fission neutrons produced:

- they might escape from the uranium fuel where they were formed without causing a further fission,
- they might be absorbed by a neighbouring nucleus, again without causing fission,
- they might cause further fission in a neighbouring nucleus.

If enough neutrons go on to cause further fission, then the reaction will sustain itself and fission will continue to take place. This is called a **chain reaction**.

An **uncontrolled** chain reaction is what takes place in an atomic bomb, releasing enormous amounts of energy in a very short time. However, the focus of this chapter is how to bring about a **controlled chain reaction** in a **fission reactor**, for example to generate electricity.

## Fission nuclear reactors

There are four common types of fission nuclear reactor: the Magnox type, the Advanced Gas-cooled Reactor (AGR), the Pressurised Water Reactor (PWR) and the Fast Reactor. The UK's oldest nuclear reactors were of the Magnox type, so-called because the natural uranium fuel was clad in a tube made of magnesium alloy. AGRs use circulating gas, almost invariably carbon dioxide, as the coolant. The 'coolant' is the material used to transfer energy away from the nuclear reactor to generate electricity. PWRs use water as the coolant, under such high pressure that even at a temperature of over 200°C it remains liquid. Fast reactors use plutonium rather than uranium as the fuel and liquid sodium as the coolant. Fast reactors tend to be used in nuclear-powered submarines. Because the AGR is now the most common type of reactor used in the UK, the remainder of our discussion shall be limited to that reactor type.

At the time of writing, around 11% of the world's electricity came from nuclear reactors. Nuclear power is viewed by many as a way of meeting the world's electricity needs while making progress towards a reduction in greenhouse gas emissions. However it does have disadvantages, as we shall discuss later in this chapter.

### Nuclear fuel and moderators

Natural uranium consists of about 99.3% uranium-238 and 0.7% uranium-235. Uranium-238 is fissile (meaning, it can undergo nuclear fission), but only with very fast neutrons. Conversely, uranium-235 is fissile only with slow neutrons (known as thermal neutrons). The neutrons emitted in the fission of uranium-235 are too slow to cause fission in uranium-238, but **need to be slowed down even**

**further** to cause further fission in uranium-235. This is achieved by the use of a material called a **moderator,** of which the most common types are graphite, water ($H_2O$) or heavy water (deuterium oxide or $D_2O$).

Because natural uranium contains only 0.7% uranium-235, it needs to be **enriched** so that the uranium within the reactor is more likely to undergo fission with slow neutrons. This involves adding extra uranium-235 to natural uranium so increasing the proportion of uranium-235 to uranium-238 within the fuel. Enrichment for the production of civil nuclear power raises the proportion of fissile uranium-235 from about 0.7% in the natural ore to about 3%. Enrichment for military purposes requires a much greater proportion of the uranium to be fissile uranium-235. Another element, plutonium-239, is also fissile with slow neutrons, and so this material is also sometimes added to natural uranium during fuel reprocessing.

### Design of a nuclear reactor

The AGR is an example of a **graphite moderated reactor**. In this reactor the enriched uranium is in long, sealed tubes, called **fuel rods** which are arranged inside a block of graphite. The neutrons released by the fission of uranium-235 collide with the atoms of the graphite moderator and are slowed down to a speed where they are more likely to cause further fission in uranium-235 than to be absorbed by the uranium-238. The general design of an AGR fission reactor is shown in the diagram below:

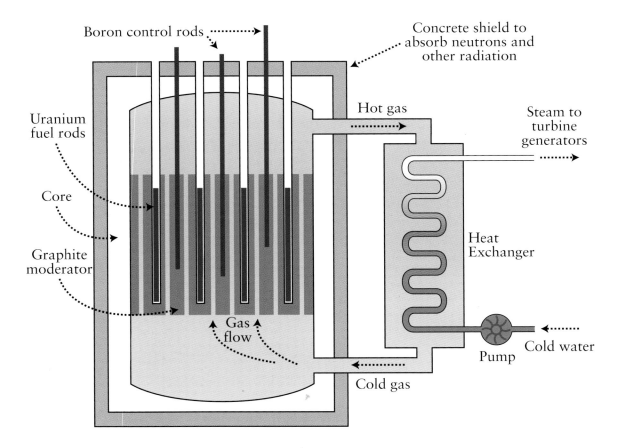

## Critical size

The bigger the size of the uranium fuel assembly in a nuclear reactor, the more likely it is that a fission neutron will go on to produce another fission event and produce a chain reaction. We can define the **critical size** of the fuel assembly as that which is **just capable of sustaining a chain reaction** within it. The critical size for uranium-235 is about that of a small football. Below the critical size, too many of the neutrons which might have induced further fission escape and the chain reaction dies away. A typical nuclear power station has a fuel assembly which is around 5% above the critical size.

*Above: The Hunterston B nuclear power station (the building on the left) in Scotland, contains a pair of AGR reactors.*

## Control rods

If, on average, much more than one of the neutrons produced by fission went on to cause further fission, then the reaction would quickly go out of control. Boron has a high affinity for absorbing neutrons. So, **boron-coated steel rods, called control rods, are used to capture excessive neutrons** before they can cause fission. When the control rods are lowered into the reactor the number of available neutrons is decreased and fewer fission events can occur.

## Coolant

The heat energy produced by the fission reaction is removed by passing a coolant through the reactor. This coolant then passes its energy to water by flowing through a **heat exchanger**, which produces steam that then drives the **turbines** which turn the **electricity-producing generators**. The part of a nuclear power station associated with the turbines and generators is exactly the same as would be seen in a conventional power station burning fossil fuels – the only difference is the source of the energy used to produce the steam.

## Reactor shielding

Every civil reactor is surrounded by a very thick concrete shield to prevent potentially dangerous radiation, particularly very penetrating gamma waves and neutrons, from reaching workers and the wider community.

# Nuclear fusion

### Fusion in the stars

Almost all of the energy we receive on Earth comes from the Sun as a result of **nuclear fusion**. All the elements which make up our material world, including the material in all living things on Earth, were formed by fusion in stars.

Stars like our Sun consist mainly of hydrogen and helium. In the previous chapter we saw how hydrogen nuclei can only fuse when their temperature is about 15 million degrees Celsius. These temperatures are achieved at the core of a star, resulting in a constant fusion of hydrogen nuclei. The reaction can be summarised by:

$${}^1_1H + {}^1_1H + {}^1_1H + {}^1_1H \rightarrow {}^4_2He + \text{other products} + \text{energy}$$

### Temperature required for nuclear fusion

In nuclear fusion, two light particles – say two protons – are brought sufficiently close together so that they fuse to form a more massive particle. However, protons are positively charged which means that as two protons come closer they repel each other. The closer they get the greater the repulsive force. For fusion to take place, they must get very close, certainly closer than the diameter of the nucleus (about $1 \times 10^{-15}$ m).

If the protons are projected towards each other the repulsion between their positive charges causes their kinetic energy to decrease and their potential energy to increase. This means that they must be projected towards each other at a very high speed if they going to get close enough to fuse.

The energy needed to bring a pair of protons sufficiently close to bring about fusion is *about* 110 keV. We can use this information to calculate the temperature to which the proton assembly must be heated.

Suppose we treat the collection of protons as a gas. Recall from chapter 4.2 that the temperature of a gas is a measure of the mean kinetic energy of the gas molecules and that:

$$\tfrac{1}{2}m<c^2> = \tfrac{3}{2}kT \qquad \text{where} \qquad \begin{array}{l} k = \text{Boltzmann's constant (J K}^{-1}) \\ T = \text{temperature (K)} \end{array}$$

What temperature is needed to give the protons an average kinetic energy of about 110 keV (where 1 keV = $1.6 \times 10^{-16}$ J)?

Mean kinetic energy $= \tfrac{3}{2}kT$, so:

$$T = \frac{2 \times \text{mean kinetic energy}}{3k} = \frac{2 \times 110 \times 1.6 \times 10^{-16}}{3 \times 1.38 \times 10^{-23}} = 850 \times 10^6 \text{ K}$$

### Plasma confinement

We have calculated that to bring protons sufficiently close to bring about fusion on a practical terrestrial scale requires a temperature of 850 million K. How can we achieve such high temperatures? Above 6000 K **all matter is in a gaseous**

first and foremost a large scale physics project, whose aim is to develop a reliable fusion reactor, and is not designed to produce electricity commercially.

## Nuclear energy, society and the environment

It is known that carbon dioxide in the Earth's atmosphere traps solar energy, by radiating infra-red radiation emitted from the planet's surface back to the Earth. In recent decades scientists have established that increasing levels of atmospheric carbon dioxide, largely driven by human activities, is causing global temperatures to rise, leading to harmful climate change.

The most effective way of halting or reducing this climate change is to reduce the amount of carbon dioxide emitted into the atmosphere by human activities. A significant source of carbon dioxide is the burning of fossil fuels to generate electricity, as shown in the pie chart. Therefore, replacing fossil fuels with other sources of energy is one way that we can reduce carbon dioxide emissions.

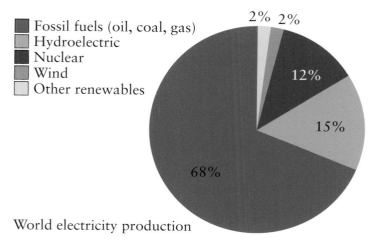

World electricity production

An increased use of nuclear energy has been proposed as a solution to the problem of carbon dioxide emissions. Nuclear power stations do not release carbon dioxide into the atmosphere. It is true that when the whole process is taken into account, including the mining, refining and recycling of uranium fuel rods, the amount of carbon dioxide released is many times more than that produced from renewable energy sources. However it is still many times less than burning fossil fuels.

Fossil fuels are also finite resources and will eventually run out, with oil likely to run out first. Due to our reliance on fossil fuels, many therefore foresee a future **energy crisis**. In order to generate sufficient power to replace fossil fuels, nuclear supporters argue that we must expand all other forms of energy production, including both renewable energy sources and nuclear power.

Opponents of nuclear energy argue that the environmental, health and security risks make it unsuitable as a replacement for fossil fuels. They argue that funds should be diverted away from nuclear power to develop renewable energy sources do not pose such risks. Some issues with nuclear power are:

- Nuclear energy (from fission) produces large quantities of toxic, radioactive waste and that must be stored safely and securely for between 10,000 years and 240,000 years in order to prevent health and environmental disasters from radioactive contamination. Finding safe storage facilities for this waste poses problems for many countries. Many would not welcome such storage facilities in their neighbourhood. One argument for ongoing research into nuclear fusion is that it does not produce waste products like this.

- Nuclear power creates employment opportunities for many people in the local area. However, those living close to nuclear power plants and radioactive waste storage sites have many concerns. The Chernobyl disaster in 1986 was the result of a flawed reactor design being operated by inadequately trained personnel. The resulting steam explosion and fire released at least 5% of the material in the radioactive reactor core into the atmosphere and downwind. Two Chernobyl plant workers died on the night of the accident, and a further 28 people died within a few weeks as a result of acute radiation poisoning. Many hundreds more probably died over the following years due to radiation. The Fukushima nuclear power plant in Japan lost power due to a tsunami in 2011, resulting in the reactor core overheating and melting, leading to around 150,000 people being evacuated from the surrounding area indefinitely. Both of these nuclear incidents caused huge economic, health and environmental damage to the area surrounding the power plants.

- Nuclear power is a secure source of energy provided the countries that provide the uranium ore have stable governments and societies. However, some sources of uranium ore are in countries that might be considered to be less stable. These source of uranium will become more important in the future as supplies from stable sources become depleted.

- Some of the technology used for nuclear power can also be used to produce nuclear weapons. A 'fast breeder' reactor uses a moderator that does not slow the fission neutrons down as effectively as a normal fission reactor would. These fast neutrons do not cause fission but are instead absorbed by uranium-238 to form plutonium-239. This plutonium can be processed either as fuel for reactors or to produce nuclear weapons. In some cases this type of reactor can produce more fuel than it actually uses, hence the name. This link between plutonium and nuclear weapons has led to concerns about the uncontrolled spread of nuclear weapons. The Nuclear Non-Proliferation Treaty of 1970 was devised as means of controlling the spread of such weapons. However, it also gave countries the right to develop nuclear energy for peaceful purposes. In recent years some countries, notably North Korea, have highlighted the dangers associated with developing nuclear weapons in conjunction with nuclear energy.

### Exercise 4.8

1 Describe fully the importance of each of the following in the functioning of a nuclear fission reactor:
   (a) Critical size
   (b) Chain reaction
   (c) Moderator
   (d) Control rods
   (e) Coolant

2 The neutrons emitted in nuclear fission reactions have an energy of 1 MeV. For U-235 to capture the neutrons leading to fission their energy must be reduced to less than 1 eV. In a reactor each collision with the atoms of the moderator reduces the kinetic energy of the

neutrons to 0.7 of their kinetic energy before collision. Calculate the number of collision required to reduce the kinetic energy of the neutrons from 1 MeV to 1 eV.

3 Nuclear fission is seen by many as a vital source of generating electricity.
(a) Make two lists, one of the environmental advantages and the other of the environmental disadvantages.
(b) List the concerns society has on the use of nuclear fission to generate electricity.

4 In order to produce a self-sustaining fusion reaction, the tritium and deuterium plasma must be heated to over 100 million K.
(a) Why is such a high temperature needed?
(b) How is plasma contained in the ITER fusion reactor?
(c) Nuclear fusion is the source of a star's energy. What type of containment is present in stars? Explain why this type of containment is not feasible on Earth.

5 (a) What is nuclear fusion?
(b) Copy and complete the deuterium–tritium reaction given below.
$$^{2}_{1}D + {}^{3}_{1}T \longrightarrow$$
(c) Give two reasons why this reaction is the most suitable reaction for terrestrial nuclear fusion.

6 (a) The ITER fusion reactor is described as a tokamak. What does this mean?
(b) Describe the three methods of plasma heating in the ITER fusion reactor.
(c) What is the function of the beryllium blanket surrounding the vacuum vessel which contains the plasma?

# Unit 5 (A2 2)
## Fields and their applications

# 5.1 Force Fields

**Students should be able to:**

5.1.1    Explain the concept of a field of force, using field lines to describe the field, indicate its direction and show the field strength.

## Fields of force

The idea of a field of force is familiar to us all. Bring a magnet close enough to a steel ball and we see the ball move towards the magnet's pole. Drop an object from a tall building and it accelerates to the surface below due to the gravitational force on it. These are both illustrations of fields of force. Indeed, one of the early experiments that physicists did on magnets was to use iron filings to reveal the shape of the field of force.

When physicists use the term **field of force**, they mean something more specific than the layperson does. For the physicist, a field of force is **a region of space within which objects with a particular property experience a force**. The table below illustrates the properties involved for three common force fields.

| Field | Property involved |
|---|---|
| Gravitational | Mass |
| Electric | Charge |
| Magnetic | Moving charge |

Note that the property and the field must match. For example, an uncharged mass will experience the gravitational force, but not the electrical force. A stationary particle with both mass and charge will experience both gravitational and electrical force, but not the magnetic force.

This enables us to state the following definitions:
- A **gravitational** field is a region of space within which **a mass** will experience a force.
- An **electric** field is a region of space within which **a charge** will experience a force.
- A **magnetic** field is a region of space within which **a moving charge** (or an electric current) will experience a force.

## Field lines

Field lines give us a visual picture of a field. The direction of the field at any point is given by the **tangent** to the field line, in the direction of the arrow, at that point. At any given point, the field has only one direction. It therefore follows that field lines **cannot cross**, because if they did it would mean that the field had more than one direction at that point, which is a contradiction.

We can draw conclusions about the field from the field lines. In general:
- **the closer** field lines are together, **the stronger** the field;

- where the field lines are **parallel and equally spaced**, we describe the field as **uniform**;
- where field lines appear to converge to or diverge from a point (ie, like radii), we describe the field as **radial**. Radial field lines are not equally spaced, so they represent a **non-uniform** field.

The diagrams below show typical field lines for three common types of field:
- the radial (non-uniform) gravitational field around the Earth;
- the radial (non-uniform) electric field around isolated electrical charges;
- the non-uniform magnetic field around a bar magnet.

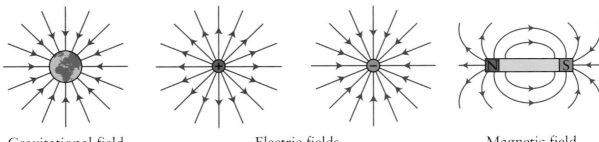

Gravitational field          Electric fields          Magnetic field

In some cases, it is possible to reveal the field by experiment. For example, magnetic fields can be disclosed using iron filings as shown below (left). The electric field between two plates held at a voltage of about 3 kV and a few centimetres apart can be disclosed by using fine semolina seeds suspended in about a 5 mm depth of warm castor oil, as shown below (right). Note that the electric field is uniform only in the space between the plates; at the edges of the plates the field lines curve.

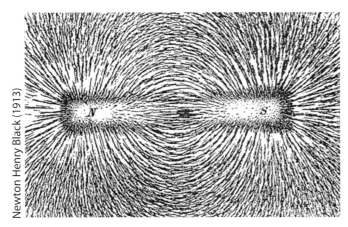

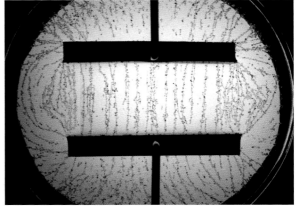

Newton Henry Black (1913)

sciencephotos / Alamy Stock Photo

# 5.2 Gravitational Fields

5.2.1    define gravitational field strength;

5.2.2    recall and use the equation $g = \dfrac{F}{m}$;

5.2.3    state Newton's law of universal gravitation;

5.2.4    recall and use the equation for the gravitational force between point masses, $F = G\dfrac{m_1 m_2}{r^2}$;

5.2.5    recall and apply the equation for gravitational field strength, $g = \dfrac{Gm}{r^2}$, and use this equation to calculate the mass, $m$;

5.2.6    apply knowledge of circular motion to planetary and satellite motion

5.2.7    show that the mathematical form of Kepler's third law ($T^2$ proportional to $r^3$) is consistent with Newton's law of universal gravitation;

5.2.8    demonstrate an understanding of the unique conditions of period, position and direction of rotation required of a geostationary satellite.

## Definition

We have already seen that a force field will exert a force on an object with the specific property associated with that field. However, it is very convenient to describe the strength of the field at any point as the force on a unit of that property.

In a gravitational field, the **gravitational field strength, g**, at a point is equal to the force which would be produced on a test mass of 1 kg at that point, ie:

$g = \dfrac{F}{m}$        where $g$ = gravitational field strength (N kg$^{-1}$)
$\qquad\qquad\qquad\quad$ $F$ = force (N)
$\qquad\qquad\qquad\quad$ $m$ = mass (kg)

**Field strength is a vector**, ie it has both magnitude and direction.

## Newton's law of universal gravitation

Following on from the work of Tycho Brahe and Johannes Kepler on the movement of the planets around the Sun, in 1687 Isaac Newton presented what today is known as **Newton's law of universal gravitation**. It states that:

**Between every two point masses there exists an attractive gravitational force, which is directly proportional to the product of the masses and inversely proportional to the square of their separation.**

Newton's law of universal gravitation can be expressed as an equation:

$F = G\dfrac{m_1 m_2}{r^2}$  where $m_1$ and $m_2$ = two respective point masses (kg)
$\qquad\qquad\qquad\quad$ $r$ = distance between $m_1$ and $m_2$ (m)
$\qquad\qquad\qquad\quad$ $G$ = a constant (the universal gravitational constant)

Note that when dealing with real objects, it is sufficient to imagine the entire mass to be concentrated at the centre of mass and to consider that point to be the point mass.

The generally accepted value of G is $6.67 \times 10^{-11}$ N m$^2$ kg$^{-2}$. The small value of G means that gravitational forces between objects can usually be ignored unless at least one of them has a particularly large mass. The gravitational force can certainly be ignored when considering forces that act on an inter-atomic and inter-molecular scale.

There are two other important facts about gravitational forces. The first is that they have **infinite range**, so they can operate over the vast distances which exist between galaxies. The second is that while we can shield objects from electrical and magnetic fields by placing them in a box made of soft iron, there is **no known way** to shield an object from a gravitational field.

## Gravitational field strength

### Field lines

In chapter 5.1 we saw how the direction of a gravitational field line at any given point shows the direction of the gravitational force on a mass at that point. For a uniform sphere the gravitational field pattern is described as **radially inwards**, because all the field lines appear to converge at the centre of mass of the sphere.

Notice that as one moves away from the surface of the sphere the field lines get further apart, which indicates that the strength of the field **decreases** with distance from the surface of the sphere. Similarly, the closer the field lines, the stronger the gravitational field.

The field lines strike the surface of the sphere at right angles. The radius of a planet such as the Earth is so large that for an observer on the surface the field lines can be considered to be parallel and equally spaced, as shown on the right. Such a field is, of course, a **uniform** field.

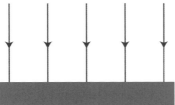

### Variation of gravitational field strength with height above the Earth's surface

Consider the gravitational force on a mass of 1 kg as it moves away from the surface of the Earth. Let the mass of the Earth be $m_E$. By Newton's law of universal gravitation, and remembering that the force on 1 kg is the gravitational field strength, $g$, we have:

$$g = F_{on\ 1\ kg} = G\frac{m_E \times 1}{r^2}$$

Therefore:

$$g = G\frac{m_E}{r^2}$$   where  $r$ = the distance from the centre of the Earth (m), and where
$r \geq$ the radius of the Earth, $R_E$.
$m_E$ = the mass of the Earth (kg)

From this equation we can see that $g$ varies inversely with $r^2$ and that $g$ has a maximum value on the surface of the Earth. At the Earth's surface the field strength, $g_0$ is given by:

$$g_0 = G\frac{m_E}{R_E^2}$$   where $g_0$ = gravitational field strength at the Earth's surface (N kg$^{-1}$), with the zero referring to the height above the surface

$R_E$ = the radius of the Earth (m)

$m_E$ = the mass of the Earth (kg)

**The mean value of $g_0$ on the Earth's surface is 9.81 N kg$^{-1}$.**

However, becauae the Earth is spinning on its axis, the radius at the equator is slightly greater than the radius at the poles. Therefore, the mean gravitational field strength at the equator is 9.78 N kg$^{-1}$ whereas at the poles it is 9.83 N kg$^{-1}$.

The graph on the right shows how gravitational field strength, $g$, varies with distance from the centre of the Earth, $r$. Note that the graph is a curve which touches neither the vertical nor the horizontal axis.

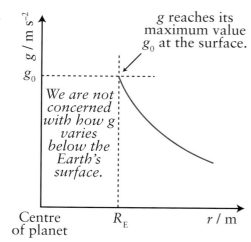

Distance from the planet's centre

### Calculating the mass of the Earth

The equation for $g_0$, above, provides an indirect way to estimate the mass of the Earth. The average value of $g$ over the surface of the Earth is generally taken as 9.81 m s$^{-2}$ and this can be measured by experiment. The radius of the planet can be found by observations of the fixed stars from points of known separation on the Earth's surface and is generally taken as around 6400 km.

Since: $g_0 = G\frac{m_E}{R_E^2}$ , we can write:

$$m_E = \frac{g_0 R_E^2}{G} = \frac{9.81 \times (6.4\times10^6)^2}{6.67\times10^{-11}} = 6.0\times10^{24} \text{ kg}$$

So, the mass of the Earth, $m_E = 6.0\times10^{24}$ kg.

---

### Worked Example

1   The Moon has a mass of $7.3\times10^{22}$ kg and orbits the Earth at a mean distance of 384 000 km. The mass of the Earth is $6.0\times10^{24}$ kg.
(a) Taking both the Moon and the Earth as point masses, locate the neutral point, P, on the line joining their centres, where the gravitational field strength is zero.
(b) Suggest why it requires more fuel to take a spacecraft from the surface of the Earth to the Moon than it does to take the same spacecraft from the Moon to the Earth.

Solution

(a) Suppose the distance from P to the Earth is $x$. The distance from P to the Moon is then $3.84\times10^8 - x$. This is shown in the diagram overleaf.

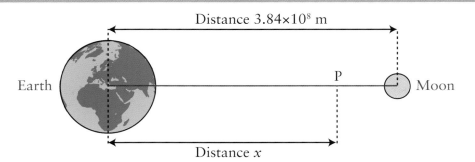

At the neutral point, field strength due to Earth = field strength due to Moon, so:

$$G\frac{m_E}{x^2} = G\frac{m_M}{(3.84\times10^8 - x)^2}$$

Cancelling $G$ and taking the square root of both sides gives:

$$\frac{\sqrt{m_E}}{x} = \frac{\sqrt{m_M}}{3.84\times10^8 - x}$$

Cross-multiplying gives:

$$(3.84\times10^8 - x) \times \sqrt{m_E} = x\sqrt{m_M}$$

This can be rearranged to give:

$$(\sqrt{m_E} + \sqrt{m_M})x = 3.84\times10^8 \times \sqrt{m_E}$$

Therefore:

$$x = \frac{3.84\times10^8 \times \sqrt{m_E}}{\sqrt{m_E} + \sqrt{m_M}}$$

Substituting in the values for the mass of the Earth and the Moon:

$$x = \frac{3.84\times10^8 \times \sqrt{6.0\times10^{24}}}{\sqrt{6.0\times10^{24}} + \sqrt{7.3\times10^{23}}} = \frac{9.41\times10^{20}}{2.72\times10^{12}} = 3.46\times10^8 \text{ m}$$

So the neutral point is approximately $3.46\times10^8$ m from the Earth and $3.84\times10^8 - 3.46\times10^8 = 3.8\times10^7$ m from the Moon.

(b) Travelling from the Earth to the Moon requires more work to be done than when travelling to Earth from the Moon, because more work is done against the greater gravitational force of the Earth for a much longer distance. In both cases, once the spacecraft reaches the neutral point, the gravitational force of the target pulls it towards its destination. Since the neutral point is much further from the Earth than the Moon, it takes more fuel to travel from the Earth to the Moon than from the Moon to the Earth.

## Planetary motion and Kepler's third law

Johannes Kepler was a seventeenth century German mathematician and astronomer. He defined three laws relating to the motion of the planets around the Sun. One of them, the third law, states that:

**The square of the period of revolution of the planets about the Sun is directly proportional to the cube of their mean distances from it.**

Expressed mathematically, Kepler's third law can be written as:

$$T^2 \propto r^3$$

or, as an equation:

$\dfrac{T^2}{r^3}$ **= a constant**     where     $T$ = period of revolution around the Sun (s)

$r$ = radius of the orbit (m)

### Showing that Kepler's third law is consistent with Newton's law of universal gravitation

**Note:** The CCEA specification requires students to be able to demonstrate that Kepler's third law is consistent with Newton's law of universal gravitation. The derivation below must therefore be memorised.

The orbit of a planet around the Sun can be considered to be an example of uniform circular motion.

Consider a planet of mass, $m$ moving about the Sun in a circular orbit of radius, $r$. Suppose the angular velocity of the planet is $\omega$ and the mass of the Sun is $m_S$. This is shown in the diagram on the right.

Gravitational attraction provides the centripetal force between the planet and the Sun.

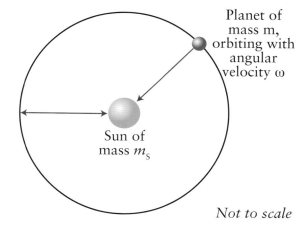

Planet of mass m, orbiting with angular velocity ω

Sun of mass $m_S$

*Not to scale*

So we can write:

$mr\omega^2 = G\dfrac{m_S m}{r^2}$     where     $\omega$ = angular velocity of the planet (rad s$^{-1}$)

$m$ = mass of the planet (kg)

Dividing both sides by $m$ and making the substitution $\omega = \dfrac{2\pi}{T}$ gives:

$$r\left(\dfrac{2\pi}{T}\right)^2 = G\dfrac{m_S}{r^2}$$

Removing the brackets gives:

$$\dfrac{4\pi^2 r}{T^2} = G\dfrac{m_S}{r^2}$$

Rearranging to make T$^2$ the subject gives:

$$T^2 = \dfrac{4\pi^2 r^3}{Gm_S} \quad \text{or} \quad \dfrac{T^2}{r^3} = \dfrac{4\pi^2}{Gm_S}$$

Since the values of $\pi$, $G$ and $m_S$ are all constant, we can conclude that $T^2$ is directly proportional to $r^3$.

### Estimating the mass of the Sun

The above mathematics also allows us to estimate the mass of the Sun. Students will know that the mass of the Sun is decreasing due to nuclear fusion. But even so, over its **entire lifetime** it is thought that this mass reduction will account for only around 0.035% of its total mass. So it is entirely reasonable to regard the Sun's mass as constant.

Let us we consider the Earth orbiting at a mean separation of 150 million km from the Sun and with a period of 365.25 days.

Rearranging the equation $T^2 = \dfrac{4\pi^2 r^3}{Gm_S}$ to make $m_S$ the subject gives:

$$m_S = \frac{4\pi^2 r^3}{GT^2}$$

Substituting in the values for $r$, $G$ and $T$ (converted to seconds) gives:

$$m_S = \frac{4\pi^2 \times (1.5\times10^{11})^3}{6.67\times10^{-11} \times (365.25 \times 24 \times 3600)^2} = 2.0\times10^{30} \text{ kg}$$

which is about 330 000 times greater than the mass of the Earth.

## Satellites orbiting the Earth

### The general case

Consider a satellite of mass, $m$ orbiting the Earth in the equatorial plane and at a distance, $r$ from the Earth's centre. We can treat this as an example of uniform circular motion. In a similar way to the orbit of a planet around the Sun, the gravitational attraction between the satellite and the Earth provides the centripetal force. So we can write:

$$mr\omega^2 = G\frac{m_E m}{r^2} \qquad \text{where} \qquad \begin{array}{l} \omega = \text{angular velocity of the satellite (rad s}^{-1}) \\ m = \text{mass of the satellite (kg)} \end{array}$$

Dividing both sides by $m$ and rearranging gives:

$$\omega^2 = G\frac{m_E}{r^3}$$

Making the substitution $\omega = \dfrac{2\pi}{T}$ and rearranging to make $T^2$ the subject gives:

$$T^2 = \frac{4\pi^2 r^3}{Gm_E}$$

Taking the square root of each side leaves us with a general equation for the period, $T$, of a satellite orbiting the Earth:

$$T = 2\pi\sqrt{\frac{r^3}{Gm_E}} \qquad \text{where} \qquad \begin{array}{l} T = \text{orbital period of the satellite (s)} \\ r = \text{orbital radius (m)} \\ m_E = \text{mass of the Earth (kg)} \end{array}$$

### Satellite orbiting just above the Earth's surface

To a good approximation, a satellite orbiting the Earth at a height of 200 km or less can be said to have an orbital radius equal to the radius of the planet itself, $r_E$. Substituting $r_E$ for $r$ in the previous equation gives:

$$T = 2\pi\sqrt{\frac{r_E^3}{Gm_E}}$$

Substituting the numerical values of $G$, $m_E$ and $r_E$, we obtain a period of:

$$T = 2\pi\sqrt{\frac{(6.4\times10^6)^3}{6.67\times10^{-11} \times 6.0\times10^{24}}} = 5085 \text{ s, or about 85 minutes}$$

**Geostationary satellites**

A geostationary satellite is one which:
- orbits the Earth directly above the equator,
- orbits in the same direction as the rotation of the Earth, and
- has an orbital period of exactly 24 hours.

These properties means that the satellite's angular velocity is the **same** as that of the Earth itself as it rotates on its polar axis. To an observer on the Earth's surface such a satellite appears to be **stationary** in the sky – hence the name 'geostationary'. This is a very useful property for satellites which are intended to serve a particular part of the Earth's surface, for example communication satellites transmitting TV signals.

We can calculate the radius of a geostationary orbit by using the equation:

$$T = 2\pi\sqrt{\frac{r^3}{Gm_E}}$$

Squaring both sides gives:

$$T^2 = \frac{4\pi^2 r^3}{Gm_E}$$

Rearranging to make $r^3$ the subject gives:

$$r^3 = \frac{Gm_E T^2}{4\pi^2}$$

Substituting values for $G$, $M_E$ and $T$ (24 hours × 60 minutes × 60 seconds) gives:

$$r^3 = \frac{6.67\times10^{-11} \times 6.0\times10^{24} \times (24 \times 60 \times 60)^2}{4\pi^2} = 7.567\times10^{22} \text{ m}^3$$

Taking the cube root gives a value of:

$r = 4.23\times10^7$ m

Since the radius of the Earth itself is $6.4\times10^6$ m, the orbital height is:

$4.23\times10^7 - 6.4\times10^6 = 3.59\times10^7$ m

The angular velocity, $\omega$, can be calculated as:

$$\omega = \frac{2\pi}{T} = \frac{2\pi}{24 \times 60 \times 60} = 7.27\times10^{-5} \text{ rad s}^{-1}$$

The orbital speed, $v$, can be calculated as:

$$v = \frac{2\pi r}{T} = \frac{2\pi \times 4.23\times10^7}{24 \times 60 \times 60} = 3076 \text{ m s}^{-1}$$

The properties of a **geostationary** satellite, therefore, are:
- The period is fixed at 24 hours.
- The orbital radius is fixed at $4.23\times10^7$ m.
- The orbital height is fixed at $3.59\times10^7$ m above the Earth's surface.
- The speed is fixed at 3076 m s$^{-1}$.

- The angular velocity, ω is fixed at $7.27 \times 10^{-5}$ rad s$^{-1}$.
- The satellite must orbit in the same direction as the Earth spins on its axis, and it must orbit directly above the equator.

Note that a **geosynchronous** orbit is one with a period equal to the Earth's rotational period. An orbit with this period and altitude $3.59 \times 10^7$ m can exist at *any* inclination to the equator but clearly a satellite in an orbit with an inclination to the equator cannot remain over a fixed point on the Earth's surface. The only geosynchronous orbit that is **geostationary** is an orbit in the plane of the Earth's equator.

### Energy requirement of satellites

Satellites high above the Earth's atmosphere do not require a source of energy to keep them in orbit, just as the planets do not require energy to remain in orbit around the Sun. A satellite orbits at a fixed speed, which means that its kinetic energy remains constant. It also orbits at a fixed height, which means that its gravitational potential energy remains constant. Satellites may, of course, generate their own energy (typically, from solar radiation) but this is used to power the electronics and other instruments on board.

### Exercise 5.2

1  By considering the mathematical form of Newton's law of universal gravitation, show that $G$ has derived units N m$^2$ kg$^{-2}$ and hence determine the SI base units in which $G$ can be measured.

2  In a hydrogen atom an electron of mass $9.11 \times 10^{-31}$ kg orbits a proton of mass $1.66 \times 10^{-27}$ kg at a radius of 50 pm. The speed of the electron is 2.2 Mm s$^{-1}$. Calculate:
   (a) the centripetal force on the electron and
   (b) the gravitational force between the proton and the electron.
   Comment on the results of these calculations.

3  Calculate the gravitational field strength on a planet where a mass of 5 kg has a weight of 180 N.

4  The gravitational force between two point masses is 36 N when they are 2 m apart. Calculate the gravitational force between the same masses when they are:
   (a) 1 m apart
   (b) 3 m apart

5  The table below shows how the magnitude of the gravitational force, $F$, on a mass of 1 kg varies with distance, $r$, from the centre of a planet.

| Force $F$ / N | 4.0 | 2.6 | 1.8 | 1.3 | 1.0 | 0.79 |
|---|---|---|---|---|---|---|
| Distance $r$ / Mm | 2.0 | 2.5 | 3.0 | 3.5 | 4.0 | 4.5 |

   (a) Plot a suitable straight line graph to show that the gravitational force $F$ is inversely proportional to $r^2$.
   (b) The value of $g$ on the planet's surface is 5 N kg$^{-1}$. Use your graph to estimate the radius of the planet.

6  The Earth has a mass of $6.0 \times 10^{24}$ kg and orbits the Sun at a mean radius of 150 million km. Assuming that gravity provides the centripetal force and that the mass of the Sun is $2 \times 10^{30}$ kg, calculate the magnitude of the gravitational constant $G$.

7  Two spherical masses of 2.0 kg and 3.0 kg are at rest on a table. The distance between their centres is 2.0 m. Calculate the gravitational force that each exerts on the other. If the friction between the table and each mass were negligible, what would be the acceleration of each mass?

8  The mass of the Sun is $2 \times 10^{30}$ kg and the mass of the planet Jupiter is $1.9 \times 10^{27}$ kg. Jupiter orbits the Sun with an average radius of $7.8 \times 10^{11}$ m. At what distance from the Sun is their gravitational neutral point?

9  Data from the Cassini space probe has indicated that there may be a planet at 630 AU (astronomical units) from the Sun. If the Earth orbits the Sun at a distance of 1 AU, calculate the time it would take for this distant planet to orbit the Sun.

10 A physicist runs a computer simulation of a fictitious solar system consisting of a star and five planets. The planets' distances from the star and their orbital period's are shown in the table.

| Planet | A | B | C | D | E |
|---|---|---|---|---|---|
| Distance to the star, $r$ / Tm | 1.00 | 1.50 | 2.25 | 3.50 | 5.00 |
| Orbital period , $T$ / Gs | 1.00 | 1.84 | 3.38 | 6.55 | 11.18 |

(a) Plot a graph of log $T$ on the vertical axis against log $r$ on the horizontal axis and use it to confirm Kepler's third law.

(b) Use your graph to show the mass of the star is approximately $5.9 \times 10^{29}$ kg.

# 5.3 Electric Fields

5.3.1    define electric field strength; and

5.3.2    recall and use the equation $E = \dfrac{F}{q}$ ;

5.3.3    state Coulomb's law for the force between point charges;

5.3.4    recall and use the equation for the force between two point charges,

$F = \dfrac{q_1 q_2}{4\pi\varepsilon_0 r^2} = \dfrac{k q_1 q_2}{r^2}$ , where $k = \dfrac{1}{4\pi\varepsilon_0}$ and $\varepsilon_0$ is the permittivity of a vacuum;

5.3.5    recall and use the equation for the electric field strength due to a point charge,

$E = \dfrac{q}{4\pi\varepsilon_0 r^2} = \dfrac{kq}{r^2}$ ;

5.3.6    recall that for a uniform electric field, the field strength is constant, and recall and use the equation $E = \dfrac{V}{d}$ ;

5.3.7    state the similarities and differences in gravitational and electric fields.

## Definition

In an electric field, the **electric field strength, $E$,** at a point is equal to the force which would be produced on a test charge of 1 C at that point, ie:

$E = \dfrac{F}{q}$ or $F = Eq$     where     $E$ = electric field strength (N C$^{-1}$)
$F$ = force (N)
$q$ = charge (C)

**Field strength is a vector,** ie it has both magnitude and direction. **Its direction is that of the force on a positive (+) charge.**

## Electric charges and Coulomb's law

In a celebrated paper in 1787 the French physicist Charles Coulomb set forth the law of electric charges which now bears his name. Coulomb's law states that:

**Between every two point charges there exists an electrical force that is directly proportional to the product of the charges and is inversely proportional to the square of their separation.**

Coulomb's law can be expressed mathematically:

$F \propto \dfrac{q_1 q_2}{r^2}$     where  $F$ = the force acting on each charge (N)
$q_1$ and $q_2$ = two respective point charges (C)
$r$ = distance between $q_1$ and $q_2$ (m)

Unlike the force between point masses, the force between electrical charges may be attractive or repulsive. The force is **attractive** when the charges have **different signs,** in which case $F$ is negative. When the charges have the **same sign,** the force is **repulsive**, in which case $F$ is positive.

With a suitable constant $k$, we arrive at the equation:

$$F = \frac{kq_1q_2}{r^2}$$ where $F$ = the force acting on each charge (N)

$q_1$ and $q_2$ = two respective point charges (C)

$r$ = distance between $q_1$ and $q_2$ (m)

$k$ = a constant $(\text{N m}^2\,\text{C}^{-2})$

The value of the constant, $k$, depends on the nature of the material which is present between the point charges. This constant can be found experimentally. For charges in a vacuum, the constant $k$ is $8.99 \times 10^9\,\text{N m}^2\,\text{C}^{-2}$. However, it is more convenient to use another constant, $\varepsilon$, known as the **permittivity** of the material.

For charges in a vacuum, Coulomb's law is usually written:

$$F = \frac{q_1q_2}{4\pi\varepsilon_0 r^2} = \frac{kq_1q_2}{r^2}$$

where $\varepsilon_0$ is known as the **permittivity of free space** (vacuum) and has the experimental value of $8.85 \times 10^{-12}\,\text{C}^2\,\text{N}^{-1}\,\text{m}^{-2}$.

It may appear at first sight that the $4\pi$ complicates the above equation, but it is a necessary consequence of the SI system of units and indeed, it brings significant simplifications later. We will explore the significance of the $4\pi$ later in this chapter.

---

### Worked Examples

1  Show from Coulomb's law that the permittivity of free space, $\varepsilon_0$, has units $\text{C}^2\,\text{N}^{-1}\,\text{m}^{-2}$. Given that the unit of capacitance, the farad (F) is equivalent to the coulomb per volt show that $\varepsilon_0$ has units of $\text{F m}^{-1}$.

   **Solution**

   Coulomb's Law can be written:

   $$F = \frac{q_1q_2}{4\pi\varepsilon_0 r^2}$$

   Rearranging gives:

   $$\varepsilon_0 = \frac{q_1q_2}{4\pi F r^2}$$

   Since $\pi$ has no units, the unit for $\varepsilon_0$ is $\text{C}^2\,\text{N}^{-1}\,\text{m}^{-2}$

   Since 1 J = 1 N m, we can write:
   Unit for $\varepsilon_0$ = $\text{C}^2\,\text{N}^{-1}\,\text{m}^{-2}$ = $\text{C}^2\,(\text{N}^{-1}\,\text{m}^{-1})\,\text{m}^{-1}$ = $\text{C}^2\,(\text{N m})^{-1}\,\text{m}^{-1}$ = $\text{C}^2\,\text{J}^{-1}\,\text{m}^{-1}$

   But the volt, V, is defined as the $\text{J C}^{-1}$, so we can write:
   Unit for $\varepsilon_0$ = $\text{C}\,(\text{J C}^{-1})^{-1}\,\text{m}^{-1}$ = $\text{C V}^{-1}\,\text{m}^{-1}$

   And since we are told that 1 F = 1 $\text{C V}^{-1}$ we can write:
   Unit for $\varepsilon_0$ = $\text{F m}^{-1}$

2 Express $\varepsilon_0$ in terms of its SI base units.

Solution

Unit for $\varepsilon_0$ = $C^2 N^{-1} m^{-2}$

Replacing C and N with their base unit equivalents gives:

Unit for $\varepsilon_0$ = $A^2 s^2 (kg\, m\, s^{-2})^{-1}\, m^{-2} = A^2 s^2\, kg^{-1}\, m^{-1}\, s^2\, m^{-2} = A^2 s^4\, kg^{-1}\, m^{-3}$

## Electric field strength

We have seen that the definition of the strength of an electric field, $E$, at a point is the force which would be produced on a test charge of +1 C at that point. This is written as:

$$E = \frac{F}{q}$$

We have also seen that Coulomb's law can be written using the equation:

$$F = \frac{q_1 q_2}{4\pi\varepsilon_0 r^2}$$

For an isolated point charge, $Q$, we can use Coulomb's law to derive an equation giving electric field strength in terms of the point charge. We substitute in the value of our isolated point charge, $Q$, for $q_1$. For $q_2$ we use the test charge, $q$ (1 C). This gives:

$$E = \frac{F}{q} = \frac{Qq}{4\pi\varepsilon_0 r^2} \div q$$

Cancelling out $q$ leaves us with:

$$E = \frac{Q}{4\pi\varepsilon_0 r^2} \quad \text{where} \quad E = \text{electric field strength (N C}^{-1}\text{)}$$
$$Q = \text{charge on the point charge (C)}$$
$$r = \text{distance between the point charge and test charge (m)}$$

### Field lines

Electric fields are similar to gravitational fields in some ways. The electric field around an isolated point charge decreases in proportion to the square of the distance, ie as $1/r^2$, just as in a gravitational field. And like the gravitational field around a point mass, the electric field around a charged sphere is also radial.

However, there is one importance difference between gravitational fields and electric fields. Around an isolated positive charge the field lines are radially **outwards**, while around an isolated negative charge the field lines are radially **inwards**. This is to satisfy the requirement that the direction of the field is the same as that of the force on a **positive** test charge. By contrast, the gravitational field around an isolated point mass is **always radially inwards**.

If the field line is curved, as shown in the diagram on the right, then the **tangent** to the curve at any point gives the direction of the electric field at that point.

$E$

field line

The diagrams below show some common electric field patterns. The two on the left show the field around an isolated charge. The two on the right show the field around two adjacent charges.

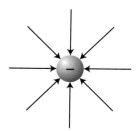 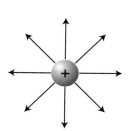 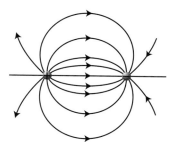 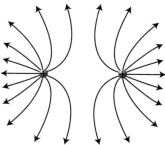

| | | | |
|---|---|---|---|
| The field pattern around a **positively** charged, isolated conductor: radially outwards. | The field pattern around a **negatively** charged, isolated conductor: radially inwards. | The field around adjacent positive and negative charges. | The field around a pair of adjacent positive charges. There is a neutral point between the charges. |

**Significance of 4π**

Let us return to explain the origin of the 4π term is the expression for the electric field strength:

$$E = \frac{Q}{4\pi\varepsilon_0 r^2}$$

The diagrams above show that the field lines around the charge spread out as they move away from the charge. This indicates that the field decreases the further we go from the charge. At any distance, $r$, from the charge, we can imagine the field lines passing through the surface of a sphere of radius $r$, as shown on the right. The field strength at distance $r$ is proportional to the density of the field lines at distance $r$.

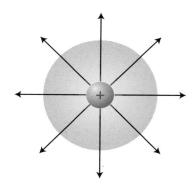

Density of field lines = $\dfrac{\text{number of lines}}{\text{surface area of the sphere}}$

Since the surface area of a sphere = $4\pi r^2$, we have:

Density of field lines = $\dfrac{\text{number of lines}}{4\pi r^2}$

Therefore the field, $E$, at distance, $r$, is directly proportional to
- the charge, $Q$, and
- $\dfrac{1}{4\pi r^2}$

The constant, $\varepsilon_0$, (known as the permittivity of free space), is now added to give the final equation:

$$E = \frac{Q}{4\pi\varepsilon_0 r^2}$$

Note that $\varepsilon_0$ is an experimental constant and it has units $C^2\ N^{-1}\ m^{-2}$, $C\ V^{-1}\ m^{-1}$ or $F\ m^{-1}$. The units are necessary for the equation to be homogeneous, but it is also a reminder that the electric field depends on the material surrounding the charge.

**Worked Examples**

1   Calculate the electrical force between a proton and an electron at a distance of 50 pm if the magnitude of the charge on each is $1.6 \times 10^{-19}$ C.

    **Solution**

    By Coulomb's Law:

    $$F = \frac{q_1 q_2}{4\pi\varepsilon_0 r^2} = \frac{(1.6 \times 10^{-19})^2}{4\pi \times 8.85 \times 10^{-12} \times (50 \times 10^{-12})^2} = 9.2 \times 10^{-8} \text{ N}$$

2   Calculate the size and direction of the electric field at a point 25 cm from an isolated point charge of $-4$ C.

    **Solution**

    Since we are calculating the force on a point charge, we can use:

    $$E = \frac{Q}{4\pi\varepsilon_0 r^2} = \frac{4}{4\pi \times 8.85 \times 10^{-12} \times (0.25)^2} = 5.75 \times 10^{11} \text{ N C}^{-1}$$

    Since the charge is negative, the direction is from the point towards the point charge.

3   At a distance of 60 pm from a certain charge the electric field strength is 400 N C$^{-1}$. Calculate the field strength at distances of (a) 120 pm (b) 150 pm and (c) 20 pm from the same charge.

    **Solution**

    (a) Around an isolated point charge the field strength obeys an inverse square law.

    120 pm is 2 × 60 pm, therefore the field strength falls to $\frac{1}{2^2}$ of its value at 60 pm.

    Thus the value of $E$ at 120 pm = $\frac{1}{2^2} \times$ ($E$ at 60 pm) = 0.25 × 400 = 100 N C$^{-1}$.

    (b) 150 pm is 2.5 × 60 pm, so $E$ at 150 pm = $\frac{1}{2.5^2} \times$ ($E$ at 60 pm) = 0.16 × 400 = 64 N C$^{-1}$.

    (c) 20 pm is $\frac{1}{3} \times$ 60 pm, so $E$ at 20 pm = $3^2 \times$ ($E$ at 60 pm) = 9 × 400 = 3600 N C$^{-1}$.

4   Charges of $+4$ C and $+8$ C are placed 1.00 m apart. At what distance from the $+4$ C charge is the electric field strength zero?

    **Solution**

    Suppose the distance from the $+4$ C to the neutral point is $x$. The distance from the neutral point to the $+8$ C is therefore $(1 - x)$. At this point, the field strength due to $+4$ C = field strength due to $+8$ C.

    Using $E = \frac{Q}{4\pi\varepsilon_0 r^2}$, at the neutral point, therefore:

    $$\frac{4}{(4\pi\varepsilon_0) x^2} = \frac{8}{(4\pi\varepsilon_0)(1 - x)^2}$$

    Cancelling out the $(4\pi\varepsilon_0)$ and taking square roots of both sides gives:

    $$\frac{2}{x} = \frac{\sqrt{8}}{(1 - x)}$$

    Cross-multiplying gives: $2(1 - x) = \sqrt{8}\ x$

    which simplifies to: $x = \frac{2}{(\sqrt{8} + 2)} = 0.41$ m (from the charge $+4$ C)

5   Charges of 5 C and –4 C are 80 cm apart in a vacuum. P is a point on the axis of symmetry between the two charges, 50 cm from each charge. Calculate the magnitude of the electric field at P and state its direction.

### Solution

This example illustrates the fact that the resultant electric field is the **vector sum** of the electric field due to the separate charges. First find the two vectors at P:

$E_1$ due to the 5 C charge $= \dfrac{Q}{4\pi\varepsilon_0 r^2} = \dfrac{5}{4\pi \times 8.85\times10^{-12} \times (0.5)^2} = 1.798\times10^{11}$ away from the 5 C charge.

$E_2$ due to the –4 C charge $= \dfrac{Q}{4\pi\varepsilon_0 r^2} = \dfrac{-4}{4\pi \times 8.85\times10^{-12} \times (0.5)^2} = 1.438\times10^{11}$ towards the –4 C charge.

We must then add these two vectors. The first stage in adding these $E_1$ and $E_2$ is to resolve them into their horizontal and vertical components. It may be helpful to sketch a diagram as you work, as shown on the right.

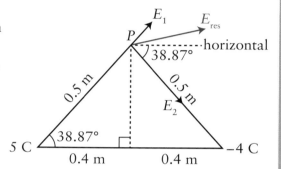

First, calculate the **horizontal** components:

Both $E_1$ and $E_2$ are at $\cos^{-1}(4 \div 5)$
$= 38.87°$ to the horizontal.

So the resultant horizontal component is:
$1.798\times10^{11}\cos(38.87°) + 1.438\times10^{11}\cos(38.87°)$
$= 2.589\times10^{11}$ N C$^{-1}$

Then, calculate the **vertical** components:

$E_1$ is at $38.87°$ above the horizontal and $E_2$ is at $38.87°$ below the horizontal. So the resultant vertical component is:

$1.798\times10^{11}\sin(38.87°) - 1.438\times10^{11}\sin(38.87°) = 2.16\times10^{10}$ N C$^{-1}$

Finally, find the **resultant** vector:

By Pythagoras' theorem, the magnitude of the resultant electric field is therefore:
$E_{res} = \sqrt{(2.589\times10^{11})^2 + (2.16\times10^{10})^2} = 2.598\times10^{11}$ N C$^{-1}$

The direction of the resultant field is $\tan^{-1}(2.16\times10^{10} \div 2.589\times10^{11})$
$= 4.8°$ above the horizontal.

**Note:**
- If the charges were of **equal** magnitude and **opposite** sign then the vertical components of the electric field at any point on the axis of symmetry would cancel and the resultant field would be **horizontal** only.
- If the charges were of **equal** magnitude and of the **same** sign then the horizontal components of the electric field at any point on the axis of symmetry would cancel and the resultant field would be **vertical** only.

## Uniform electric field

Consider a pair of parallel metal plates, a distance, $d$. Suppose that between them we maintain a constant potential difference, $V$. Between such plates, and away from the edges, there is a uniform electric field as illustrated below.

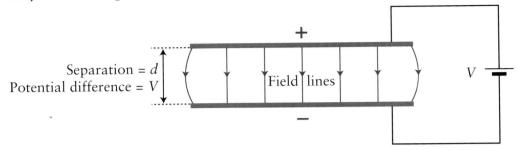

From the definitions of electrical potential, $V$, and electric field strength, $E$, it is possible to establish the relationship between them:

$$E = -\frac{V}{d} = -\text{ potential gradient}$$

where   $E$ = electric field strength (N C$^{-1}$)
$V$ = electrical potential (V)
$d$ = distance between the plates (m)

**Note:** You do not need to know the derivation of this equation, but you do need to remember it. The minus sign indicates that the electric field strength, $E$, is in the direction of **decreasing** potential. However it is often omitted, for example when we are only interested in the magnitude of the field.

The graph below illustrates how the potential varies as we move from the top (positive) plate to the bottom (negative) plate.

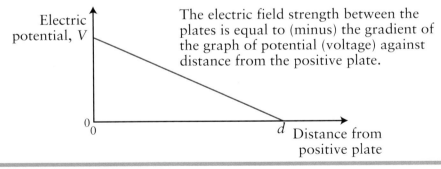

The electric field strength between the plates is equal to (minus) the gradient of the graph of potential (voltage) against distance from the positive plate.

---

**Worked Example**

1   Two parallel metal plates, 4 cm apart, are connected to a 12 V battery as shown in the diagram. (a) Copy the diagram showing the polarity of the plates, by writing "+" and "−" in the appropriate circles. (b) Calculate the size of the electric field between the plates.

Identical charges are now placed at points X, Y and Z. (c) At which point (if any) will the charge experience the greatest force? (d) At which point (if any) is the electrical potential greatest?

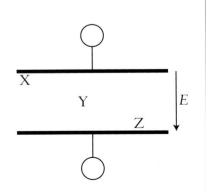

Solution

(a) The direction of an electric field between two charged plates is from positive to negative. So mark the upper plate as positive, and the lower plate is negative.

(b) $E = \dfrac{V}{d} = \dfrac{12}{0.04} = 300$ V m$^{-1}$

(c) The force is the same at all points because the field is uniform.

(d) Electric potential decreases as we move away from the positive plate. Therefore, potential is greatest at point X.

## Differences and similarities between gravitational and electric fields

The CCEA specification requires candidates to be able to state the differences and similarities between gravitational and electric fields. These are summarised in the table below.

|  | Gravitational fields | Electric fields |
|---|---|---|
| **Differences** | • Acts on masses.<br>• Always produces an attractive force on a mass.<br>• It is impossible to shield an object from a gravitational field. | • Acts on charges.<br>• Can produce both attractive and repulsive forces because there are two types of charge (positive and negative).<br>• Shielding is possible with a suitable material. |
| **Similarities** | • The field around a point mass decreases according to an inverse square law (falls off as 1/$r^2$).<br>• Field is of infinite range. | • Field around a point charge decreases according to an inverse square law (falls off as 1/$r^2$).<br>• Field is of infinite range. |

## Exercise 5.3

1  In the ground state of the hydrogen atom, the electron orbits the proton at an average speed of 2.2 Mm s$^{-1}$. Given that the mass of the electron is $9.11 \times 10^{-31}$ kg, calculate the radius of the orbit. Hint: Remember the electrical force between the charges provides the centripetal force.

2  A point charge, $Q$, is placed at the centre of a sphere of radius 1.0 m. The radial field at the surface if the sphere is 1 N C$^{-1}$. Calculate the size of $Q$.

3  Two point charges, +5 C and +3 C, are placed 1 m apart in a vacuum. Calculate the distance between the neutral point between them and the smaller charge.

4  A potential difference of 200 V is maintained between two parallel metal plates, which are placed 40 mm apart in a vacuum.
   (a) Calculate the size and direction of the force on a proton in the electric field between the plates, if the proton is 5 mm from the plate of higher potential and well away from the edges of the plates.
   (b) If what way, if at all, would the size and direction of the force on the proton be different if it was placed 5 mm from the plate of lower potential?

5 An electron is travelling parallel to the field lines in a uniform electric field at an initial speed on $1\times10^6$ ms$^{-1}$. The electron is decelerated to rest over a distance of 0.4 m. Calculate the size of the field.

6 ABC is an equilateral triangle of side 10 cm. Charges of +5 nC are located at points A and B. Calculate the size and direction of the electric field at point C, assuming that the line AB is horizontal.

7 Two identical, small, charged spheres, A and B, each carry the same electrical charge. A is suspended by an insulated thread. B is attached to an insulated rod. When the distance between the centres of the spheres is 40 mm, the supporting thread deflects by 30° from the vertical and the tension in this thread is 0.3 mN.

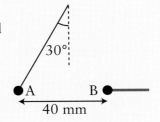

   (a) Calculate the magnitude of the repulsive force between the spheres.
   (b) Calculate the magnitude of the charge on each sphere.
   (c) State the magnitude of the electric field midway between the spheres.

8 A negatively charged oil drop of weight $3.84\times10^{-14}$ N is held stationary in the electric field maintained between two metal plates 40 mm apart in a vacuum, as shown. The p.d. between the plates is held at 1.6 kV.

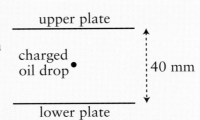

   (a) Calculate the strength of the electric field between the plates.
   (b) State the polarity of the upper plate and the direction of the electric field.
   (c) Calculate the number of excess electrons on the oil drop.

# 5.4 Capacitors

5.4.1     define capacitance;

5.4.2     recall and use the equation $C = \dfrac{Q}{V}$;

5.4.3     define the unit of capacitance, the farad;

5.4.4     recall and use the equation $\frac{1}{2}QV$ or its equivalent for calculating the energy of a charged capacitor;

5.4.5     recall and use the equations for capacitors in series and in parallel;

5.4.6     perform and describe experiments to demonstrate the charge and discharge of a capacitor;

5.4.7     confirm the exponential nature of capacitor discharge using $V$ or $I$ discharge curves;

5.4.8     use the equations $Q = Q_0 e^{-t/CR}$, $V = V_0 e^{-t/CR}$ and $I = I_0 e^{-t/CR}$;

5.4.9     define time constant and use the equation $\tau = RC$;

5.4.10    perform and describe an experiment to determine the time constant for R-C circuits;

5.4.11    apply knowledge and understanding of time constants and stored energy to electronic flash guns and defibrillators;

A capacitor is an electrical component that can store energy in the electric field between a pair of metal plates separated by an insulator. The process of storing energy in the capacitor is called **charging**. It involves allowing electric charges of equal magnitude, but opposite polarity, to build up on each plate.

Capacitors come in many different types as shown in the picture. The simplest design of a capacitor is two parallel metal plates separated by an insulator as shown in the diagram on the left below. The metal plates are made of thin metal foil and the insulator is either a plastic strip or waxed paper sandwiched between the metal foils. The diagram on the right below shows a typical design for the capacitors shown in the photograph. In this design, the layers are rolled up into a cylinder to make the capacitor easier to handle.

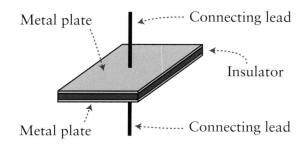

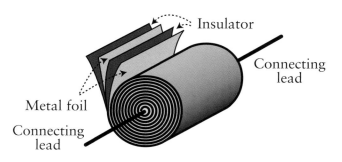

A capacitor's ability to store charge is measured by its **capacitance**. Capacitance is defined as **the charge stored per volt** and is given in units of **farads**, symbol F. This can be written in the form of an equation:

$C = \dfrac{Q}{V}$    where  $C$ = capacitance (F)
  $Q$ = charge stored (C)
  $V$ = potential difference between the plates (V)

The farad is a very large unit and in practice microfarads ($\mu$F) and picofarads (pF) are more common: 1 $\mu$F = $1\times10^{-6}$ F and 1 pF = $1\times10^{-9}$ F.

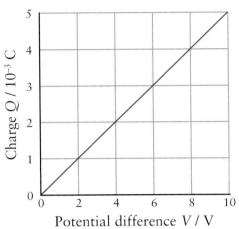

When electric charge is stored on the plates of a capacitor the potential difference between the plates rises. The equation above shows that potential difference is proportional to the amount of charge stored. Therefore a graph of charge, $Q$, against the potential difference, $V$, is a straight line that passes through the origin. The capacitance is equal to the gradient of the graph.

An example of such a graph is shown on the right. The gradient of the graph gives the capacitance of this particular capacitor:

Gradient = $C = \dfrac{Q}{V} = \dfrac{4\times10^{-3}}{8} = 5\times10^{-4}$ F = 500 $\mu$F

## Capacitors in parallel

The three capacitors shown in the diagram below, $C_1$, $C_2$ and $C_3$ when connected to a potential difference, $V$, store electric charge $Q_1$, $Q_2$ and $Q_3$ respectively. Since they are connected in parallel the potential difference across each capacitor is the **same** and is equal to $V$. The three capacitors are equivalent to a single capacitor of some value $C$ which will store a charge $Q$, the sum of the individual charges stored on each capacitor ($Q = Q_1 + Q_2 + Q_3$), when connected to the same potential difference. How do we calculate the capacitance of $C$?

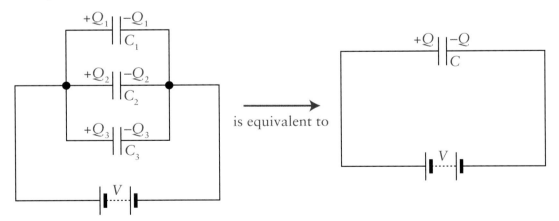

is equivalent to

The charge on each capacitor is given by:
$Q_1 = C_1 V$,  $Q_2 = C_2 V$ and $Q_3 = C_3 V$

For the single capacitor that is equivalent to these three in parallel the charge is:
$Q = CV$

Since the total charged stored is the sum of the charged stored by each of the three capacitors, we can say:

$$Q = Q_1 + Q_2 + Q_3$$

and therefore that:

$$CV = C_1V + C_2V + C_3V$$

Dividing both sides by $V$ gives:

$$C = C_1 + C_2 + C_3$$

Therefore, **the total capacitance of any number, N, of capacitors in parallel is the sum of the capacitance of each.** This can be written as:

$$C = C_1 + C_2 + C_3 + \ldots\ldots C_N$$

This shows that we can obtain a larger capacitance by connecting a number of smaller capacitors in parallel.

## Capacitors in series

The diagram below shows three capacitors, $C_1$, $C_2$ and $C_3$ connected in series. When the capacitors are connected to a potential difference electrons move on to plate G of capacitor $C_3$. This causes the same number of electrons to move from plate F of $C_3$ to plate E of capacitor $C_2$ and in turn this causes the same number of electrons to leave plate D and move to plate B of capacitor $C_1$. And finally, the same number of electrons leave plate A of capacitor $C_1$.

This means that the total amount of charge that has moved around the circuit when the potential difference is applied is $Q$. It is **not** the $3Q$ that you might think when looking at the circuit. Another way to think about this is to consider plates A and G as the plates of the single capacitor, $C$, that can replace the three in series. This is shown in the equivalent circuit on the right hand side of the diagram. How do we calculate the capacitance of $C$?

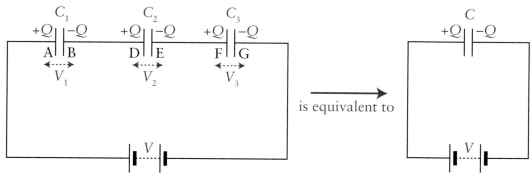

It is important to note that the potential differences across each capacitor are **not** equal (they would only be equal if all the capacitors had the same capacitance). However we can say that:

$$V = V_1 + V_2 + V_3$$

From the equation for capacitance we can also say that:

$$V_1 = \frac{Q}{C_1}, \; V_2 = \frac{Q}{C_2} \text{ and } V_3 = \frac{Q}{C_3}$$

Therefore the total potential difference, $V$ is given by:

$$\frac{Q}{C} = \frac{Q}{C_1} + \frac{Q}{C_2} + \frac{Q}{C_3}$$

Dividing both sides by Q gives:

$$\frac{1}{C} = \frac{1}{C_1} + \frac{1}{C_2} + \frac{1}{C_3}$$

Therefore, **the total capacitance of any number, N, of capacitors in series is given by the equation:**

$$\frac{1}{C} = \frac{1}{C_1} + \frac{1}{C_2} + \frac{1}{C_3} + \text{.......} \frac{1}{C_N}$$

This shows that we can obtain a smaller capacitance by connecting a number of larger capacitors in series.

---

**Worked Example**

1. Find the capacitance between the points A and B of the circuit shown.

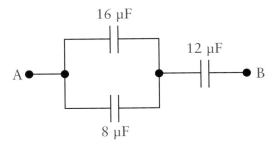

**Solution**

The 8 μF and the 16 μF capacitors are in parallel so their total capacitance is 8 + 16 = 24 μF. The circuit is then effectively a 24 μF capacitor in series with a 12 μF capacitor as shown below.

$$A \bullet \quad\text{24 μF}\quad \dashv\vdash \quad\text{12 μF}\quad \dashv\vdash \quad\bullet B$$

The total capacitance, $C$, is then calculated using the rule for capacitors in series:

$$\frac{1}{C} = \frac{1}{24} + \frac{1}{12} = \frac{3}{24} = \frac{1}{8}, \text{ giving } C = 8 \text{ μF}$$

---

## Energy of a charged capacitor

We have already seen that the charge stored by a capacitor is proportional to the potential difference across the plates, and that a graph of charge against the potential difference is therefore a straight line through the origin as shown on the next page.

Suppose the potential difference across the capacitor is $V$ when it stores a charge $Q$. To move a small amount of charge $\Delta Q$ from the negative plate to the positive plate requires **work** to be done against the repulsive force of the charges already on that plate. How do we calculate the work done charging the capacitor, ie the energy that is stored by the capacitor?

Potential difference = work done per unit charge.

This can be written as: $V = E \div Q$

Therefore, work done, $E = QV$

So in the case of moving a small amount of charge, $\Delta Q$, the work done $E = \Delta Q \times V$ = area of shaded strip

The **total** energy stored, therefore is equal to the area between the graph and the charge, $Q$, axis. We can therefore write an equation for the energy stored in charged capacitor, $E$:

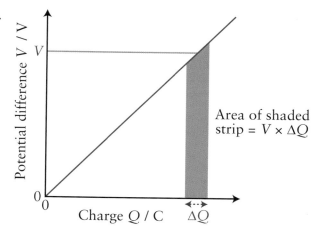

Area of shaded strip = $V \times \Delta Q$

$E = \frac{1}{2}QV$   where  $E$ = energy stored (J)
$Q$ = total charge in the capacitor (C)
$V$ = potential difference across the capacitor (V)

Using the relationship $C = \frac{Q}{V}$ we can also gives the energy stored as:

$E = \frac{1}{2}\frac{Q^2}{C}$   where  $E$ = energy stored (J)
$Q$ = total charge in the capacitor (C)
$C$ = capacitance (F)

We can also eliminate the charge and give the energy stored as:

$E = \frac{1}{2}CV^2$   where  $E$ = energy stored (J)
$C$ = capacitance (F)
$V$ = potential difference across the capacitor (V)

### Verifying the relationship $E = \frac{1}{2}CV^2$

This relationship can be verified by experiment by using the equipment arranged as shown on the right.

The capacitor is initially charged by closing switch $S_1$ for a short time and then opening it. The joule meter, which measures the energy supplied by the capacitor, is then reset to read zero.

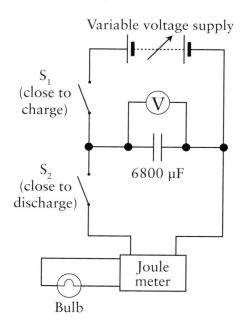

Next, the capacitor is discharged by closing switch $S_2$. The bulb will be seen to light and then dim as the energy stored in the capacitor is dissipated as heat and light by the bulb. The joule meter measures this energy. The discharging switch is kept closed until the reading on the joule meter no longer changes.

This process is repeated several times and an average obtained.

Next, the voltage is changed and the above procedure repeated. Typically, the voltage might be varied from 5 V to 25 V in steps of 5 volts. An example of a set of readings from an experiment like this is shown overleaf.

| Energy readings / J | | | | |
|---|---|---|---|---|
| Potential difference / V | 1st reading | 2nd reading | 3rd reading | Average energy / J |
| 5 | 0.1 | 0.1 | 0.1 | 0.1 |
| 10 | 0.4 | 0.4 | 0.4 | 0.4 |
| 15 | 0.8 | 0.8 | 0.9 | 0.83 |
| 20 | 1.7 | 1.7 | 1.7 | 1.7 |
| 25 | 2.5 | 2.5 | 2.5 | 2.5 |

If the values of $E$ and $V$ are plotted on a graph, the result is a curve as shown in the graph on the left below. However, a graph of $E$ against $V^2$ will be a straight line that passes through the origin. This shows that the energy $E$ is directly proportional to the square of the potential difference, $V^2$, verifying the relationship $E = \frac{1}{2}CV^2$.

The equation of a straight line graph that passes through the origin is $y = mx$. Comparing this to the energy relationship $E = \frac{1}{2}CV^2$ we can see that the gradient of the graph of $E$ against $V^2$ is equal to $\frac{1}{2}C$.

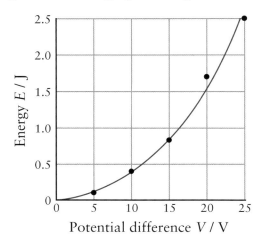

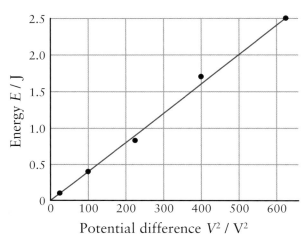

### Worked Example

1. (a) A capacitor of capacitance 100 µF is charged by a battery of e.m.f. 6.0 V. Calculate the charge on the capacitor.
   (b) Calculate the energy stored in the capacitor when it is fully charged.
   (c) The charged capacitor in (a) and (b) is now disconnected from the battery and connected in parallel with an uncharged capacitor of capacitance 50 µF. Calculate the potential difference across the capacitors.
   (d) Calculate the energy now stored in the two capacitors in (c). Account for any difference between your answer and the initial energy stored in the 100 µF capacitor.

   Solution

   (a) $Q = CV = 100{\times}10^{-6} \times 6.0 = 6.0{\times}10^{-4}$ C

(b) Energy stored, $E = \frac{1}{2}QV = \frac{1}{2}(6.0\times10^{-4} \times 6) = 1.8\times10^{-3}$ J

Alternatively you could use $E = \frac{1}{2}CV^2 = \frac{1}{2}(100\times10^{-6} \times 6^2) = 1.8\times10^{-3}$ J

It is also possible to use $E = \frac{1}{2}\dfrac{Q^2}{C} = \frac{1}{2}\left(\dfrac{(6.0\times10^{-4})^2}{100\times10^{-6}}\right) = 1.8\times10^{-3}$ J

(c) The total capacitance of the two capacitors in parallel is 100 + 50 = 150 μF. The electric charge that was solely on the 100 μF capacitor is now shared between it and the 50 μF capacitor. Electric charge is conserved.

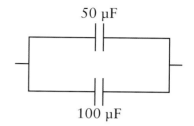

$Q = CV$, so:

$V = Q \div C = 6.0\times10^{-4} \div 150\times10^{-6} = 4.0$ V

(d) The energy stored in the combination, $E = \frac{1}{2}CV^2 = \frac{1}{2}(150\times10^{-6} \times 4^2) = 1.2\times10^{-3}$ J
The initial energy stored in the 100 μF capacitor was $1.8\times10^{-3}$ J. The loss of energy is due to the transfer of electrons between the two capacitors when they are connected together. This movement of electrons is a current and the connecting leads have a small amount of resistance so some of the stored energy is dissipated as heat.

## Charging and discharging capacitors

### Charging a capacitor

The R-C circuit on the right shows a capacitor, $C$, connected in series with a battery of e.m.f. $V$, a switch and a resistor, $R$. When the switch is closed the capacitor **charges**. Electrons flow onto one plate and are repelled from the other plate. This movement of electrons constitutes a current. The charging

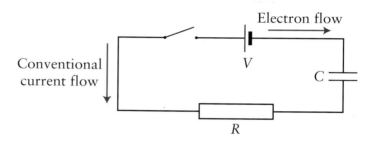

current decreases and eventually stops flowing once the potential difference across the capacitor is exactly equal to the e.m.f. of the battery.

The rate at which the charging current decreases and the rate at which the potential differences across the capacitor rises depends on the **capacitance** of the capacitor and the **resistance** of the circuit.

The graph on the right shows how the **charging current** varies with time. Notice how the charging current **decreases** with time. It decreases because it becomes more difficult to push electrons onto the plate because of the repulsion of the electrons already there. The lower the resistance of the circuit, the more rapidly the capacitor charges, and hence the charging current falls more quickly.

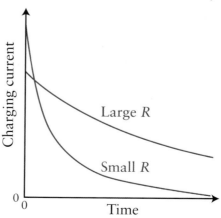

The graph on the right shows how the **potential difference** across the capacitor varies with time. Notice how the potential difference gradually **increases** with time until it is equal to the e.m.f. of the battery. However the potential difference is in the opposite sense to the battery, so that it opposes the further movement of electrons. The lower the resistance of the circuit, the more rapidly the capacitor charges, and hence the potential difference rises more quickly.

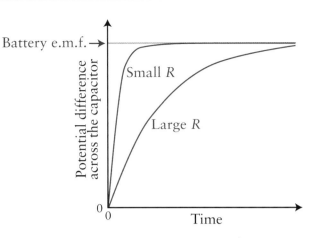

### Discharging a capacitor

The R-C circuit on the right shows a capacitor, C, a battery of e.m.f. 9 V, a switch and a resistor, R. There is also a microammeter, which should have a range of 0–100 µA and a switch which can be toggled between two positions, A and B. This circuit can be used to investigate the discharge of a capacitor. Suitable values for this circuit are $R = 100$ kΩ ($1 \times 10^5$ Ω) and $C = 470$ µF ($470 \times 10^{-6}$ F).

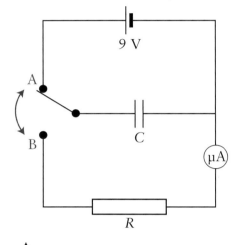

When the switch is moved to position A the capacitor is charged from the 9 V battery. The capacitor becomes fully charged very quickly since the resistance of the charging circuit is very small.

Moving the switch to position B will start the capacitor discharging through the resistor R. The reading on the microammeter will start high and gradually fall. Values of the current should be recorded at 10 or 20 second intervals.

The results from such an experiment are shown in the graph on the right. Note that as the capacitor discharges, the current flowing decreases **exponentially** with time.

### The time constant

The product of the capacitance and the resistance of a circuit is known as the **time constant, τ,** of the circuit. This can be expressed in the form of an equation:

$\tau = RC$     where   τ = time constant (s)
                      R = resistance of the circuit (Ω)
                      C = capacitance (F)

The product of capacitance and resistance can be shown to have the units of time (in seconds) as follows:

Unit of $RC = \Omega.F = VA^{-1} . CV^{-1} = CA^{-1} = As.A^{-1} = s$

**Worked Example**

1. A capacitor of capacitance 470 µF is placed in a circuit in series with a resistor of resistance 100 kΩ. What is the time constant of the circuit?

**Solution**

Time constant $\tau = RC = 100 \times 10^3 \times 470 \times 10^{-6} = 47$ s

We have seen that the current flowing in a discharging capacitor decreases exponentially. The equation that describes this decrease is as follows:

$$I = I_0 e^{\frac{-t}{\tau}}$$     where $I_0$ = the initial current (A)
$I$ = current at time $t$ (A)
$t$ = time (s)
$\tau$ = time constant (s)

Since $\tau = RC$, this equation is also sometimes written as: $I = I_0 e^{\frac{-t}{CR}}$

**Note:** The CCEA specification does not require you to know the derivation of this equation, but you do have to be able to use it.

**Measuring the time constant experimentally**

To explain the significance of the time constant $\tau$, consider what value the discharging current has after a period of time equal to the time constant has passed, ie at time $t = \tau$.

$$I = I_0 e^{\frac{-t}{\tau}} = I_0 e^{-1} = \frac{I_0}{e}$$

The value of $e$ is approximately 2.7183, we can write:

$$I = \frac{I_0}{2.7183} \approx 0.37 \times I_0$$

So after a period of time equal to the time constant, the discharging current falls to 0.37 of the value that it had at the start of that period. For the circuit in the worked example above the time constant was 47 s. If the initial discharging current was 60 µA, after 47 s it will have fallen to $0.37 \times 60$ = 22.2 µA and after another 47 s it will have fallen to $0.37 \times 22 = 8.2$ µA. This is an exponential decline and is shown in the graph on the right.

So if the initial current is $I_0$, then the current after successive time constants is:

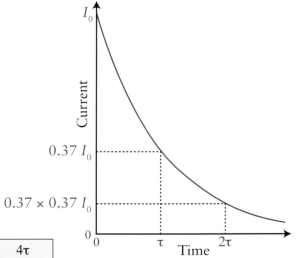

| Time | 0 | $\tau$ | $2\tau$ | $3\tau$ | $4\tau$ |
|---|---|---|---|---|---|
| **Current in terms of $e$** | $I_0$ | $\dfrac{I_0}{e}$ | $\dfrac{I_0}{e^2}$ | $\dfrac{I_0}{e^3}$ | $\dfrac{I_0}{e^4}$ |
| **Current** | $I_0$ | $0.37\,I_0$ | $0.14\,I_0$ | $0.050\,I_0$ | $0.019\,I_0$ |

This approach can be used determine the time constant of a R-C circuit by carrying out the discharge experiment already discussed, ie using the graph of current against time to determine the time that it takes for the current to fall to 0.37 of its initial value. For greatest accuracy, values for $\tau$, $2\tau$, $3\tau$ etc should be read from the graph and an average found. Once the time constant has been determined, the capacitance can be found if the resistance of the circuit is known (or the resistance can be found if the capacitance is known).

Note that the charge stored by the capacitor and the potential difference across the capacitor also decrease in a exponential way. The equation that describes the decrease in **charge** is as follows:

$Q = Q_0 e^{\frac{-t}{\tau}}$   where  $Q_0$ = the initial charge (C)
$Q$ = charge at time $t$ (C)
$t$ = time (s)
$\tau$ = time constant (s)

Since $\tau = RC$, this equation is also sometimes written as: $Q = Q_0 e^{\frac{-t}{CR}}$

The equation that describes the decrease in **potential difference** is as follows:

$V = V_0 e^{\frac{-t}{\tau}}$    where  $V_0$ = the initial potential difference (V)
$V$ = potential difference at time $t$ (V)
$t$ = time (s)
$\tau$ = time constant (s)

Since $\tau = RC$, this equation is also sometimes written as: $V = V_0 e^{\frac{-t}{CR}}$

**Points to remember**

- The value of $V_0$ is the e.m.f. of the battery or power supply used to charge the capacitor.
- The value of $Q_0 = CV_0$ (from the equation for capacitance, $C = \frac{Q}{V}$).
- The value of $I_0 = \frac{V_0}{R}$ (from Ohm's Law, $I = \frac{V}{R}$).
- The value of $R$ is that of the resistor through which the capacitor discharges.

**Measuring the time constant more accurately**

As already discussed, the graph of current against time can be used to find the time constant directly, ie the time taken for the current to fall to 0.37 of the initial value. However, a problem with this approach is the difficulty of drawing an exponential curve by hand. A straight line graph is much easier to draw and can be achieved as follows.

Beginning with:

$I = I_0 e^{\frac{-t}{\tau}}$

Taking natural logarithms (ie, log to base $e$, or ln) of both sides gives:

$\ln I = \ln I_0 - \frac{t}{\tau}$

Plotting a graph of ln $I$ on the $y$–axis against $t$ on the $x$–axis will produce a straight line as shown on the right.

The gradient of the line will give $\frac{1}{\tau} \times -1$.

**Note:** Logarithms, natural or to the base 10, **do not have a unit.** If you wanted to make it explicit that $I$ was measured in A, then the vertical axis label should be labelled **ln ($I$ / A)**. Note carefully the position of the brackets. The brackets indicate that only $I$ is measured in A, and that ln $I$ itself has no unit.

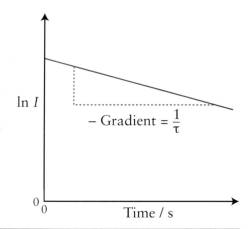

## Worked Example

1 A capacitor, C, of value 1 μF may be connected either to a 100 V DC supply or to a resistor, R, of value 22 MΩ by means of a two-way switch, S, as shown on the right.

(a) Explain the meaning and significance of the time constant.

(b) Calculate the value of the time constant for this circuit.

(c) The capacitor is fully charged by moving the switch to the position shown. The switch is then moved so that capacitor discharges through the resistor. Determine the time taken for the voltage across the capacitor (ie between points X and Y) to fall to 10 V.

**Solution**

(a) The time constant $\tau$ is the product of the capacitance and resistance.

When the switch is changed so that the capacitor is connected to the resistor the charge stored on the capacitor will fall to a value of $1/e$ or 0.37 of the charge stored before the switch was changed over, in one time constant period.

Alternatively you could explain the significance in terms of the discharge current. After a period equal to $\tau$ the discharge current will have decreased to $0.37\,I_0$, where $I_0$ is the value of the current at the moment the switch was changed over.

(b) $\tau = RC = 22 \times 10^6 \times 1 \times 10^{-6} = 22$ s

(c) Using $V = V_0 e^{\frac{-t}{\tau}}$ gives:

$10 = 100 \times e^{\frac{-t}{22}}$, which can be rearranged to give: $0.1 = e^{\frac{-t}{22}}$

Taking natural logs of both sides gives:

$\ln (0.1) = \frac{-t}{22}$

This can be rearranged to give:

$t = 2.3026 \times 22 = 51$ s

## Uses of capacitors

### Flash gun

An electronic flash gun uses an electric discharge in a suitable gas such as xenon to produce an intense flash of light that lasts a short time. In the case of the type of flash gun used with a camera, the system is operated from a small battery, say, 6 V. To achieve such an intense flash of light from such a small battery, electronic circuitry has to be used to generate a high voltage (several hundred volts) which then charges a capacitor. When the shutter on the camera is pressed the charged capacitor is discharged rapidly through the gas filled flash tube to producing the intense flash of light. The diagram on the right below shows a simplified version of the circuit used.

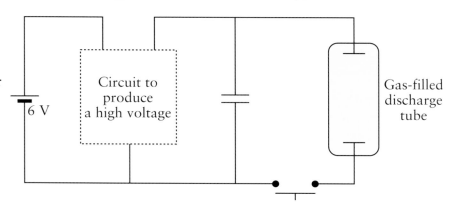

Shutter on the camera: when pressed, allows the capacitor to discharge through the gas

### Defibrillators

When functioning normally, the heart muscles depend upon regularly-timed electrical signals which causing them to contract (and relax) in a delicate rhythm. The heart beats at an average of about 70 beats per minute throughout our life, and has its own natural pacemaker which produces electrical signals at around 70 pulses per minute.

If this rhythm becomes disturbed, for example as a result of a heart attack, the heart may undergo ventricular fibrillation which is a rapid, uncoordinated twitching of the heart muscles. If this happens the heart cannot properly pump blood, which means that fresh oxygen will not be delivered to the cells of the body. If this situation is not rectified quickly, it can lead to death. A defibrillator is a device that is used to deliver a carefully controlled shock to the victim's heart. The shock is designed to stop the ventricular fibrillation and allow the heart to resume a normal rhythm.

A defibrillator needs to transfer a precise amount of energy to a patient in a short time. The best way to do this is to use a capacitor. The diagram on the right shows a simplified version of the circuit used. The capacitor stores the electric charge by means of the electric field that is

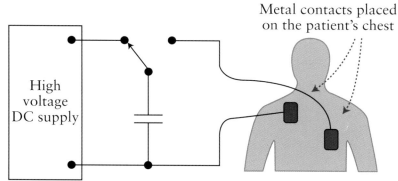

Metal contacts placed on the patient's chest

created between its plates. Modern designs of defibrillators use energies of 120 – 200 J to stop fibrillation – these are much lower energies than have been used in the past. This energy is delivered as a pulse lasting just a few milliseconds.

The charging circuit has minimal resistance so that the capacitor charges quickly. But the resistance must not be so small that the large current produced damages the power supply unit.

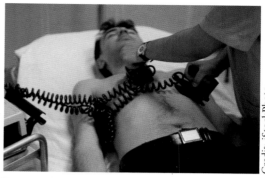

Credit: iStockPhoto

**Note:** The first portable defibrillator was developed by a cardiologist, Professor Frank Pantridge, at the Royal Victoria Hospital in Belfast. Today they are used across the world and have saved many lives.

## Exercise 5.4

1 Show how you would connect three 4 µF capacitors to form a network with a total capacitance of (a) 1.33 µF and (b) 6.0 µF. In each case draw a circuit diagram and provide suitable calculations for your answer.

2 An arrangement of capacitors is shown in the diagram on the right. The only accessible terminals are X, Y and Z. The central common point is not accessible. State the pair of terminals between which the maximum capacitance is obtained. Make suitable calculations to support your answer.

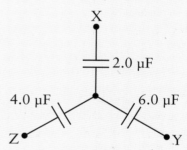

3 A number of capacitors, each of value 10 µF, are connected in a network as shown on the right.
  (a) Calculate the capacitance of the network between the points X and Y.

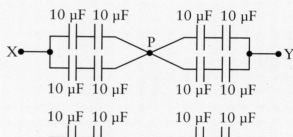

  (b) Later, the wires crossing at P become separated as shown on the right. Calculate the new capacitance of the network between X and Y.

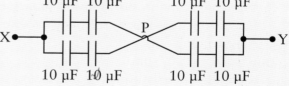

4 The diagram on the right shows six identical capacitors. The total capacitance of the network is 33 µF. What is the value of each capacitor?

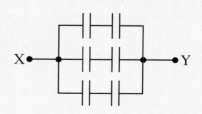

5  Two capacitors of values 1 μF and 100 pF are each given a charge of 1.5 nC.
   (a) Calculate the potential difference across each capacitor.
   (b) Calculate the energy stored in each capacitor.

6  A capacitor $C_1$ of value 12.0 μF is charged from a 400 V supply. It is then disconnected from the supply and connected across a second capacitor $C_2$ of value 4.0 μF , which is initially uncharged. $C_2$ is then disconnected from $C_1$ and discharged.
   (a) What charge remains on $C_1$?
   (b) Find the minimum number of times that $C_2$ has to be connected to $C_1$, then disconnected from $C_1$ and discharged, in order to reduce the charge on $C_1$ to below 50% of its initial value.

7  The diagram on the right shows a circuit containing three capacitors connected to a 12 V battery.
   (a) State which capacitors are in parallel.
   (b) Calculate the capacitance of the single capacitor, connected across the battery, which is equivalent to the network of the three capacitors.
   (c) Calculate the energy stored in the network of capacitors.

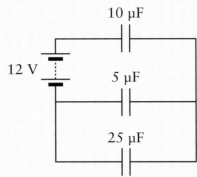

8  A 300 μF capacitor stores 4.8 mC of charge when it is connected across a battery.
   (a) Calculate the e.m.f. of the battery and the energy stored in the capacitor.

   The battery is disconnected and the 300 μF charged capacitor is then connected to an uncharged capacitor of capacitance 500 μF as shown in the diagram on the right. The switch S is then closed.
   (b) Calculate the potential difference across the capacitors.

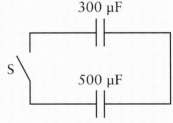

9  A charged capacitor is connected in series with a switch and a resistor as shown in the diagram. Before the switch is closed the potential difference across the capacitor is $V_0$.
   (a) Sketch a graph to show how the potential difference across the capacitor (y-axis) varies with time (x-axis) after the switch is closed.
   (b) Explain what is meant by the time constant of the circuit. Mark the time constant τ on the horizontal axis of your graph and label the corresponding voltage on the vertical axis.
   (c) The capacitor has a capacitance of 47 nF and the resistor has a resistance of 22 MΩ. How long after the switch is closed will it take for the potential difference across the capacitor fall to 14% of its initial value?

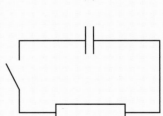

10 An uncharged capacitor is connected in series with a
resistor, a battery and a switch as shown on the right.
Initially, the switch is open.

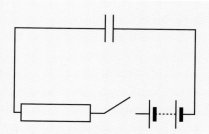

(a) The switch is now closed. Sketch a graph to show the
variation of the charge ($y$-axis) on the capacitor with
time ($x$-axis).

(b) Sketch a graph to show the variation of the current,
$I$ ($y$-axis) drawn from the battery with time ($x$-axis)
after the switch is closed.

11 A capacitor of value 470 µF is connected in series with a battery of e.m.f. 20 V, a resistor of
value 10 kΩ, a milliammeter and a switch.
(a) Draw a circuit diagram of this arrangement.
(b) The switch is closed. Calculate the initial current shown by the milliammeter.
(c) Calculate the time constant of the circuit.
(d) Calculate how long it is before the discharge current has fallen to ¼ of its initial value.

12 A charged capacitor of value 8 µF is discharged through a milliammeter and resistor. The
current is recorded at 5 second intervals. The measurements obtained are shown below.

| Time / s | 0 | 5 | 10 | 15 | 20 | 25 | 30 | 35 |
|---|---|---|---|---|---|---|---|---|
| Current / mA | 72 | 54 | 41 | 31 | 23 | 17 | 13 | 10 |

(a) Use the results to plot a suitable linear graph from which the time constant of the circuit
can be found.

(b) Calculate the resistance of the resistor used in the circuit.

13 Defibrillators use capacitors specially designed for use in portable devices.
(a) What charging potential difference would be needed to store 100 J in a 50 µF capacitor?
(b) Doctors need to use the defibrillator over and over again so they require a charging time
of 3 seconds. What average charging current is needed?
(c) Calculate the mean charging power.
(d) A defibrillator uses a 50 µF capacitor charged to 1500 V. How would you use a number
of 50 µF capacitors that can withstand a maximum of 500 V to construct a circuit with a
capacitance of 50 µF and that can withstand the charging voltage of 1500 V? Draw a
circuit diagram to illustrate your answer.

14 A 47 µF capacitor in a flash gun supplies an average power of $1.5 \times 10^4$ W for 20 µs. What is
the potential difference across the capacitor before it is discharged?

15 In the circuit shown on the right, $C_1$ is a capacitor of
capacitance 250 µF, and R is a resistor of resistance 500 kΩ.
The resistor-capacitor combination is connected to 1.5 V cell.
Calculate:

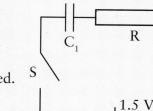

(a) the current in the circuit at the instant the switch S is closed.
(b) the charge stored in the capacitor when the potential
difference across its plates reaches its maximum.
(c) the energy stored in the capacitor when it is fully charged.

16 (a) A capacitor in a catalogue is marked "47 µF, 12 V". What information does this give the person considering buying this capacitor?
   (b) A 2 mF capacitor is required to work at 600 V. The only capacitors available are marked "2 mF, 200 V". How could these capacitors be arranged to provide a capacitor of 2 mF capable of withstanding 600 V?

17 A capacitor of unknown capacitance, C, is charged by a battery of e.m.f. 6.0 V and then the battery is disconnected. The charged capacitor is now connected across an uncharged capacitor of capacitance 47 µF, as shown on the right. The potential difference across the combination is then 4.0 V. Calculate the capacitance, C, of the unknown capacitor.

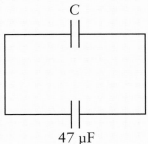

18 How would you connect three capacitors of capacitances 3 mF, 6 mF and 9 mF together to give a combined capacitance of 11 mF?

19 A 30 µF capacitor is charged and then disconnected from the supply. Over the next 60 seconds the potential difference across the plates is seen to fall by 4 V. Calculate the average leakage current.

20 A 1 µF capacitor is charged to a potential difference of 200 V. It is then allowed to discharge through a 100 MΩ resistor.
   (a) How long does it take before the potential difference across the capacitor has fallen to 100 V?
   (b) How much longer will it take before the potential difference reaches 50 V? Comment on your answer.
   (c) Calculate the potential difference across the capacitor 200 seconds after the start of the discharge. Give your answer to the nearest volt.

# 5.5 Magnetic Fields

## Definition

The space surrounding a magnet where a magnetic force is experienced is called a magnetic field. This magnetic force is experienced by other magnets, objects made of metals such as iron and steel and also by current carrying conductors. The direction of a magnetic field at a point is taken as **the direction of the force that acts on a north pole placed at that point.**

The shape of a magnetic field can be represented by a magnetic field lines (lines of magnetic force). Arrows on the lines show the direction of the magnetic force. Since a north pole is repelled from another north pole and attracted by a south pole **the direction of a magnetic field is from north to south.**

Magnadur magnets are commonly used in school laboratories to produce a strong magnetic field. Two are arranged on a U-shaped steel yoke as shown in the diagram on the next page. The diagram also shows the shape and direction of the magnetic field that is created by this arrangement.

The field lines in the central portion of the magnetic field are parallel and uniformly spaced. This indicates a magnetic field that is uniform, ie it has the same strength at all points in the region. The field weakens at the edges as indicated by the increased spacing between the lines of force.

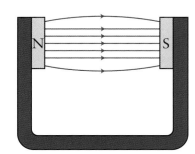

## Direction of the magnetic field produced by the current in a long straight wire

The direction of the magnetic field around a long straight current-carrying wire can be investigated using the apparatus shown on the right. A current is passed through a long straight vertical wire which passes through a small hole in a horizontal, rectangular piece of hardboard. The size of the current can be changed using a rheostat in series with the battery.

The **shape** of the field can be disclosed using iron filings sprinkled on the hardboard, while plotting compasses on the hardboard can be used to disclose the **direction** of the magnetic field.

The experiment will show that the field lines are **closed circles around the vertical wire**.

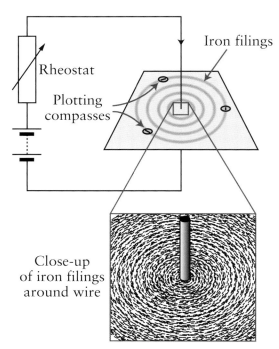

### The right hand grip rule

The direction of the field around a long straight wire can be recalled by using the **right hand grip rule**. Grip the conductor with the right hand so that the thumb points in the direction of the conventional current, as shown in the diagram on the right. The direction in which your fingers are turning gives the direction of the magnetic field.

It is easier to show this situation with a two dimensional diagram. In the diagram below, the symbol $\otimes$ represents a current flowing **into** the page (away from you) and the symbol $\odot$ represents a current flowing **out** of the page (towards you).

Apply the right hand grip rule to each of the diagrams to confirm the magnetic field direction in each case.

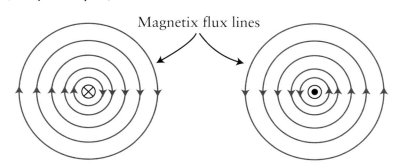

Current carrying wire with current direction **into** the page

Current carrying wire with current direction **out of** the page

# Direction of the magnetic field produced by the current in a coil of wire

### Single coil

The diagram on the right shows the shape of the magnetic field around a single loop of wire when it carries an electric current. At A, the current is flowing **out of** the plane of the paper and the magnetic field lines there turn anti-clockwise. At B, the current is flowing **into** the plane of the paper and the magnetic field lines there point clockwise. In the middle, the fields from each part of the loop combine to produce a magnetic field pointing from bottom to top. Note

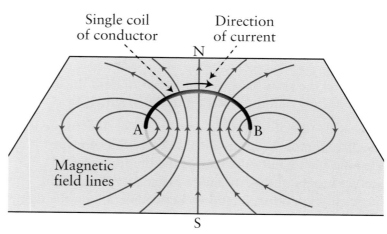

the field lines at the top diverging away from the north pole and at the bottom converging towards the south pole.

### Coil with many turns

The diagram on the right shows the shape of the magnetic field caused by the current in a long, cylindrical coil or **solenoid**. Note that the magnetic field produced is very similar to that around a bar magnet. Within the solenoid the field lines are parallel and equally spaced (so the field there is uniform). Outside the solenoid the field lines loop, in a way which is similar to that around a bar magnet. As they leave the solenoid

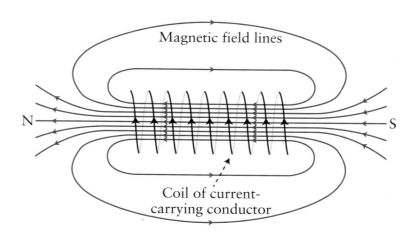

the field lines diverge as the strength of the field at that point decreases.

The direction of the field can be found by using the **right hand grip rule**. Imagine gripping the coil with the right hand with the fingers pointing in the direction of conventional current, as shown on the right. Then the thumb will point to the north pole of the solenoid.

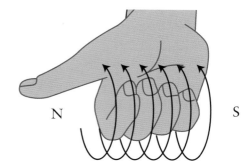

The strength of the magnetic field produced can be increased by:

- increasing the current in the coil.
- increasing the number of turns in the coil.
- placing a rod of soft iron in the coil with its axis perpendicular to the plane of the coil.

## Force on a current-carrying conductor in a perpendicular magnetic field

When a current flows through a conductor in a magnetic field the conductor **experiences a force**. This can be demonstrated using the apparatus shown on the right. When a current is passed along the flexible wire, the wire moves up.

Note that the force acts at right angles to **both** the direction of the current **and** the direction of the magnetic field.

The CCEA specification requires you to be able to predict the direction of the force. This is best obtained using **Fleming's left hand rule**. Extend the thumb, first and second fingers of the left hand so that they are at right angles to each other, as shown in the diagram on the right.

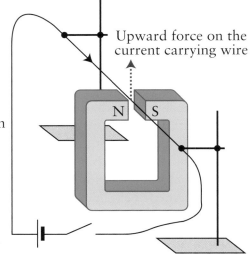

Upward force on the current carrying wire

- The first finger represents the magnetic field direction. Remember that the magnetic field direction is from the north pole (N) to the south pole (S).

- The second finger represents the conventional current direction, ie from positive to negative.

- The thumb represents the force acting on the current carrying wire.

**You must be able to use Fleming's left hand rule to predict the direction of the force on a current-carrying conductor in a magnetic field.**

This force arises because of the interaction of the two magnetic fields: firstly, the uniform field of the permanent magnet and, secondly, the field due to the current in the wire. The magnetic field lines of force are **vectors** and the field lines due to two fields have to be combined vectorially. This interaction of magnetic fields is illustrated below. The resultant field is sometimes called a **catapult field**: the field lines resemble the stretched rubber band in a catapult, and the conductor experiencing a force in the direction shown.

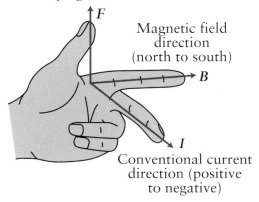

Force on the current-carrying conductor

Magnetic field direction (north to south)

Conventional current direction (positive to negative)

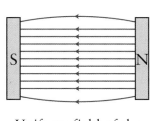

Uniform field of the permanent magnet

+

Magnetic field due to the current which is **into** the page

=

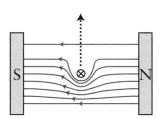

The resultant magnetic field is sometimes known as a **catapult field**

## Magnetic flux density

The force acting on the current-carrying wire is at a **maximum** when the current and the magnetic field are perpendicular to each other. The force is **zero** when the current and the magnetic field are in the same direction or act at 180° to each other. The term **magnetic flux density** is used to indicate the strength of a magnetic field. Magnetic flux density is measured in a unit called the **tesla**, symbol T.

In the case where the magnetic field and the current are at right angles the force is given by:

$F = BIl$   where  $F$ = force (N)

$B$ = magnetic flux density (T)

$I$ = current in the conductor (A)

$l$ = length of the conductor in the magnetic field (m)

## Definition of the tesla

Re-arranging the above equation gives:

$$B = \frac{F}{Il}$$

This shows that magnetic flux density, $B$, is **the force per unit current carrying length**. A 'current carrying length' is the product of the current and the length of the conductor in the magnetic field. For example, a current of 2.0 A and a length of 0.5 m is a current carrying length of 1.0 Am.

This allows us to define the tesla. If a current of 1 A flowing in a conductor at right angles to a magnetic field, causes a force of 1 N to be produced on each metre of conductor within the field, then the strength of the magnetic field is 1 tesla, or 1 T. Note that the force, current and magnetic field directions are perpendicular to each other in accordance with Fleming's left hand rule.

---

### Worked Examples

1 A straight wire, of length 60 cm, carries a current of 1.25 A. Calculate the value of the force that acts on this wire when a length of 25 cm of the wire is placed at right angles to a magnetic field of flux density $4.5 \times 10^{-2}$ T as shown in the diagram.

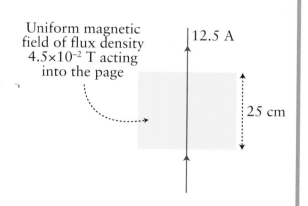

Uniform magnetic field of flux density $4.5 \times 10^{-2}$ T acting into the page

12.5 A

25 cm

#### Solution

The figure of 60 cm is not relevant, since only 0.25 m of the wire is in the magnetic field. So:

$F = BIl = 4.5 \times 10^{-2} \times 1.25 \times 0.25 = 0.014$ N

Application of Fleming's left hand rule tells us that the force on the wire acts to the left.

2  A straight wire carrying a current of 500 mA is placed in a magnetic field of flux density 0.2 T. The length of the wire in the magnetic field is 30 cm and the wire makes an angle of 50° with the magnetic field direction. Calculate the force on the current carrying wire due to the magnetic field.

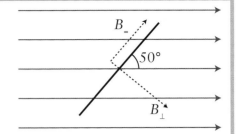

**Solution**

The magnetic flux density must be resolved into a component perpendicular to the wire $B_\perp$ and a component parallel to the wire, $B_=$, as shown in the diagram on the right. Only the perpendicular component produces a force on the wire. So:

$B_\perp = 0.2 \times \sin 50° = 0.153$ T

Therefore:

$F = B_\perp Il = 0.153 \times 0.5 \times 0.3 = 0.023$ N

## Verification of $F = BIl$

The apparatus shown on the right can be used to investigate how the force acting on a current carrying conductor depends on the **current, $I$,** flowing in the conductor and the **length of the conductor, $l$,** in the magnetic field.

An aluminium rod (the upright from a retort stand is suitable) is clamped horizontally above a sensitive electronic balance. The rod is connected to a variable low voltage power supply. An ammeter connected in series with both will allow the current to be measured.

A permanent magnet is placed on the balance and the aluminium rod positioned so that it is located in the centre of the magnetic field. The balance is reset to read zero after the magnets have been placed on it.

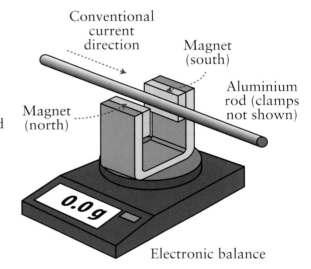

A current is then passed along the clamped aluminium rod, which causes the rod to experience a force because of the interaction of the permanent magnetic field and the magnetic field due to the current in the aluminium rod. In the case shown in the diagram, the force is upwards: you can use Fleming's left hand rule to verify that this is the case. Since the magnet is exerting an upward force on the rod, then by Newton's third law, the rod must exert an equal but opposite force on the magnets. This downward force will cause the reading on the electronic balance to increase.

The current should be varied and readings of the force taken with a single magnet in place. This ensures that the length of the conductor in the magnetic field remains constant. A graph of the force ($y$-axis) against current ($x$-axis) produces a straight line through the origin as shown in the first graph on the right. This is verification that the force on the current carrying conductor in the magnetic field is directly proportional to the current.

The experiment is then repeated. This time, the current is fixed and a number of identical magnets are placed side by side. This changes the length of the conductor in the magnetic field. A graph of force (*y*-axis) against the length of

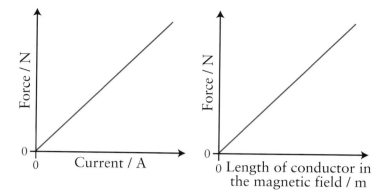

conductor in the magnetic field (*x*-axis) also produces a straight line through the origin as shown in the second graph on the right. This is verification that the force on the current carrying conductor in the magnetic field is directly proportional to the length of the conductor in the magnetic field. This experiments therefore verifies the equation $F = BIl$.

## The principle of the electric motor

The diagram on the upper right shows the basic principle of an electric motor. Current from a battery flows in the horizontal coil of wire. Fleming's left hand rule predicts that the left side of the loop will experience an upward force and the right side will experience a downward force. These two forces produce a resultant moment which causes the coil to turn.

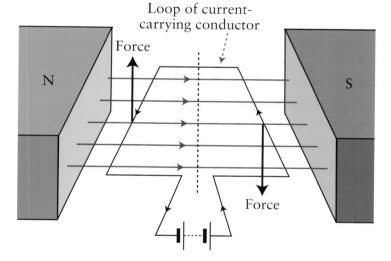

Practical motors involve a coil of many turns, as shown on the lower right, mounted on a former (not shown) between the poles of a permanent magnet and free to rotate about a central axle. When current flows in the coil, it rotates.

A component called the commutator causes the direction of the current to reverse each time the coil passes through the vertical position, so that the coil continues to rotate in the same direction.

**Note:** You do not need to know the details of the action of the commutator.

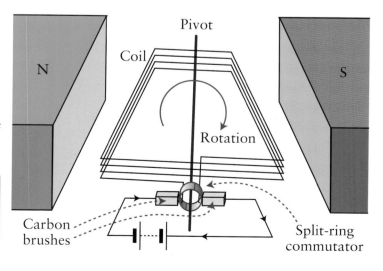

When the coil is horizontal the force on the longer sides of the coil is:

$F = NBIL$    where   $N$ = the number of turns in the coil
$B$ = strength of the magnetic field (T)
$I$ = the current (A)
$L$ = the length of the side of the coil (m).

## Magnetic flux $\phi$

As previously discussed, gravitational fields, electric fields and magnetic fields can be visualized using lines of force. Magnetic flux lines (magnetic field lines) show the direction of a magnetic field. Their spacing indicates the strength of the field, the closer the field lines, the stronger the magnetic field.

**Magnetic flux $\phi$**, represents the total number of magnetic flux lines that pass at 90° through a given area, such as the area within a coil of a current-carrying conductor. Magnetic flux is measured in **webers**, symbol Wb.

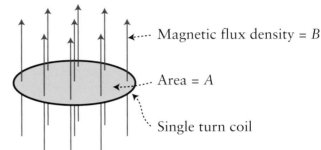

Magnetic flux density = $B$

Area = $A$

Single turn coil

If the field, $B$, is normal to the area, $A$, then

$\phi = BA$         where    $\phi$ = magnetic flux (Wb)
$B$ = magnetic flux density (T)
$A$ = area (m²)

If the field, $B$, is at an angle $\theta$ to the normal of the area, $A$, then the magnetic flux linked with the area is the component of B normal to the area (B cos $\theta$) times the area itself, ie:

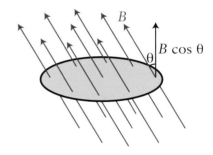

$\phi = BA \cos \theta$         where    $\phi$ = magnetic flux (Wb)
$B$ = magnetic flux density (T)
$A$ = area (m²)
$\theta$ = angle of magnetic flux to normal of the area (degrees)

## Magnetic flux linkage $N\phi$

The term **magnetic flux linkage, $N\phi$**, is used when calculating the total magnetic flux passing through (or 'linking') a coil of $N$ turns of current-carrying conductor and area of cross section $A$. Magnetic flux linkage is also measured in webers (Wb).

If the coil has $N$ turns, then:

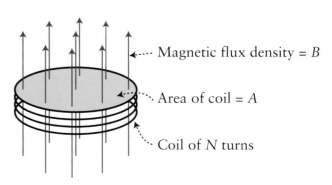

Magnetic flux density = $B$

Area of coil = $A$

Coil of N turns

$N\phi = BAN$     where     $N\phi$ = magnetic flux linkage (Wb)
$B$ = magnetic flux density, perpendicular to the
     plane of the coil (T)
$A$ = area (m$^2$)
$N$ = number of turns in the coil

If the magnetic field passes through the coil so that the angle between the normal to the plane of the coil and B is θ, then:

$N\phi = BAN \cos \theta$     where     $N\phi$ = magnetic flux linkage (Wb)
$B$ = magnetic flux density (T)
$A$ = area (m$^2$)
$N$ = number of turns in the coil
$\theta$ = angle of magnetic flux to
     normal of the area (degrees)

## Worked Example

1   A coil of 250 turns each of area 80 cm$^2$ is placed in a
    uniform magnetic field of flux density 0.25 T. The
    magnetic field direction makes an angle of 30° with the
    normal to the plane of the coil.
    (a) Calculate the magnetic flux linked with the coil.
    (b) Calculate the maximum flux that this field could
        produce in the coil and state the angle between the
        normal and the direction of $B$ when it occurs.

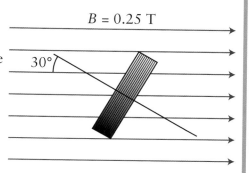

### Solution

(a)   $N\Phi = BAN \cos \theta = 0.25 \times 80 \times 10^{-4} \times 250 \times \cos 30° = 0.433$ Wb

(b)   $N\Phi = BAN = 0.25 \times 80 \times 10^{-4} \times 250 = 0.5$ Wb is produced when angle = 0°.

## Electromagnetic induction

An electromotive force (e.m.f.) can be **induced** in a
coil of wire by moving a magnet towards or away
from the coil or by moving a wire so that it cuts
across the magnetic lines of flux. For an e.m.f. to be
induced, **there must be relative motion** between the
magnet and the conductor, the wire or coil of wire.

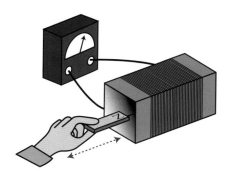

The magnitude of the induced e.m.f. is proportional
to:

* the strength of the magnet
* the number of turns on the coil
* the speed of the moving magnet

This can be stated formally as **Faraday's law of
electromagnetic induction:**

**The magnitude of the induced e.m.f. is equal to the
rate of change of magnetic flux linkage.**

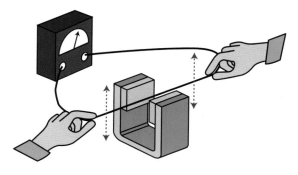

The direction of the induced e.m.f. depends on the direction in which the magnet is moving and on the type of magnetic pole that is nearest the coil. We can demonstrate this using the simple apparatus shown on the right.

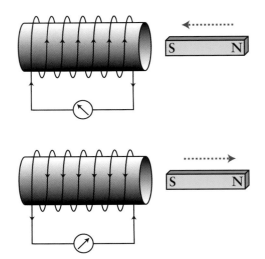

Moving the south pole of the magnet **towards** the coil causes the induced current to flow so that it creates a south magnetic pole in the coil opposing the incoming south pole of the magnet. Work has to be done against this opposing force.

Moving the south pole of the magnet **away from** the coil causes the induced current to reverse direction. It now flows so that it creates a north magnetic pole in the coil attracting the retreating pole of the magnet. Work again has to be done against this opposing force.

These observations can be stated formally as **Lenz's law:**

**The direction of the induced current is such that it opposes the change in the magnetic flux that is producing it.**

Note that Lenz's law is the principle of conservation of energy in action. The kinetic energy of the moving magnet is converted to electrical energy when work is done against the opposing force.

### Calculation of induced e.m.f.

Faraday's law tells us that the magnitude of the induced e.m.f. is equal to the rate of change of the number of magnetic flux lines. As we have seen, the number of magnetic flux lines that passes through a coil is calculated as the magnetic flux $\phi = BA$ and for a coil of $N$ turns it is calculated as the magnetic flux linkage $N\phi = BAN$.

The diagrams on the right illustrate the role magnetic flux linkage plays in Faraday's model of electromagnetic induction. In the upper diagram, a bar magnet is moved towards to a coil of wire. At this instant the number of magnetic flux lines linking the coil is 3. A short time later the magnet has been moved closer to the coil and the number of magnetic flux lines linking the coil has increased to 5.

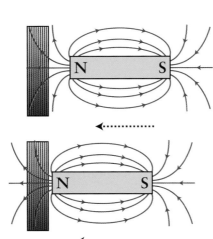

So in this example there has been a change of 2 in the magnetic flux linkage in the coil. This change results in an e.m.f. being induced in the coil. The more rapidly this change takes place, the larger the induced e.m.f. The average induced e.m.f. can be calculated as follows:

**Average induced e.m.f. = rate of change of magnetic flux linkage with time**

$E = -\dfrac{\Delta N\phi}{\Delta t}$   where   $E$ = induced e.m.f (V)

$\Delta N\phi$ = change in the magnetic flux linkage (Wb)

$\Delta t$ = time in which the change occurs (s)

The minus is a consequence of Lenz's Law.

## AC generator

The diagram on the right shows the structure of a simple AC (alternating current) generator which can be used to create an electric current from rotational kinetic energy. It consists of a coil of wire that is rotated at a constant angular velocity in a magnetic field. As the coil turns, the magnetic flux

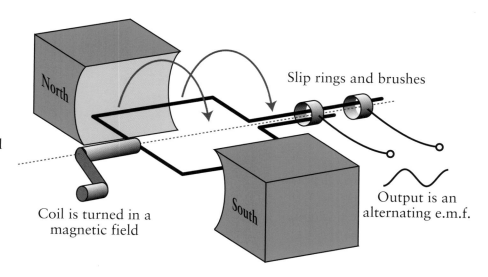

Coil is turned in a magnetic field

Slip rings and brushes

Output is an alternating e.m.f.

linking it changes. This change in magnetic flux linkage results in the induction of an alternating e.m.f. in the coil. The output from the rotating coil is led to the outside by means of carbon brushes that rub against metal slip rings.

**Note:** In a practical generator there would be many more turns on the coil and the coil would be formed around a soft iron core. These two changes result in an alternating output voltage that has a much greater peak value.

The following diagrams illustrate the change in magnetic flux linkage as the coil turns.

In this position the plane of the coil is **parallel** to the magnetic flux lines. The magnetic flux linking the coil, therefore $N\phi$ = **zero**.

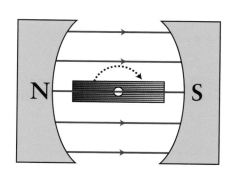

In this position the coil has turned through 90°. The plane of the coil is now **perpendicular** to the magnetic flux lines. The magnetic flux linkage is now at a maximum and has the value $N\phi = BAN$.

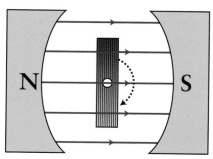

In this diagram, the coil has rotated through an angle θ. The dotted line is the normal to the plane of the coil. To calculate the magnetic flux linking the coil at this position it is necessary to resolve the magnetic flux density into two components. The component used to calculate the magnetic flux linking the coil is $B_\perp$, ie the one that is perpendicular to the plane of the coil, where $B_\perp = B \cos \theta$. Therefore:

$N\phi = B_\perp AN = B \cos \theta \, AN$

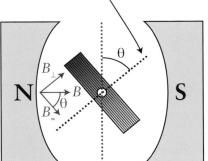

Normal to the plane of the coil

This is more conveniently written as:

$N\phi = BAN \cos \theta$

Since the coil is rotating with a constant angular velocity, ω, the angle $\theta = \omega t$. So therefore at any given time, $t$:

$N\phi = BAN \cos \omega t$

The magnetic flux linking the coil therefore varies as a cosine function as shown in the graph on the right. The diagram below the graph shows the position of the coil in relation to the magnetic field.

The lower graph shows the induced e.m.f.. Notice that when the flux linking the coil is momentarily zero the induced e.m.f. is at a maximum. Although at this instant the magnetic flux linkage is zero, its rate of change is a maximum so the induced e.m.f. is a maximum.

Because the equation $E = -\dfrac{\Delta N\phi}{\Delta t}$

we can obtain the e.m.f. by taking the negative of the gradient of the flux linkage graph, ie:

$E = -\dfrac{\mathrm{d}(N\phi)}{\mathrm{d}t} = \dfrac{\mathrm{d}(BAN \cos \omega t)}{\mathrm{d}t}$

From the rules of trigonometry, this results in a sine function:

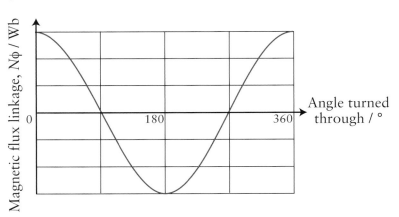

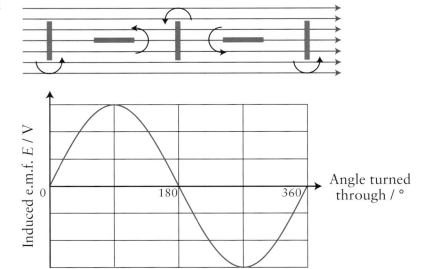

**$E = BAN\omega \sin \omega t$**  where

$E$ = induced e.m.f (V)
$B$ = magnetic flux density (T)
$A$ = area (m$^2$)
$N$ = number of turns in the coil
$\omega$ = angular velocity (rad s$^{-1}$)
$t$ = time (s)

## Worked Examples

1  A circular coil of wire has a radius of 2 cm and 500 turns. It is situated in a magnetic field so that its plane is perpendicular to a magnetic field of flux density 20 mT. The magnetic field is then reduced in strength to zero and then increased to 20 mT in the opposite direction. This change, which takes 60 ms, takes place at a constant rate. Calculate the magnitude of the e.m.f. induced in the coil.

### Solution

Area of coil = $\pi r^2 = \pi \times (2\times10^{-2})^2 = 1.26\times10^{-3}$ m²

Change of magnetic flux density, $\Delta B$, = 20 − (−20) = 40 mT

Change of magnetic flux linkage:

$\Delta N\phi = \Delta BAN$

= $40\times10^{-3} \times 1.26\times10^{-3} \times 500 = 25.2\times10^{-3}$ Wb

Therefore induced e.m.f. $E = \dfrac{\Delta N\phi}{\Delta t} = \dfrac{25.2\times10^{-3}}{60\times10^{-3}} = 0.42$ V

We have omitted the minus sign from this equation since the question only asks us for the magnitude, not the direction, of the induced e.m.f..

2  A long solenoid is connected to a signal generator. A short coil is wound over the longer coil as shown below.

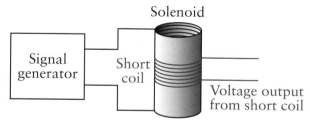

The voltage delivered by the signal generator varies with time as shown below.

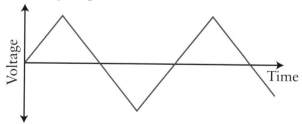

Sketch a graph to show the voltage induced in the short coil.

### Solution

The voltage causes a current to flow in the longer coil. This current varies with time in the same way as the voltage does. This current creates a magnetic field which also varies in the same manner as shown in the graph. This means that the magnetic flux linking the shorter coil changes, which means that an e.m.f. is induced in this coil. The size of the induced e.m.f. is proportional to the rate of change of magnetic flux linkage. The size of the induced e.m.f. is obtained by taking the gradient of the voltage-time graph and its direction is the negative of this gradient.

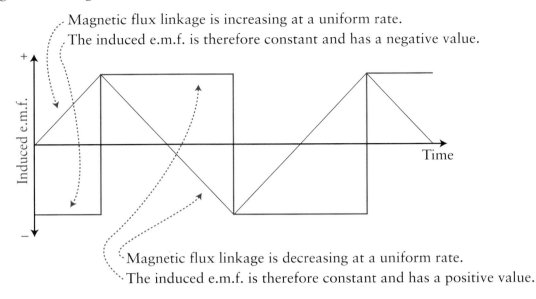

Magnetic flux linkage is increasing at a uniform rate.
The induced e.m.f. is therefore constant and has a negative value.

Magnetic flux linkage is decreasing at a uniform rate.
The induced e.m.f. is therefore constant and has a positive value.

3  An electrical generator has a rectangular coil of 250 turns and measuring 40 cm × 40 cm. The coil is in a uniform magnetic field of strength 20 mT. The coil turns on an axle at 3000 revolutions per minute.
   (a) Calculate the maximum output voltage from this generator and state its frequency.
   (b) State the magnetic flux linked with the coil when the output e.m.f. is (i) zero (ii) a maximum.
   (c) Sketch a graph to show how the output voltage changes with time.
   (d) On the same graph, show how the output voltage changes if the coil rotates at 6000 rpm.

Solution

(a) $f$ = 3000 ÷ 60 = 50 Hz
    Angular velocity, $\omega = 2\pi f \approx 314$ s$^{-1}$
    Induced e.m.f. $E = BAN\omega \sin \omega t$,
    So $E_{max} = BAN\omega = 0.02 \times (0.4 \times 0.4) \times 250 \times 314 = 251.2$ V
(b) (i) $N\phi = BAN = 0.02 \times 0.16 \times 250 = 0.8$ Wb  (ii) 0 Wb
(c) Sinusoidal wave of peak value 251.2 V, period 20 ms.
(d) Sinusoidal wave of peak value 502.4 V, period 10 ms.

# The transformer

A transformer is a device that is used to either increase ('step up') or decrease ('step down') the supplied voltage. This is very useful for applications such as power transmission, as shall be discussed later.

The principle of the transformer can be demonstrated using two coils arranged as shown in the diagram on the right. The primary coil is connected to an AC power supply and a switch. The secondary coil is connected to a sensitive ammeter. A soft iron core passes through both coils.

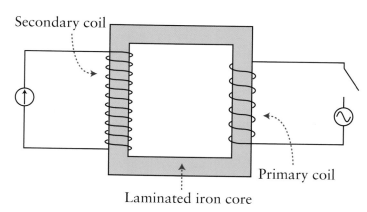

Secondary coil

Primary coil

Laminated iron core

An alternating current passed through the primary coil produces an alternating magnetic field, a field whose strength varies continuously and whose direction reverses periodically. This changing magnetic field causes the magnetic flux linking the secondary coil to change so that an e.m.f. is induced in the secondary coil. The iron core maximizes the magnetic flux linking both coils.

**In all transformers:**

The ratio of the turns on each coil determines the ratio of the two voltages.

$$\frac{N_S}{N_P} = \frac{V_S}{V_P}$$

where $N_P$ = number of turns on the primary coil

$N_S$ = number of turns on the secondary coil

$V_P$ = voltage applied to the primary coil (input)

$V_S$ = voltage developed across the secondary coil (output)

If we assume that the efficiency of the transformer is 100% then we can write:

Input power = output power

So: $I_P \times V_P = I_S \times V_S$

Therefore, **in transformers where there are no energy losses:**

$$\frac{I_P}{I_S} = \frac{V_S}{V_P}$$

where $I_P$ = current in the primary coil

$I_S$ = current in the secondary coil

$V_P$ = voltage applied to the primary coil (input)

$V_S$ = voltage developed across the secondary coil

The diagrams on the right show two types of transformer. In a **step up** transformer, there are more turns in the secondary coil than the primary. In a **step down** transformer, there are more turns in the primary coil than the secondary.

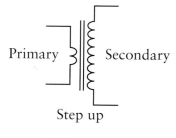

Primary     Secondary

Step up

In general, in a **step up transformer:**

*   $N_S$ is greater than $N_P$
*   $V_S$ is greater than $V_P$
*   $I_P$ is greater than $I_S$

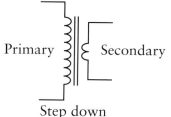

Primary     Secondary

Step down

In general, in a **step down transformer**:
- $N_p$ is greater than $N_S$
- $V_p$ is greater than $V_S$
- $I_S$ is greater than $I_p$

### Power losses in a transformer

In the discussion above, we assumed that the transformer had an efficiency of 100%. In practice, a real transformer has an efficiency of less than 100%. Modern transformers are among the most efficient electrical devices with some designs having an efficiency of around 99%. Nevertheless, it means that not all of the input electrical energy appears as useful output electrical energy. Some of the various ways in which energy is wasted, and steps that can be taken to minimise these losses, are as follows.

1  There are **resistive heat losses due to the wires** in the primary and secondary coils. As the coils heat up the resistance increases so that the amount of energy lost also increases. Many large transformers use oil as a coolant to reduce this type of energy loss.

2  **Not all of the magnetic flux** of the primary **passes through the secondary coil.**

3  Repeatedly magnetising the iron core in one direction and then reversing the direction of magnetisation results in heating of the iron core.

4  The iron is a conductor in a changing magnetic field so currents are induced to flow in it. These are called eddy currents and are very large. They result in heating of the core. These eddy current are reduced by **laminating the iron core.**

---

### Worked Example

1  A transformer, which is 95% efficient, is used with a supply voltage of 240 V. The primary winding has 5000 turns. The output voltage is 12 V. The output power is 36 W.
   (a) Name this type of transformer.
   (b) Calculate the number of turns in the secondary coil.
   (c) Calculate the current supplied to the primary coil.

   **Solution**

   (a) Step down transformer (because $V_p$ is greater than $V_p$).

   (b) $\dfrac{N_S}{N_P} = \dfrac{V_S}{V_P}$, so $N_S = 5000 \times \dfrac{12}{240} = 250$ turns

   (c) Input power, $P_{in}$ = output power ÷ efficiency = 36 ÷ 0.95 = 37.89 W

   $P_{in} = V_p \times I_P$

   $37.89 = 240 \times I_p$

   Therefore $I_p = 37.89 \div 240 = 0.158$ A = 158 mA

---

## Use of transformers in transmission of electricity

Transformers play an important role in the transmission of electricity from where it is generated in power stations to consumers. At the generating end they step the voltage **up** before it is connected to the transmission cables. At the consumer end, they step the voltage **down** for use in appliances. The process is illustrated below.

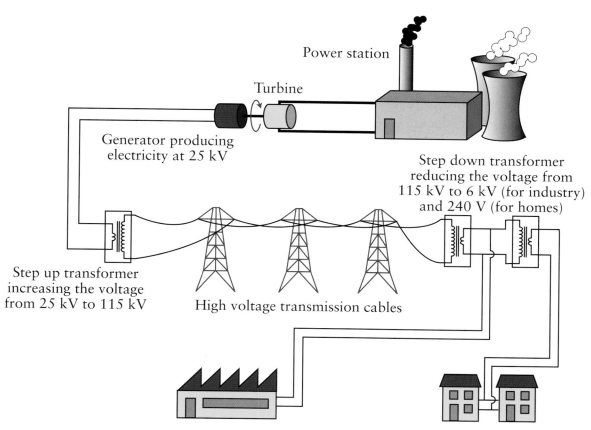

Power station

Turbine

Generator producing electricity at 25 kV

Step down transformer reducing the voltage from 115 kV to 6 kV (for industry) and 240 V (for homes)

Step up transformer increasing the voltage from 25 kV to 115 kV

High voltage transmission cables

## Advantages of high voltage electricity transmission

The cables used to transmit the electrical power from the generator to the consumer have electrical resistance. This means energy is lost as heat due to resistive heating.

The diagram on the right is a simplified picture of the electricity generation and transmission system. The power loss in the cables $P_{Loss} = I^2R$.

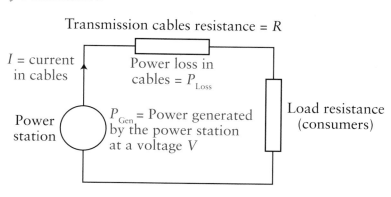

Transmission cables resistance = $R$

$I$ = current in cables

Power loss in cables = $P_{Loss}$

Power station

$P_{Gen}$ = Power generated by the power station at a voltage $V$

Load resistance (consumers)

This equation suggests that one way to reduce the power loss would be to reduce the resistance, $R$, of the cables. This could be achieved by using cables of a very large cross section area. However this would considerably increase their weight and hence the cost of construction.

The alternative way to reduce the power loss is to reduce the current, $I$, using a transformer. This is the function of the step up transformer at the generating station. As the voltage is stepped up, the current is reduced. The electrical power is then transmitted at a high voltage and a low current.

What is the impact of reducing the current in this way?

If the power generated $P_{Gen} = IV$, so the current $I = \dfrac{P_{Gen}}{V}$.

Since $P_{Loss} = I^2R$, the power loss in the cables $P_{Loss} = \dfrac{P^2_{Gen}R}{V^2}$

Since $P_{Gen}$ and $R$ are both constants this shows that the power loss in the cables $P_{Loss}$ is inversely proportional to the square of the voltage at which the electricity is transmitted to the consumer. Therefore if the voltage is **doubled** the power loss is reduced by a factor of **four**.

The advantage of the high voltage transmission can be illustrated if we calculate the power loss for a 1 km transmission line at two different voltages.

Consider a power station which generates 300 MW of electrical power at a voltage of 25 000 V (25 kV) and suppose the transmission lines have a resistance of 0.2 Ω per kilometre.

**At 30 kV** the current, $I = \dfrac{P}{V} = \dfrac{300 \times 10^6}{25 \times 10^3} = 1.2 \times 10^4$ A

The power loss in the cables = $P_{Loss} = I^2R = (1.2 \times 10^4)^2 \times 0.2 = 28.8$ MW

This represents a power loss of 9.6% over a 1 km length of transmission line.

**At 115 kV** the current is $I = \dfrac{P}{V} = \dfrac{300 \times 10^6}{115 \times 10^3} = 2.6 \times 10^3$ A

The power loss in the cables = $_{Loss} = I^2R = (2.6 \times 10^3)^2 \times 0.2 = 1.35$ MW

This represents a power loss of 0.45% over a 1 km length of transmission line.

## Exercise 5.5

1 The horizontal component of the Earth's magnetic field has a flux density of $2.0 \times 10^{-5}$ T. A straight piece of wire XY, 1.2 m long of mass 0.8 g, is resting on a wooden bench so that it is at right angles to the magnetic field direction as shown in the diagram. A current is passed through the wire which just causes the wire to lift off the bench.
   (a) State the direction of the current in the wire.
   (b) Calculate the current.

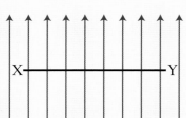

2 A current carrying conductor is placed in the magnetic field between the poles of a permanent magnet as shown on the right. The direction of the current in the conductor is out of the page.
   (a) Copy the diagram, and on it mark clearly the direction of the force on the conductor.

Conductor

(b) When the magnitude of the force on the conductor is 1.44 mN the current is 2.40 A. The length of the conductor in the field is 4.00 cm. Calculate the magnetic flux density of the field.

3 The graph below shows how the magnetic flux linkage through a coil varies over a period of 13 seconds. Draw second set of axes, with induced e.m.f. on the y-axis aand time of the x-axis. On this set of axes show how the e.m.f. induced in this coil varies during the same time. Place values on both of the axes.

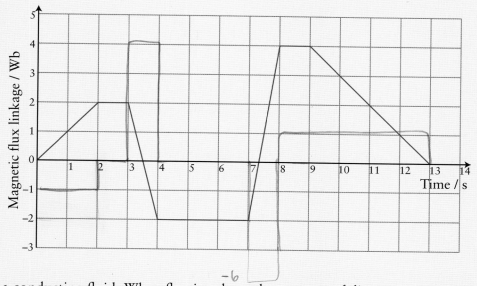

EMF
-gradient

−6

4 Blood is a conducting fluid. When flowing through an artery of diameter 10 mm which is subject to a constant magnetic field of strength 60 mT, an e.m.f. of 0.3 mV appears across the width of the artery. Calculate the speed of the blood.

5 A mains generator produces a sinusoidal output of peak voltage 325 V and 50 Hz using a rectangular coil spinning between the poles of an electromagnet.
(a) Calculate the angular velocity of the rotating coil.
(b) Calculate the maximum flux linked with the coil.

6 An iron-cored solenoid has 1000 turns of insulated copper wire. The magnetic field in the core changes uniformly over a 5 second interval from 300 mT in one direction to 600 mT in the opposite direction. The core has a cross section area of 25 cm² and the coils are connected to an external circuit of resistance 9.0 Ω.
(a) Find the instantaneous current when the flux density threading the coil is zero.
(b) Does the current change direction during this process? Give a reason for your answer.

7 (a) Describe how a suitable input voltage, applied to the primary coil of a transformer, results in an output being obtained from the secondary coil.
(b) A power supply of fixed peak voltage is available. A voltage of half this peak value is to be obtained, using a transformer. What type of transformer should be used? State the relation which must apply between the number of turns on the primary coil $N_p$ and the number of turns on the secondary coil $N_s$.

8  A generator in a power station produces 176 MW of power at 11.0 kV. This is transformed to 275 kV for transmission to a nearby town.

(a) Calculate the ratio of turns in the primary coil to the number of turns in the secondary coil of the transformer.

(b) Calculate the current in the primary coil and the current in the secondary coil, assuming the transformer has an efficiency of 100%.

(c) Calculate the maximum resistance of the transmission lines if the power loss in the lines is not to exceed 2% of the power generated.

(d) In practice, transformers are less than 100% efficient. State three sources of power loss in a transformer.

# 5.6 Deflection of Charged Particles in Electric & Magnetic Fields

**5.6.1** demonstrate an understanding that a charge in a uniform electric field experiences a force;

**5.6.2** recall and use the equation $F = qE$ to calculate the magnitude of the force and determine the direction of the force;

**5.6.3** demonstrate an understanding that a moving charge in a uniform, perpendicular magnetic field experiences a force;

**5.6.4** recall and use the equation $F = Bqv$ to calculate the magnitude of the force, and determine the direction of the force.

## Motion of electrons in an electric field

Beams of electrons are found in traditional television tubes, cathode ray oscilloscopes, X–ray tubes and electron microscopes. They are produced by an electron gun, as shown in the diagram below.

The source of the electrons is a heated wire filament. Electrons with sufficient energy escape from the surface of the filament by a process called **thermionic emission**. The electrons emerge into an electric field created by a large potential difference between the cathode and the anode. This electric field accelerates the electrons, such that they lose electric potential energy and gain kinetic energy (we can apply the principle of conservation of energy and say that the kinetic energy gained equals the loss of electric potential energy). An electron beam emerges through a opening in the anode.

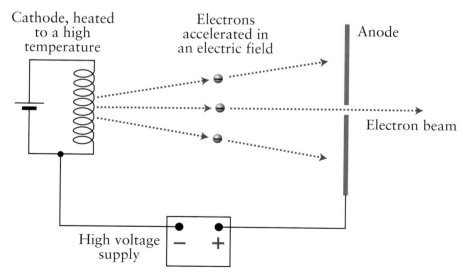

The picture and diagram on the next page show a typical electron beam tube found in most school laboratories. The electron gun directs a beam of electrons towards the fluorescent screen, which emits green light when struck by electrons. When the Maltese cross electrode is made positive it deflects the electrons away from their original path preventing them reaching the fluorescent screen so a black shadow is seen on the screen.

Source: Giorgio Basile
http://lampes-et-tubes.info

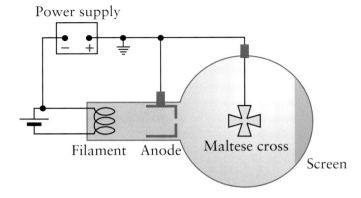

## Energy changes

Electrical potential difference is measured in volts. The volt is defined as a joule per coulomb (J C$^{-1}$), which means that a charge of 1 coulomb accelerated through a potential difference of 1 volt will gain 1 joule of energy. Using this definition of the volt and applying the principle of conservation of energy we can say that: **loss of electrical potential energy = gain of kinetic energy**. This can be written in the form of an equation as:

$eV = \frac{1}{2}m_e v^2$     where     $e$ = charge on the electron ($1.6 \times 10^{-19}$ C)
$V$ = potential difference between anode and cathode (V)
$m_e$ = mass of the electron (kg)
$v$ = velocity of the electron (m s$^{-1}$)

Re-arranging the above expression we obtain the equation below for the velocity of the electron after it has been accelerated from rest through a potential difference $V$:

$$v = \sqrt{\frac{2eV}{m_e}}$$

If the charged particles have a mass, $m$, and a charge, $q$, the expression for the velocity can be written as:

$$v = \sqrt{\frac{2qV}{m}}$$

---

### Worked Examples

1  A potential difference of 50 V is applied between two electrodes. An electron is emitted from the negative electrode with negligible speed.
   (a) Calculate the increase in kinetic energy of the electron when it reaches the positive electrode.
   (b) Calculate the speed of the electron when it reaches the positive electrode.
   Solution

   (a) Gain in kinetic energy = change in electric potential energy
       $= eV = 1.6 \times 10^{-19} \times 50 = 8.0 \times 10^{-18}$ J

---

(b) $v = \sqrt{\dfrac{2qV}{m}} = \sqrt{\dfrac{2 \times 8 \times 10^{-18}}{9.1 \times 10^{-31}}} = 4.2 \times 10^6$ m s⁻¹

2  Positive ions, each of mass $8.35 \times 10^{-27}$ kg and charge $3.20 \times 10^{-19}$ C are accelerated in a vacuum from rest to a speed of $5.75 \times 10^4$ m s⁻¹.

(a) Calculate the potential difference through which the ions are accelerated to give them this speed.

(b) If ions with twice this charge but of the same mass were accelerated through the same potential difference how would this affect their final kinetic energy and final speed?

**Solution**

(a) Using $v = \sqrt{\dfrac{2qV}{m}}$ and substituting in the known values gives:

$5.75 \times 10^4 = \sqrt{\dfrac{2 \times 3.2 \times 10^{-19} \times V}{8.35 \times 10^{-27}}}$, giving $V = 43.1$ V

(b) Gain of kinetic energy $= qV$. Therefore, twice the charge and same potential difference means twice the kinetic energy.

Thus, with twice the charge, the new final speed $v_{new}$ is:

$v_{new} = \sqrt{\dfrac{4qV}{m}} = \sqrt{2}\sqrt{\dfrac{2qV}{m}} = \sqrt{2}v = \sqrt{2} \times 5.75 \times 10^4 = 8.13 \times 10^4$ m s⁻¹

3  Charged particles of different charges and masses are accelerated from rest through the same potential difference. Sketch graphs to show how:

(a) The kinetic energy of the particles depends on their mass.

(b) The velocity of the particles depends on the charge of the particle.

**Solution**

(a) kinetic energy = loss of electric potential energy
$E_k = qV$
$E_k$ does not depend on the mass, only on $q$ and $V$.
Therefore the graph is a horizontal line as shown.

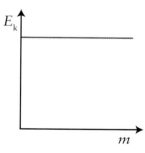

(b) $v = \sqrt{\dfrac{2qV}{m}}$.

In this case, $v \propto \sqrt{q}$
Therefore the graph is a square root curve as shown.

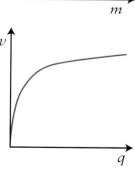

## Force on a charged particle

As we have seen, a charged particle in an electric field experiences a force. This force is given by the equation:

$F = qE$ 　　　where 　$F$ = the force (N)
　　　　　　　　　　　$q$ = the charge on the particle (C)
　　　　　　　　　　　$E$ = electric field strength (V m$^{-1}$ or N C$^{-1}$)

If the field is **non-uniform** then this force **varies** from point to point within the field. However in the case of a **uniform** electric field, which has the same field strength throughout, the force is **constant.**

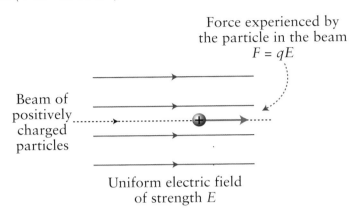

Force experienced by
the particle in the beam
$F = qE$

Beam of positively charged particles

Uniform electric field
of strength $E$

In the first diagram on the right, a beam of positively charged particles is directed into an electric field so that its direction is **parallel to** the electric field lines. The particles in the beam experience a force in the same direction as the electric field. As a result, the particles will accelerate to the right.

In this second diagram on the right, a beam of positively charged particles is directed into an electric field so that its direction is **parallel to but in the opposite direction** to the electric field lines. The particles in the beam experience a force in the same direction as that of the electric field, but opposite to the direction of motion of the particles. As a result, the particles will experience a deceleration to the left.

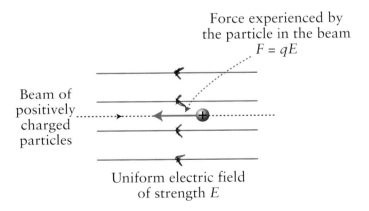

Force experienced by
the particle in the beam
$F = qE$

Beam of positively charged particles

Uniform electric field
of strength $E$

## Deflection of charged particles in an electric field

The diagram on the next page shows a beam of negatively charged particles moving with velocity, $v$, entering a uniform electric field of strength, $E$. A uniform electric field has the same field strength throughout its region. The parallel, uniformly spaced field lines indicate this uniformity. The charged particles enter the electric field at right angles to the electric field lines. The particles experience a **constant** force, $qE$, towards the positively charged plate.

The charged particle experiences **a force in the vertical direction** only. There is no horizontal force. This means that we treat its motion in the following way:
- Horizontally – constant velocity
- Vertically – uniform acceleration from rest

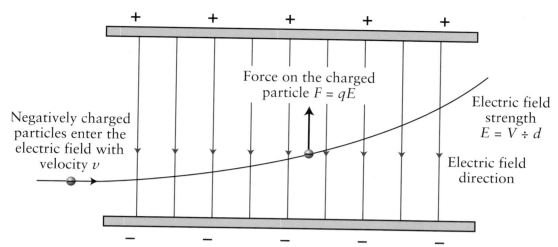

The vertical force F is given by $F = qE$. If the separation of the plates is $d$, then electrical field strength, $E = \dfrac{V}{d}$. So we can write:

$$F = qE = q\dfrac{V}{d}$$

where

$F$ = the force (N)
$q$ = the charge on the particle (C)
$E$ = electric field strength (V m$^{-1}$ or N C$^{-1}$)
$V$ = potential difference between the plates (V)
$d$ = the separation of the plates (m)

The acceleration of the particle is obtained from Newton's second law of motion. Since $F = ma$, we have $a = \dfrac{F}{m}$. So for the charged particle:

$$a = \dfrac{qE}{m} = \dfrac{qV}{dm}$$

where

$a$ = acceleration of the particle (m s$^{-2}$)
$m$ = mass of the particle (kg)

### Calculating the path of a charged particle in an electric field

The above equations allow us to plot the path of a charged particle. It enters the electric field with a velocity, $v$, and travels a horizontal distance, $x$, in a time, $t$. The vertical deflection of the charged particle in the same time is $y$. This situation is shown in the diagram on the right.

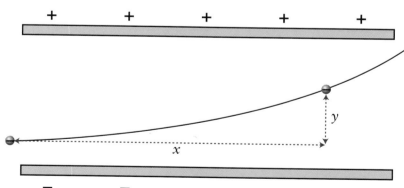

There is no horizontal force and hence no horizontal acceleration, so at any time, $t$, the horizontal displacement $x = vt$.

Since the vertical motion is one of uniform acceleration, from rest, it is necessary to use the equations of motion to determine the vertical displacement, $y$.

From the equation $s = ut + \frac{1}{2}at^2$, and since the initial speed $u = 0$, the vertical displacement, $y$, is given by:

$y = \frac{1}{2}at^2$

Since $x = vt$, we have $t = \dfrac{x}{v}$. Therefore:

$y = \frac{1}{2}a\dfrac{x^2}{v^2}$

Since the acceleration, $a$, and the initial horizontal velocity, $v$, are constant we have can say that $\dfrac{a}{v^2} = k$ and write:

$y = kx^2$

From geometry, we know that this is the equation of a parabola, which tells us that **within the electric field the path of the charged particles is a parabola.** When they exit the field, and no longer experience a force, they move in a straight line once again.

> **Note:** This should remind the student of the parabolic motion of a projectile under gravity, a topic studied in AS 1.

If the length of the electric field is $L$, then the **total** time, $T$, taken to cross the electric field, t, is given by:

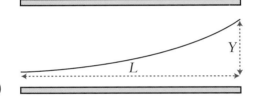

$T = \dfrac{L}{v}$  where  $T$ = time to cross the electric field (s)
  $L$ = horizontal length of the field (m)
  $v$ = horizontal velocity of particle (m s$^{-1}$)

The vertical acceleration, $a = \dfrac{qV}{dm}$.

Therefore the **total** vertical distance moved, $Y$, is given by:

$Y = \frac{1}{2}aT^2 = \frac{1}{2}a\dfrac{L^2}{v^2} = \frac{1}{2}\dfrac{qV}{dm}\dfrac{L^2}{v^2}$

The initial vertical velocity of the charged particles is 0.

The time to move vertically is equal to the time to move horizontally.

---

### Worked Example

1  The diagram shows two horizontal metal plates. The plates are 120 mm long and are separated by 40 mm. The upper plate is maintained at a potential of −20 V with respect to the lower one. The region between the plates is a vacuum. An electron beam enters the electric field along a line midway between the plates. The electrons in the beam have a velocity of $6\times10^6$ ms$^{-1}$.

   (a) Calculate the electric field strength at the point P. State the direction of the electric field at P.

   (b) Calculate the force on an electron as it enters the electric field.

   (c) Sketch the path of the electron beam as it passes between the plates.

   (d) Calculate the acceleration of an electron in the beam as it passes between the plates. State the direction of the acceleration.

(e) Calculate the time taken for an electron in the beam to pass from one end of the plates to the other.

(f) Calculate the distance from the mid-line at which the electron beam leaves the region between the plates.

(g) Calculate the final velocity of an electron in the beam as it leaves the electric field.

**Solution**

(a) $E = \dfrac{V}{d} = \dfrac{20}{40 \times 10^{-3}} = 500$ V m$^{-1}$ (or N C$^{-1}$)

Direction is upwards towards the upper plate.

(b) $F = qE = 1.6 \times 10^{-19} \times 500 = 8.0 \times 10^{-17}$ N

(c) The electrons in the beam experience a force towards the lower plate, because they are being repelled by the upper negative plate. The path is a parabola:

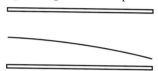

(d) $a = \dfrac{F}{m} = \dfrac{8.0 \times 10^{-17}}{9.1 \times 10^{-31}} = 8.8 \times 10^{13}$ m s$^{-2}$. Direction is towards the lower plate.

(e) $t = \dfrac{120 \times 10^{-3}}{6 \times 10^{6}} = 2.0 \times 10^{-8}$ s

(f) Vertical motion is uniform acceleration from rest.
$y = ut + \frac{1}{2}at^2 = 0 + \frac{1}{2} \times 8.8 \times 10^{13} \times (2 \times 10^{-8})^2 = 1.76 \times 10^{-2}$ m = 17.6 mm

(g) The final velocity is the resultant of the constant horizontal velocity, $v_x$ and the final vertical velocity, $v_y$. We know that $v_x = 6 \times 10^6$ m s$^{-1}$.

$v_y = u + at = 0 + 8.8 \times 10^{13} \times 2 \times 10^{-8} = 1.76 \times 10^6$ m s$^{-1}$.

By Pythagoras theorem, $v_{resultant}^2 = v_x^2 \times v_y^2$ which gives:
$v_{resultant} = 6.25 \times 10^6$ m s$^{-1}$.

The direction of the final velocity makes an angle $\theta$ with the horizontal, where:
$\tan\theta = \dfrac{v_y}{v_x} = \dfrac{1.76 \times 10^6}{6 \times 10^6} = 0.2933$, so $\theta \approx 16.3°$

2  A beam of singly charged positive ions is directed, at an angle, into a uniform electric field and follow the parabolic path shown in the diagram. The potential difference between the plates is 1200 V. The separation of the metal plates is 100 mm. The velocity of the ions as they enter the electric field is $5 \times 10^5$ m s$^{-1}$ and they make an angle of 30° with the vertical as shown in the diagram.

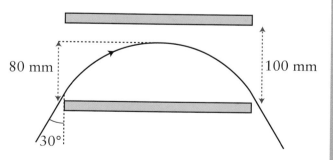

(a) Calculate the electric field strength between the plates and state its direction.

(b) Calculate the acceleration of the ions in the beam.

(c) Calculate the electric force acting on the ions in the beam.

(d) Calculate the mass of an ion in the beam.

**Solution**

(a) $E = \dfrac{V}{d} = \dfrac{1200}{0.1} = 1.2 \times 10^4$ V m$^{-1}$ (or N C$^{-1}$)

The direction is downwards, towards the lower plate because the positive ions are being repelled by the positively charged upper plate.

(b) The vertical motion of the ions is one of uniform acceleration. The initial vertical velocity, $u_y$ of the ions is:

$u_y = u \cos 30° = 5 \times 10^5 \times \cos 30° = 4.33 \times 10^5$ m s$^{-1}$

When the vertical displacement of the ions in the electric field is 80 mm, the final velocity $v_y$ is zero. Therefore using the equation of motion $v^2 = u^2 + 2as$:

$0 = v_y^2 + 2ay = (4.33 \times 10^5)^2 + 2 \times a \times 80 \times 10^{-3}$
giving $a = -1.17 \times 10^{12}$ m s$^{-2}$

(c) Electric force on an ion in the beam:
$F = qE = 1.6 \times 10^{-19} \times 1.2 \times 10^4 = 1.92 \times 10^{-15}$ N

(d) We can find the mass of an ion using Newton's second law:

$F = ma$, so $a = \dfrac{F}{m} = \dfrac{1.92 \times 10^{-15}}{1.17 \times 10^{12}} = 1.64 \times 10^{-27}$ kg

## Deflection of charged particles in a magnetic field

A moving charge in a magnetic field experiences a force which is perpendicular to both the velocity of the particle and the direction of the magnetic field. the The direction of this force Fleming's left hand rule (discussed in section 5.5).

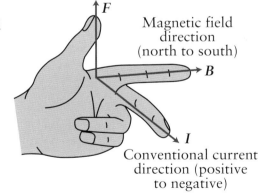

Force on the current-carrying conductor

Magnetic field direction (north to south) B

F

I

Conventional current direction (positive to negative)

To determine the direction of the force on an electron moving in a magnetic field you must remember that the movement of the electron is **opposite** to that of conventional current:

Current direction ⟶
⟵ Electron flow

Since the force always acts at right angles to the velocity of the charged particles it causes the particles (electrons, protons, ions) to move in circular paths. The diagrams on the next page show the paths taken by beams of negatively charged and positively charged particles when they enter a magnetic field (indicated by the yellow rectangle).

An important point to remember is that the basic conservation laws of physics apply when antimatter is produced, for example conservation of electric charge or conservation of momentum.

---

**Worked Example**

1 A high-energy gamma ray passes close to a heavy nucleus and produces a positron and an electron as shown. A magnetic field acts perpendicularly into the plane of the paper

(a) Why would it not be possible for the gamma ray to produce only an electron (or only a positron)?

(b) Calculate the minimum energy of the gamma-ray photon.

(c) The initial directions of the positron and the electron are slightly above and below the velocity vector of the photon. Why could both particles not be slightly above (or both slightly below) the direction of this vector?

(d) Which particle is the positron and which is the electron? Explain how you found your answer.

**Solution**

(a) To conserve electric charge.

(b) Two particles of equal mass are produced. Therefore:
$E = mc^2 = (2 \times 9.11 \times 10^{-31}) \times (3 \times 10^8)^2 = 1.64 \times 10^{-13}$ J = 1.02 MeV

(c) To conserve momentum. The gamma ray is travelling to the right, so the electron-positron pair must have no resultant vertical momentum.

(d) The upper particle is the positron, the lower is the electron. The initial direction of the upper particle is to the right and the force on it is vertically upwards. Since the field is into the plane of the paper, then by Fleming's left hand rule, the current is to the right, so the particle is positively charged: it is therefore a positron. A similar argument shows the lower particle must be negatively charged, and is therefore an electron.

---

## Annihilation

You may already be wondering what happens when a matter particle encounters its antimatter particle. The answer is that, in general, both particles are annihilated (cease to exist) in line with the principle of conservation of charge. In their place we observe two gamma ray photons, as shown on the right.

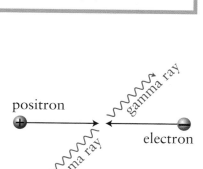

Why two photons? This is an essential requirement if both energy and momentum are to be conserved:

- Conservation of mass. Each of the particles has a mass. When the particles are annihilated, this mass cannot disappear. Instead, it is converted into energy in the form of photons. When annihilation or pair production occurs the conversion formula is $E = mc^2$.

- Conservation of momentum. A single photon would travel in one direction only. In order to conserve momentum, there must be two photons, travelling in opposite directions.

## Worked Example

1   A proton and an antiproton collide with minimal kinetic energy. Calculate the energy and wavelength of each gamma ray produced.

**Solution**

The rest energy of the two particles, $E = mc^2 = (2 \times 1.67 \times 10^{-27}) \times 9 \times 10^{16} = 3.006 \times 10^{-10}$ J

Energy of each photon $= \frac{1}{2}(3.006 \times 10^{-10}) = 1.503 \times 10^{-10}$ J

Wavelength of each photon $= \frac{hc}{E} = \frac{6.63 \times 10^{-34} \times 3 \times 10^8}{1.503 \times 10^{-10}} = 1.32 \times 10^{-15}$ m

### Medicine with antimatter – Positron-Emission Tomography

Carbon-11 or $^{11}$C is a radioactive isotope of carbon that decays to boron-11 mainly by positron emission. It is produced from nitrogen by collision with fast protons in an accelerator by the reaction:

$$^{14}_{7}\text{N} + ^{1}_{1}\text{p} \longrightarrow ^{11}_{6}\text{C} + ^{4}_{2}\text{He}$$

A compound containing $^{11}$C is injected into the patient's blood. After a short time the active molecule becomes concentrated in tissues of interest. Then the patient is placed in the imaging scanner.

The radioisotope emits a positron which travels in tissue for a short distance until it meets an electron. The encounter annihilates both the electron and the positron, producing a pair of annihilation (gamma) photons moving in approximately opposite directions. These are detected when they reach a scintillator in the scanning device, and the scintillations (flashes of light) are used to produce an image of the tissue.

### Exercise 5.7

1   Why is it necessary for the magnetic field to be increased as protons are accelerated in a synchrotron?

2   Explain why protons, but not neutrons, can be accelerated in a synchrotron.

3   By what percentage is the relativistic mass of an electron travelling at 99% of the speed of light greater than its rest mass?

4   Identify the three particles you would find in the nucleus of $^3$He if it were composed entirely of antimatter.

5   Why is antimatter so uncommon in interstellar space?

6   Write the equation to describe what happens when an electron collides with a positron.

7   Potassium-40, $^{40}_{19}$K decays by positron emission to Argon-40, $^{40}_{18}$Ar by positron emission. Write the equation to represent the decay process. (In the positron decay process another particle, called a neutrino, is also produced, but ignore that until you have read the chapter on fundamental particles.)

8   In Dan Brown's book, *Angels and Demons*, matter and antimatter are kept apart by a magnetic field. Calculate how much energy is released when 0.500 grams of matter annihilates 0.500 grams of antimatter.

# 5.8 Fundamental Particles

| Students should be able to: |

5.8.1    explain the concept of a fundamental particle;

5.8.2    identify the four fundamental forces and their associated exchange particles;

5.8.3    classify particles as gauge bosons, leptons and hadrons (mesons and baryons);

5.8.4    state examples of each class of particle;

5.8.5    describe the structure of hadrons in terms of quarks;

5.8.6    demonstrate an understanding of the concept of conservation of:
– charge;
– lepton number;
– baryon number;

5.8.7    describe β-decay in terms of the basic quark model.

## What is a fundamental particle?

An elementary particle or fundamental particle is **a particle not known to be made up of smaller particles**. A fundamental particle has no substructure, it is one of the basic building blocks of the universe from which all other particles are made.

In the 1930s our understanding of the structure of matter seemed almost complete. Our picture of the atom was one of a relatively tiny but massive nucleus orbited by electrons. Scientists had made sense of atomic spectra, electron orbits and the link between the two. The neutron had been detected and its discovery explained nuclear isotopes. Some eighty years ago, the fundamental particles, the building blocks of all matter, were considered to be the proton, neutron and electron.

However some questions had yet to be answered. Firstly, **what force holds the protons and neutrons together to form the nucleus,** ie why does the electrical repulsion of the positively charged protons not split the nucleus apart? Secondly, **what are the forces involved in the radioactive decays of nuclei** that make α-particles, β-particles, and gamma rays?

Particle accelerators allowed physicists to study the nucleus and the interactions of neutrons and protons that form it. Their experiments studied the collisions of high energy particles produced by accelerators and sophisticated detectors surrounding the collision point were used to identify each of the many particles that may be produced in a single collision.

Accelerator experiments revealed many more particles of a type similar to protons and neutrons. A whole new family of particles called **hadrons** was also discovered. By the 1960s hundreds of different particles had been identified, and physicists had no complete understanding of how they were related to each other or of the fundamental forces that are involved with them.

These new particles had a wide range of properties. Some were very massive, some had no mass, some seemed to consist of smaller parts while others were apparently point-like, some were stable and some decayed almost as soon as they were created and they had various different charges. Patterns began to emerge from the many discoveries and experiments, and a simpler picture gradually formed. Today that picture is called the **Standard Model**.

Today all particles are classified as:
- Gauge bosons
- Leptons
- Hadrons (pronounced haedrons)

These are discussed in the following sections. However, before we examine them in more detail we need to outline the **four fundamental forces** that occur in nature.

## The four fundamental forces of nature

In order of strength, from strongest to weakest, the four fundamental forces are:

- The **strong nuclear force** exists between neutrons and protons in the nucleus. It is clearly strong enough to overcome the electrical repulsion of the protons. It is a **very short range** force and only acts when hadrons are within a distance of around $10^{-15}$ m of each other. The strong nuclear force determines the structure of the nucleus and is always attractive.

- The **electromagnetic force** affects particles with charge and has an **infinite range**. Electromagnetic forces determine the structure of atoms as well as determining the properties of materials and the results of chemical processes. The electromagnetic force can be **repulsive or attractive**.

- The **weak interaction** is the name given to the force that induces beta decay. Beta decay occurs when a neutron decays to a proton and creates an electron and an antineutrino in the process. The neutral antineutrino is not affected by the electromagnetic force or the strong nuclear force. The weak interaction is the **short range force** needed to explain this effect.

- **Gravity** affects particles with mass. It is very weak and is only noticeable when at least one large mass is present. Our weight is due to the gravitational attraction between ourselves and the Earth which has a mass of $6 \times 10^{24}$ kg. Gravity is **always attractive** and has an **infinite range**. Gravity is the force that determines the structure of large scale matter such as stars and galaxies.

## Gauge bosons – exchange particles and the fundamental forces

The modern understanding of the four fundamental forces comes from what is known as Quantum Field Theory. According to this theory, all the fundamental forces can be treated as the **exchange of particles**.

These exchange particles are the **gauge bosons**. Each fundamental force is attributed to the exchange of at least one gauge boson. Physicists have found that, using the idea of exchange particles, they can explain very precisely the force of one particle acting on another.

**Note:** Bosons are named after the Indian physicist Satyendra Nath Bose. The word 'gauge' comes from Quantum Field Theory.

There are four kinds of gauge bosons:

- **Photons** are the gauge bosons of the electromagnetic interaction, such as the repulsion between two electrons.
- The **W and Z bosons** are the exchange particles of the weak interaction which governs beta decay.
- **Gluons** play a role in the strong interaction, ie the force that exists between neutrons and protons.
- **Gravitons** are believed to play a similar role in gravity. Although gravitational waves were first detected in 2015, the existence of the graviton, unlike the other exchange particles, has yet to be confirmed experimentally.

**Table of the fundamental forces and their exchange particles**

| Force | What it does | Strength (Comparative) | Range | Exchange particle (gauge boson) |
|---|---|---|---|---|
| Strong nuclear | Holds the nucleus together | 1 | $1 \times 10^{-15}$ ~ diameter of a nucleus | Gluons |
| Electromagnetic | Attractive and repulsive force between charged particles | ~$\frac{1}{150}$ | Infinite | Photon |
| Weak interaction | Induces beta decay | $1 \times 10^{-6}$ | $1 \times 10^{-18}$ m ~ diameter of a proton | W and Z bosons |
| Gravity | Attractive force between masses | ~$1 \times 10^{-39}$ | Infinite | Graviton (by analogy only) |

## Leptons

All leptons are **fundamental particles,** ie they cannot be broken into smaller particles. They are assigned to three 'generations' which correspond to the times when they were discovered. Their properties are as follows:
- Leptons are not affected by the strong interaction.
- Charged leptons are affected by the electromagnetic force. Neutral leptons are not affected by the electromagnetic force.

- Leptons are affected by the weak interaction in beta decay.
- Leptons with mass are affected by gravity. Leptons without mass are not affected by gravity.
- There are six leptons in the present structure, the electron (e), the muon (μ), and the tau (τ) particle and their associated neutrinos. There are six corresponding anti-leptons.
- Each lepton is given a lepton number of 1 and their antiparticle –1.
- The lepton number, $L$, is conserved during interactions which involve leptons.

**Table of leptons**

| Genera-tion | Particle | Symbol | Relative mass | Relative charge | Lepton number $L$ | Antiparticle | Symbol | Relative mass | Relative charge | Lepton number $L$ |
|---|---|---|---|---|---|---|---|---|---|---|
| 1 | electron | $e^-$ | 1 | –1 | 1 | positron | $e^+$ | 1 | +1 | –1 |
| 1 | electron-neutrino | $\nu_e$ | 0 | 0 | 1 | antielectron-neutrino | $\overline{\nu}_e$ | 0 | 0 | –1 |
| 2 | muon | $\mu^-$ | 207 | –1 | 1 | antimuon | $\mu^+$ | 207 | +1 | –1 |
| 2 | muon-neutrino | $\nu_\mu$ | 0 | 0 | 1 | antimuon-neutrino | $\overline{\nu}_\mu$ | 0 | 0 | –1 |
| 3 | tau | $\tau^-$ | 3490 | –1 | 1 | antitau | $\tau^+$ | 3490 | +1 | –1 |
| 3 | tau-neutrino | $\nu_\tau$ | 0 | 0 | 1 | antitau-neutrino | $\overline{\nu}_\tau$ | 0 | 0 | –1 |

## Hadrons

These particles are **not** fundamental, that is they are made up of other particles, a point which will be discussed later in the chapter. Hadrons are all affected by the strong interaction.

As more hadrons were discovered it became convenient to divide the hadrons into two sub-groups, **baryons** and **mesons**. Our picture of the subatomic particles we have encountered to this point is as shown below.

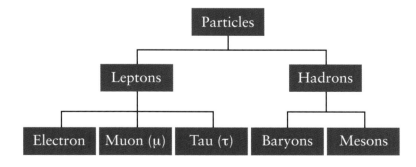

The neutron and the proton are the most familiar members of the hadron family. They are both **baryons** (the prefix 'bary-' means heavy). Baryons are all given a baryon number, $B$ of 1. Anti-baryons have a baryon number of $-1$. Mesons and leptons all have a baryon number of zero. In interactions where baryons are involved, baryon number is conserved.

**Table of baryons**

| Particle | Symbol | Relative mass | Relative charge | Baryon number $B$ | Antiparticle | Symbol | Relative mass | Relative charge | Baryon number $B$ |
|---|---|---|---|---|---|---|---|---|---|
| neutron | $n^0$ | 1 | 0 | 1 | antineutron | $\overline{n}^0$ | 1 | 0 | $-1$ |
| proton | $p^+$ | 0.999 | $+1$ | 1 | antiproton | $p^-$ | 0.999 | $-1$ | $-1$ |

**Mesons** have a mass less than the proton but greater than the electron. The pi-meson family, consisting of two charged particles $\pi^+$, $\pi^-$ and the neutral $\pi^0$, play a role in the strong nuclear force. Altogether there are around 140 different types, or families, of mesons. You need to be able to quote examples only and to know their structure (quark-antiquark doublet). Details are not required.

**Table of mesons**

| Particle | Symbol | Relative mass | Relative charge | Baryon number $B$ | Antiparticle | Symbol | Relative mass | Relative charge | Baryon number $B$ |
|---|---|---|---|---|---|---|---|---|---|
| pion | $\pi^+$ | 0.149 | $+1$ | 0 | pion | $\pi^-$ | 0.149 | $-1$ | 0 |
| pion | $\pi^0$ | 0.144 | 0 | 0 | pion | $\overline{\pi}^0$ | 0.144 | 0 | 0 |

---

**Worked Examples**

1 Apply the laws of conservation of charge and lepton number to identify the unknown particles, X, Y and Z in the following interactions.
The n, p and e⁻ are the neutron, proton and electron respectively.
The $\pi^+$ and $\mu^+$ are the positive $\pi$ meson and the antimuon respectively.
The $\pi^+$, being a meson and not a lepton, has a lepton number of zero.

(a) n $\rightarrow$ p + e⁻ + **X**

(b) **Y** + n $\rightarrow$ p + e⁻

(c) $\pi^+$ $\rightarrow$ $\mu^+$ + **Z**

Solution

(a) To conserve charge, X must be neutral. The neutron and proton are not leptons, so their lepton numbers are zero. The lepton number for the electron is 1. So to conserve lepton number, X must be a lepton, with lepton number $-1$. All the uncharged leptons with lepton number $-1$ are anti-neutrinos. We cannot take this argument further; we can only conclude X is an antineutrino. (It is, in fact, the antielectron – neutrino.)

(b) To conserve charge, Y must be neutral. To conserve lepton number, Y must have a lepton number of 1. It is therefore a neutrino.

(c) To conserve charge, Z must be neutral. To conserve lepton number, Z must have a lepton number of 1. It is therefore a neutrino.

2 Apply the laws of conservation of charge, baryon number and lepton number to find out whether the following reactions are possible.

(a) $p^+ \rightarrow e^+ + \gamma$

(b) $n^0 + p^+ \rightarrow e^+ + \pi^0$

(c) $p^+ \rightarrow n^0 + e^+ + \nu_e$

**Solution**

(a) Charge is conserved, but baryon number is not. On LHS, $B = 1$, on RHS, $B = 0 + 0 = 0$. Therefore the reaction is not possible.

> **Note:** Interestingly, no reaction has been observed by which the proton decays to another particle. However, theoretical physicists believe that the proton does indeed decay, with a half life of around $10^{30}$ years – which is longer than the universe has been in existence!

(b) Charge is conserved. However, baryon number is not conserved.
On LHS, $B = 1 + 1 = 2$, on RHS, $B = 0 + 0 = 0$.

Lepton number is not conserved either.
On LHS, $L = 0$, on RHS, $L = -1 + 0 = -1$

Therefore the reaction is not possible.

(c) Charge, baryon number and lepton number are all conserved. Therefore the reaction is possible.

## The quark

In 1964 physicists Murray Gell-Mann and George Zweig independently suggested that the properties of hundreds of the particles known at the time could be explained as combinations of just three fundamental particles.

> **Note:** Gell-Mann chose the strange name **quarks** for these three particles, a nonsense word used by Irishman James Joyce in the novel Finnegan's Wake: "Three quarks for Muster Mark!"

Eventually six kinds or 'flavours' of quark were discovered. Physicists still talk about quarks having flavours: they really mean kinds of quark, but the word flavour has stuck, because it was the word used by both Gell-Mann and Zweig. These flavours are: up, down, charm, strange, top and bottom. At A-level it is only necessary to know about the up and the down quarks.

Until 1964 the charge of the electron was considered to be the smallest electric charge possible. In the quark model, however, electric charges of $\pm\frac{2}{3}e$ and $\pm\frac{1}{3}e$ are possible.

Antiquarks are the antimatter partners of quarks. They have the same masses as, but the opposite charge from, the corresponding quarks. The quark model has been confirmed by many experiments. It is now part of the Standard Model of Fundamental Particles and Interactions. Note that free quarks cannot exist; they are always combined in twos (forming mesons) or in threes (forming baryons).

The following table shows the properties of these quarks and their corresponding antiquark. Notice that they also have three generations, just as the leptons have, with each generation having an increasing mass.

**Table of quarks**

| Generation | Quark | Symbol | Charge Q | Baryon number B |
|---|---|---|---|---|
| 1 | up | u | $+\frac{2}{3}e$ | $\frac{1}{3}$ |
| 1 | down | d | $-\frac{1}{3}e$ | $\frac{1}{3}$ |
| 2 | strange | s | $-\frac{1}{3}e$ | $\frac{1}{3}$ |
| 2 | charm | c | $+\frac{2}{3}e$ | $\frac{1}{3}$ |
| 3 | top | t | $+\frac{2}{3}e$ | $\frac{1}{3}$ |
| 3 | bottom | b | $-\frac{1}{3}e$ | $\frac{1}{3}$ |

| Antiquark | Symbol | Charge Q | Baryon number B |
|---|---|---|---|
| anti-up | $\bar{u}$ | $-\frac{2}{3}e$ | $-\frac{1}{3}$ |
| anti-down | $\bar{d}$ | $+\frac{1}{3}e$ | $-\frac{1}{3}$ |
| anti-strange | $\bar{s}$ | $+\frac{1}{3}e$ | $-\frac{1}{3}$ |
| anti-charm | $\bar{c}$ | $-\frac{2}{3}e$ | $-\frac{1}{3}$ |
| anti-top | $\bar{t}$ | $-\frac{2}{3}e$ | $-\frac{1}{3}$ |
| anti-bottom | $\bar{b}$ | $-\frac{1}{3}e$ | $-\frac{1}{3}$ |

## The quark model for mesons

In the quark model mesons consist of two quarks, a quark and an anti-quark, known as a doublet.

| Meson | Features | | | | | | Diagram |
|---|---|---|---|---|---|---|---|
| **Neutral pion $\pi^0$** consists of: 1 up quark 1 anti-up quark | Quark Charge Baryon number | u $\frac{2}{3}e$ $\frac{1}{3}$ | + + | $\bar{u}$ $(-\frac{2}{3}e)$ $(-\frac{1}{3})$ | = = | 0 0 | |
| **Positive pion $\pi^+$** consists of: 1 up quark 1 anti-down quark | Quark Charge Baryon number | u $\frac{2}{3}e$ $\frac{1}{3}$ | + + | $\bar{d}$ $\frac{1}{3}e$ $(-\frac{1}{3})$ | = = | 1e 0 | |

## The quark model for baryons

In the quark model baryons consist of three quarks, known as a triplet.

| Baryon | Features | | | | | | | Diagram |
|---|---|---|---|---|---|---|---|---|
| **Proton** consists of: 2 up quarks 1 down quark | Quark | u | | u | | d | | |
| | Charge | $\frac{2}{3}e$ + | | $\frac{2}{3}e$ + | | $(-\frac{1}{3}e)$ = | 1e | |
| | Baryon number | $\frac{1}{3}$ + | | $\frac{1}{3}$ + | | $\frac{1}{3}$ = | 1 | |
| **Neutron** consists of: 2 down quarks 1 up quark | Quark | u | | d | | d | | |
| | Charge | $\frac{2}{3}e$ + | | $(-\frac{1}{3}e)$ + | | $(-\frac{1}{3}e)$ = | 0 | |
| | Baryon number | $\frac{1}{3}$ + | | $\frac{1}{3}$ + | | $\frac{1}{3}$ = | 1 | |
| **Anti-proton** consists of: 2 anti-up quarks 1 anti-down quark | Quark | $\bar{u}$ | | $\bar{u}$ | | $\bar{d}$ | | |
| | Charge | $(-\frac{2}{3}e)$ + | | $(-\frac{2}{3}e)$ + | | $(\frac{1}{3}e)$ = | $-1e$ | |
| | Baryon number | $(-\frac{1}{3})$ + | | $(-\frac{1}{3})$ + | | $(-\frac{1}{3})$ = | $-1$ | |
| **Anti-neutron** consists of: 2 anti-down quarks 1 anti-up quark | Quark | $\bar{d}$ | | $\bar{d}$ | | $\bar{u}$ | | |
| | Charge | $\frac{1}{3}e$ + | | $\frac{1}{3}e$ + | | $(-\frac{2}{3}e)$ = | 0 | |
| | Baryon number | $(-\frac{1}{3})$ + | | $(-\frac{1}{3})$ + | | $(-\frac{1}{3})$ = | $-1$ | |

## Beta decay and the quark model

The weak interaction force induces beta decay. Inside the nucleus a neutron changes to a proton plus an electron ($\beta^-$) and an antineutrino. The following equation illustrates this process:

$$^1_0 n + {}^1_1 p \longrightarrow {}^0_{-1} e + {}^0_0 \bar{\nu}$$

In terms of the quarks that make up the neutrons, the process involves one of the down quarks that make up the neutron changing into an up quark.

This process is represented in the diagram on the right.

Note that this is a two stage process:

$d \rightarrow u + W^-$    followed by:    $W^- \rightarrow e^- + \bar{\nu}_e$

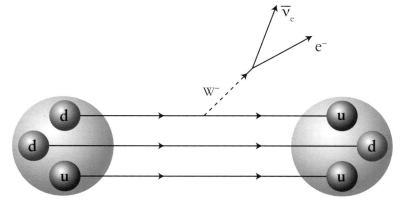

**Exercise 5.8A**

1 (a) What is meant by a 'fundamental particle'?
  (b) From the following list of subatomic particles select those which are not fundamental:
    **neutron  neutrino  pi-meson  electron  tau particle  proton**
  (c) State two differences between leptons and hadrons.
  (d) State the quark structure of (i) mesons and (ii) baryons.

2 Consider the neutral atom of lithium, $^7_3\text{Li}$.
  (a) State, with an explanation, the number of leptons, baryons and mesons that this neutral atom contains.
  (b The following equation represents the reaction in which a proton changes to a neutron, and a positron is emitted with particle X.

  $$p^+ \rightarrow n^0 + e^+ + X$$

  By applying the conservation of charge and the conservation of lepton number, identify particle X.

3 (a) State the quark structure of (i) the proton and (ii) the neutron.
  (b) Use your answer to (a) to show that the charge on the proton is +1e, and that the neutron is a neutral particle.
  (c) (i) What is meant by a 'gauge boson'?
      (ii) Write down two equations representing a reaction which describes $\beta^-$ decay in terms of quarks. Each equation should include the gauge boson involved in the process.
      (iii) Name the force responsible for this process.

4 (a) (i) What is a gauge boson?
      (ii) Identify the gauge bosons associated with the strong nuclear force and the weak force.
  (b) In terms of quarks, state the structure of the antiproton and the antineutron.
  (c) In nuclear research, electrons – rather than protons or neutrons – are used to bombard nuclei. Suggest a reason why this is so.

5 Copy and complete the table below to show the structure of the proton and the neutron and the properties of the quarks of which they are composed.

| Particle | Quark structure | Quark charges | Particle charge | Particle Baryon number |
|----------|-----------------|---------------|-----------------|------------------------|
| Proton   |                 |               |                 |                        |
| Neutron  |                 |               |                 |                        |

6 Using only up quarks, down quarks and their antiparticles state the structure of the four possible mesons that can be generated. State also the charge on each meson.

# Unit 6 (A2 3):
# Practical Techniques and Data Analysis

# 6.1 Implementing

6.1.1 Assemble and use measuring apparatus correctly, skilfully and effectively with full regard for safety, including:
- spring and top-pan balances (mass)
- rule, micrometer and callipers (length)
- graduated cylinder (liquid volume)
- clock and stopwatch (time)
- thermometer and sensor (temperature)
- ammeter (electric current)
- voltmeter (potential difference)
- protractor (angle)

(Note: digital versions of the apparatus are acceptable);

6.1.2 Use and describe how the cathode ray oscilloscope (CRO) can be used to determine the voltage and frequency;

6.1.3 Make and record sufficient relevant, reliable and valid observations and measurements to the appropriate degree of precision and accuracy, using data loggers where suitable;

6.1.4 Show familiarity with analogue and digital displays.

Physics relies on accurate measurements of physical quantities such as mass, length, time and temperature. To improve the accuracy and precision of such measurements instruments such as metre rules, vernier callipers, stop clocks and thermometers are used. It is important that you know how to use these devices properly.

In measuring any quantity there is always some degree of uncertainty. Appreciation of the uncertainty associated with each measuring instrument is equally important. In this book the uncertainty in a reading will be taken as ± ½ the smallest division shown on the scale of the measuring instrument. However, it is equally acceptable to take the uncertainty in a reading as ± the smallest division on the scale.

## Measuring length

### Using a metre rule

Although this may be one of the simplest length measuring instruments to be found in a school laboratory, care must be taken with its use to avoid errors.

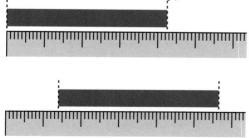

**This is bad practice.** The end of the metre rule may be worn giving rise to a zero error and an inaccurate measurement of the length.

**It is good practice** to place the metre rule against the object so that you have two readings to take.

Subtracting them will give you the length of the object. It avoids a zero error in the measurement. Of course the measurement of length still has an uncertainty associated with it.

The smallest division on the metre is usually 1 mm. If we say that each reading of the metre rule has an uncertainty of ± 0.5 mm then subtracting the two readings to obtain the length has an associated uncertainty of ± 1 mm.

For example, if the two readings are 14.0 cm and 56.5 cm, the length is 42.5 cm and if we quote the length with the associated uncertainty then we would write this as (42.5 ± 0.1) cm, ie an uncertainty in the length of about 0.25%.

For lengths greater than 1 m it is better to use a tape measure, with 1 mm divisions. Tape measures can be used to measure distances up to several metres with good accuracy.

## Parallax error

Parallax error occurs when any scale is not viewed at right angles (or **normally**) as shown. Failure to view the scale at right angles will give a reading which is either too high or too low.

Having the scale of the metre rule as close as possible to the object will reduce the possibility of a parallax error.

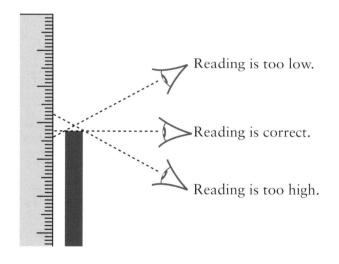

Reading is too low.

Reading is correct.

Reading is too high.

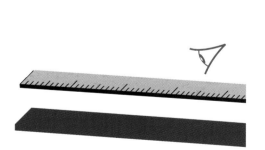

The object to be measured is too far from the scale increasing the possibility of parallax error.

Moving the object closer to the scale as shown is good practice since it reduces the possibility of parallax error.

# Vernier calliper

The vernier calliper is a precision instrument that can be used to measure internal and external distances extremely accurately. The example shown below is a manual calliper. Measurements are interpreted from the scale by the user.

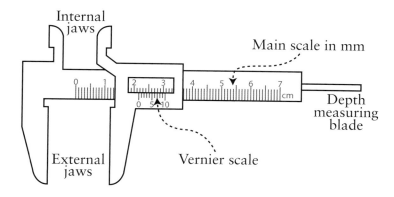

The internal jaws can be used to measure the internal diameter of, say, a tube, and the external jaws can be used to measure the external diameter of a tube or the width of a block. The depth measuring blade can be used to measure the depth of, say, a hole drilled in a metal bar.

The calliper in the diagram below can read to ± 0.1 mm. To take the reading you should follow the two steps shown below.

**Step 1**
To get an approximate reading use the first division of the vernier scale (zero mark). The zero here is between 2.1 cm and 2.2 cm.

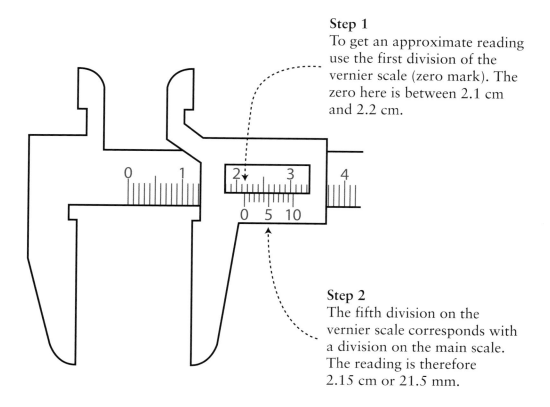

**Step 2**
The fifth division on the vernier scale corresponds with a division on the main scale. The reading is therefore 2.15 cm or 21.5 mm.

### Exercise 6.1A

Work out the following readings.

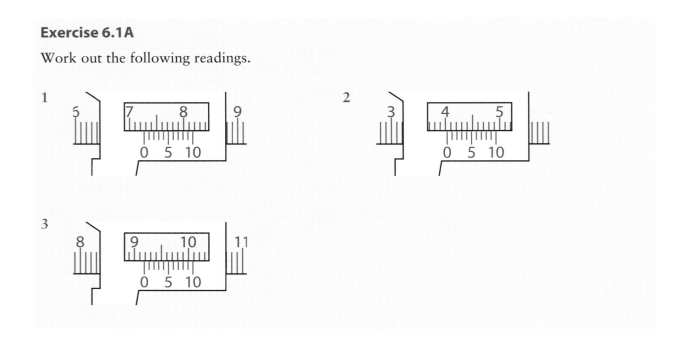

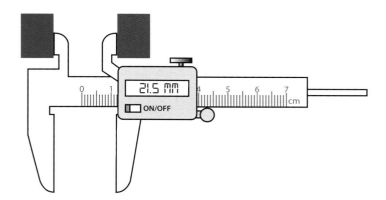

## Digital (vernier) calliper

An increasing number of schools are now using digital vernier callipers like the one shown in the diagram below. Just like the manual type, a digital calliper can be used to measure internal and external distances extremely accurately.

The measurement is shown on a LCD display. The parts are the same as those on the manual type, the only addition is an on/off switch for the LCD to extend the life of the small battery used to power it.

The digital display needs to be set to zero before it can be used to measure a distance accurately. The display is turned on and the external jaws are brought together until they touch. The zero button should then be pressed. This procedure should be followed when turning on the digital calliper for the first time.

**Note:** Remember to record all readings as they are taken. Do not allow for zero error 'in your head' and then write down the adjusted value.

### Parallax error

Parallax error occurs when the scale is not viewed normally when taking a reading. To reduce parallax errors, always:

- have the scale as close as possible to the pointer.
- view the scale normally.

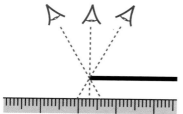

Reading too high  Correct reading  Reading too low

### Over-tightening a micrometer

Over-tightening a micrometer gauge when taking a measurement will lead to a systematic error that will always give a smaller value than the true value.

Always use the ratchet for the final turn, because this will slip when the jaws meet any resistance. This is particularly important if you are measuring the diameter of a wire.

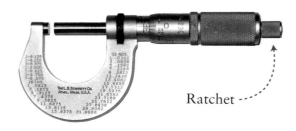

Ratchet ----

## Techniques designed to improve the accuracy of your measurements

### Timing oscillations

Start your timing when the oscillation is at one extreme, ie when the vibrating object is momentarily at rest. In the case of the simple pendulum shown on the right, one oscillation would be from C to A to B and back to C again. Start the object oscillating before you start timing and watch the object until the vibrations are no longer noticeable. This will determine how many oscillations are noticeable. When you decide to start timing, begin by saying zero as you start.

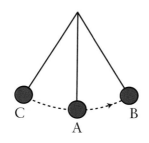

C    A    B

It is poor practice to measure the period by timing just 1 oscillation. The error in human timing is likely to be around 0.2 s. It is better to time 20 such oscillations, as this will reduce the uncertainty. However, in some circumstances the oscillations may die out quickly and only 3 or 5 complete oscillations may be noticeable. A simple pendulum with a period of just 1 second would have an error of 0.2 s, ie 20%. However, if you time 20 such oscillations the error is only 0.2 s in 20 seconds, ie 1%.

When you take measurements, vary the quantity in a logical manner, for example, increase the length of the pendulum in equal sized steps. This will allow trends to be more noticeable.

Measuring current and potential difference

Always draw the circuit diagram before you start building the circuit. Start at the positive terminal and insert components as you follow the circuit from positive to negative.

Voltmeters should be left until all the series components have been connected. Remember voltmeters are connected in parallel. Ammeters and voltmeters are always connected as positive to positive or red to red.

When using analogue meters establish what each division on the scale represents. When taking a reading, look vertically down on the scale (at a right angle). This reduces the possibility of parallax error in your reading. If you are using a digital meter, do not change the scale in the middle of the experiment.

In many cases try to change the potential difference in equal steps. However, when dealing with light emitting diodes (LEDs) it may be necessary to change the potential difference in very small steps when the current is beginning to increase.

## Cathode ray oscilloscope (CRO)

A cathode ray **oscilloscope** is an instrument that allows voltages to be viewed as a graph with voltage on the vertical axis ($y$-axis) plotted as a function of time on the horizontal axis ($x$-axis). The CRO is one of the most versatile and widely-used electronic instruments. The CRO can be used as a voltmeter to measure the size of a d.c. voltage and the amplitude of an a.c. voltage.

The CRO is essentially a voltmeter with a very high resistance. It can be used to measure both alternating and direct voltages, display waveforms and measure time intervals. The display seen on the CRO screen depends on the type of voltage (a.c. or d.c.) and on whether the timebase is on or off.

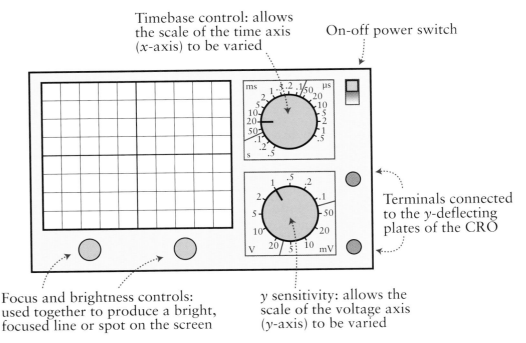

Timebase control: allows the scale of the time axis ($x$-axis) to be varied

On-off power switch

Terminals connected to the $y$-deflecting plates of the CRO

Focus and brightness controls: used together to produce a bright, focused line or spot on the screen

$y$ sensitivity: allows the scale of the voltage axis ($y$-axis) to be varied

You can regard the screen of the CRO as a graph, the vertical scale ($y$-axis) being voltage and the horizontal scale ($x$-axis) time. The voltage scale can be changed using a control known as the $y$ sensitivity and is marked in V cm$^{-1}$ or mV cm$^{-1}$. The time scale can also be changed using the timebase control; this control is marked in ms cm$^{-1}$ or μs cm$^{-1}$.

A modern oscilloscope may have a lot more functions but the most important ones are shown in the diagram on the previous page.

### Measuring voltage

The diagrams below show the appearance of the screen for a.c. and d.c. voltages with the timebase on and off.

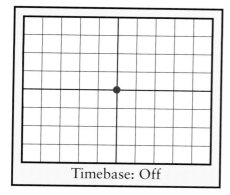

No voltage is applied to the $y$ plates. The CRO is adjusted until the beam is at the centre of the screen. When the timebase is OFF this appears as spot, with the timebase ON a line is seen.

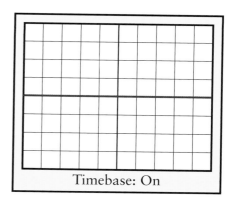

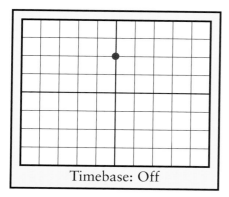

A + d.c. voltage is applied to the y plates.

With the timebase OFF the beam is deflected upwards by 2 cm.

If the $y$-sensitivity is set at 2 V cm$^{-1}$ then d.c. voltage is
2 cm × 2 V cm$^{-1}$ = 4 V.

With the timebase ON the line is seen.

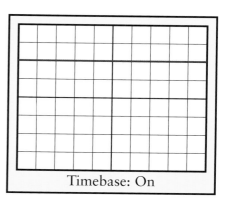

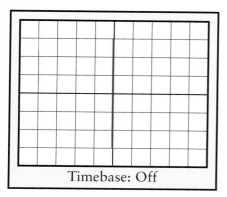

An a.c. voltage is applied to the $y$ plates.

With the timebase OFF the beam is deflected upwards and downwards.

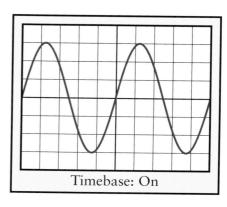

If the $y$ sensitivity is set at 100 mV cm$^{-1}$ this represent a voltage that varies from +300 mV to −300 mV. The peak value of this voltage is 300 mV. If this voltage were measured using a meter a value less than this would be displayed since the meter gives an average value of the voltage.

With the timebase ON the CRO displays the waveform of the alternating voltage.

### Measurement of time and frequency

Since the screen of the CRO shows a graph of voltage against time the instrument can be used to measure the time interval between two events. Since time can be measured the CRO also provides us with a method of measuring the frequency of an alternating voltage.

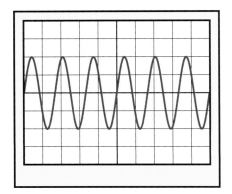

The waveform on the left was displayed with the CRO settings below:

$y$ sensitivity = 2 V cm$^{-1}$ and timebase setting = 5 ms cm$^{-1}$

6 complete waves are shown and width of the screen shows a total time of 10 cm × 5 ms cm$^{-1}$ = 50 ms

The period, $T$, of 1 wave = $\dfrac{50}{6}$ = 8.33 ms

Frequency, $f = \dfrac{1}{T} = \dfrac{1}{8.33 \times 10^{-3}}$ = 120 Hz

# 6.2 Analysis

The first step in the analysis of your data is the recording of measurements in a suitable table. The table should have sufficient columns for all the measurements and possible calculations you need to make.

Columns need headings. These should state the quantity and the appropriate units for that quantity.

Below is an example of a table that could be used for the investigation of the period of a simple pendulum and the length of the pendulum.

Measurement repeated three times to give an average

Units shown on all column headings

Systematic and a good range

| Length of the pendulum / m | Time for 20 oscillations / s | | | Average time for 20 oscillations / s | Period / s |
|---|---|---|---|---|---|
| | 1st | 2nd | 3rd | | |
| 1.2 | | | | | |
| 1.0 | | | | | |
| 0.8 | | | | | |
| 0.6 | | | | | |
| 0.4 | | | | | |
| 0.2 | | | | | |

The length is varied in a systematic manner: it is gradually increased in length using steps of 0.2 m. Increasing the length from 0.2 to 1.2 m covers a good range of values. For each length the time for 20 oscillations is measured. To improve the accuracy and ensure reliability, this is done 3 times and the average taken. The final step is to calculate the period of the pendulum by dividing the average time by 20.

The measurements could be entered into a spreadsheet to process the data and present it in a form suitable for use in graph plotting software. However, it is essential that you develop your own graph plotting skills, as these will be required in any practical examination.

To reduce the uncertainty in the measurement of the periodic time of any vibrating system, it is advisable to time sufficient oscillations so that a total time of around 20 seconds or better is to be measured. In the case on page 183, a pendulum with length of 0.2 m would yield around 18 seconds and the length of 1.2 m would yield a total time of around 40 seconds.

However, it is not always possible to obtain sufficient oscillations to achieve a total time of at least 20 seconds. In this case you need to determine the maximum number of oscillations that you can detect before they cease to be noticed.

## Worked Example

In this practical experiment, a bifilar pendulum was set up for you. The pendulum was made to vibrate about its centre. The length of the vertical cords was to be varied and the effect this had on the periodic time of oscillation was to be investigated.

The timing was to be carried out using a stopwatch or stopclock. The length of the supporting cords, $L$, was to be decreased from 400 mm to about 200 mm and 5 sets of readings were to be taken.

The results were to be recorded in a table that was partly completed with the first value of $L$ and the period $T$ shown with the appropriate unit.

When the bifilar pendulum was set swinging it was found that 5 oscillations were easily observable. More than this and they became very difficult to see. As you can see from the table, it was decided that 5 oscillations should be timed.

| $L$ / mm | Time for 5 oscillations / s | | | | $T$ / s |
| --- | --- | --- | --- | --- | --- |
| | **1st** | **2nd** | **3rd** | **Average** | |
| 400 | 9.55 | 9.40 | 9.51 | 9.48 | 1.90 |
| 350 | 8.90 | 8.85 | 8.82 | 8.85 | 1.77 |
| 300 | 8.21 | 8.30 | 8.25 | 8.25 | 1.65 |
| 250 | 7.35 | 7.51 | 7.53 | 7.46 | 1.49 |
| 200 | 6.52 | 6.75 | 6.62 | 6.63 | 1.33 |

The relationship between $T$ and $L$ is given by one of the following equations. Which one?

$$1 \quad T = A\sqrt{L} \qquad 2 \quad T = \frac{A}{\sqrt{L}} \qquad 3 \quad T = \frac{A}{L^2}$$

From the trend shown by the results it is clear that **1** is the correct relationship. As the length $L$ increases the period $T$ also increases. Equations **2** and **3** indicate that as $L$ increases $T$ would decrease.

To draw a suitable straight line graph from the results to find the constant A then $\sqrt{L}$ should be plotted on the $x$-axis and $T$ on the $y$-axis. A new table containing the appropriate values is then produced.

| $\sqrt{L}$ / mm$^{\frac{1}{2}}$ | 14.14 | 15.81 | 17.32 | 18.71 | 20.0 |
|---|---|---|---|---|---|
| $T$ / s | 1.33 | 1.49 | 1.65 | 1.77 | 1.90 |

The graph obtained using these values is shown below.

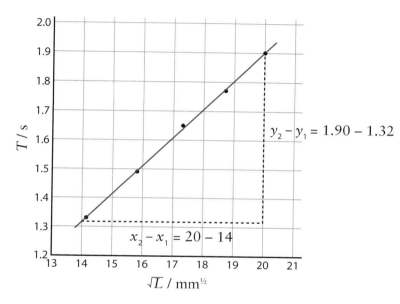

To find the value of $A$ we need to take the gradient of this line. Why?

The relationship between $L$ and $T$ is given by $T = A\sqrt{L}$. This corresponds to $y = mx$, the equation for a straight line that passes through the origin $(0,0)$. Note that in this case there is no requirement to find the intercept so there is no need to plot the graph from the origin.

By comparing the two equations we see that $y \equiv T$   $x \equiv \sqrt{L}$ and the gradient $m \equiv A$.

The gradient $= \dfrac{y_2 - y_1}{x_2 - x_1} = \dfrac{1.90 - 1.32}{20.0 - 14.0} = \dfrac{0.58}{6.0} = 0.097$

The gradient may have units and in this case it has the units of s mm$^{-\frac{1}{2}}$.

## Graphs

Graphs are commonly used to show the results of experiments. Graphs allow you to deduce relationships much more quickly than using a table. They provide a visual picture of how two quantities depend on each other: they show up anomalous readings and, if straight lines, the gradient can be used to find an average value of the ratio of the two quantities.

### Dependent and independent variables

Plot the independent variable (the one you have been changing) along the horizontal axis and the dependent variable along the vertical axis. The exception to this rule occurs where you need to plot a particular graph to find a required quantity. For example, in the case of stretching a spring, the equation $F = kx$ applies. $F$ is the force, $x$ is the extension and $k$ is the spring constant. In this instance $F$ is the independent variable but to find the spring constant, the force $F$ is plotted along the $y$-axis and the extension along the $x$-axis, because the gradient is then the spring constant.

### Labels and units

Label both axes to show the quantity that is being plotted. Indicate on the axes the unit of measurement used for the quantity. Sometimes the quantity may just be a number so a unit is not required.

### Scales

Choose scales on the axes to make the plotting of values simple. Generally this means letting 10 small divisions on the graph paper equal 1, 2, 5, 10 or some multiple of these numbers. Do not make life difficult for yourself by letting small divisions equal 3 or 7. This will take you longer to plot the graph, increase your chances of mis-plotting points and makes it difficult for others to read the data.

Choose the range of the scales on the axes so that the points are spread out. As a general rule the graph you draw should fill at least three quarters of the graph paper grid in both the $x$ and $y$ directions.

### Plotting points

Plot the results clearly, and use a sharp pencil rather than a pen. Pencil is much easier to erase should you make a mistake in plotting. Use crosses or dots with circles around them.

### Lines and curves

The graphs that you will encounter during an A level course will generally represent a smooth variation of one quantity with another, so a smooth curve or straight line will be appropriate. Draw a best fit line, which may be a smooth curve or a straight line that passes through or close to all your points as shown below. In general you should **not** join the points with short straight lines.

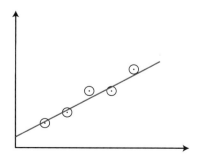 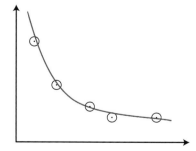

## Worked Examples

1  A ball rolls from rest down a sloped plane. Measurements are made of the distance travelled along the slope, $d$, and the time taken, t.
   The relationship between $d$ and $t$ is: $d = \frac{1}{2}at^2$ where $a$ is the acceleration of the ball.
   (a) What **straight line** graph would you plot to display your results?
   (b) How could you find the acceleration from the graph?

   Solution

   (a) The equation of a straight line that passes through the origin (0,0) is $y = mx$. By comparing this with the relationship above we see that $d$ should be plotted on the $y$-axis and $t^2$ on the $x$-axis.
   (b) In the equation for the straight line $m$ represents the gradient. The gradient of the graph of $d$ against $t^2$ is equal to $\frac{1}{2}a$.

2  The unknown e.m.f. of a cell, $E$, is linked to the terminal voltage, $V$, and the current, $I$, by the equation $E = V + Ir$ where $r$ is the unknown internal resistance of the cell.
   In an experiment, corresponding values of $V$ and $I$ are recorded as the resistance in an external circuit is changed. The e.m.f. and the internal resistance are both constant.
   (a) What **straight line** graph would you plot? Which variable would be on the vertical axis?
   (b) Draw a sketch of the graph you would expect to obtain.
   (c) How would you find the e.m.f. of the cell and the internal resistance from this graph?

   Solution

   (a) First the equation has to be arranged so that $V$ becomes the subject of the equation. This gives $V = E - Ir$. The equation of a straight lines is $y = mx + c$. By comparing these two equations we see that $V$ should be plotted on the $y$-axis and $I$ on the $x$-axis.
   (b)

   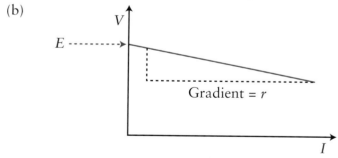

   (c) The intercept on the $y$-axis is $c$ and in this case it will give us a value for $E$. The gradient of the graph is negative and will give a value for $r$.

3  The focal length $f$, of an inaccessible lens (inside a cylinder) can be found by a technique called 'the displacement method'. The distance between an illuminated object and a screen is measured, this is $s$, as shown in the diagram. The cylinder containing the lens is moved until a sharp image is obtained on the screen. The position of the cylinder is noted. The cylinder is moved again until a new image on the screen is obtained. The distance between the two positions of the cylinder containing the lens is found, this is $d$, as shown in the diagram.

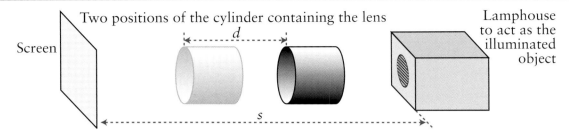

The mathematical relationship between the quantities is $f = \dfrac{s^2 - d^2}{4s}$

Below is a table of results of $s$ and $d$.

| $s$ / cm | 50.0 | 54.0 | 58.0 | 62.0 | 66.0 | 70.0 |
|---|---|---|---|---|---|---|
| $d$ / cm | 22.4 | 27.5 | 32.3 | 36.9 | 41.4 | 45.8 |
| | | | | | | |
| | | | | | | |

(a) What **straight line** graph should you plot so that the gradient can be used to calculate the focal length of the lens?

(b) Copy the table above and calculate the values required to plot the graph. Insert the values in the appropriate spaces in your table and add appropriate labels.

(c) Plot the graph, labelling carefully the units on each axis and use it to find the focal length of the lens.

**Solution**

Rearrange the equation to give:

$s^2 = d^2 + 4sf$

Divide both sides by $s$:

$s = \dfrac{d^2}{s} + 4f$

Plot $s$ on the $y$-axis and $\dfrac{d^2}{s}$ on the $x$-axis. The intercept is equal to $4f$.

Alternatively, rearrange the equation to give:

$4fs = s^2 - d^2$

$(s^2 - d^2) = 4fs$

Plot $(s^2 - d^2)$ on the $y$-axis and $s$ on the $x$-axis. The slope is $4f$.

# 6.3–6.5 Evaluation, Refinement and Communication

6.3.1   Assess the reliability of data, results and conclusions drawn from the data;

6.3.2   Evaluate and demonstrate an appreciation of the limitations of the methodology used in and the impact of the experimental activity;

6.3.3   Calculate the absolute and percentage uncertainty in a quantity;

6.4.1   Suggest improved effective and safe procedures, after considering quantitative and qualitative methods;

6.4.2   Modify procedures in response to serious sources of systematic and random error in order to generate results that are as accurate and reliable as the apparatus allows;

6.5.1   Communicate observations, measurements, results and conclusions in an appropriate and effective manner.

## Reliability and methodology

When you evaluate the result of an experiment, the reliability of the data is of major concern. For the data to be reliable, the variation of the values must be small. There will always be some variation in any set of measurements.

In an experiment to measure a particular quantity, three experimenters (A, B and C) obtained the values shown in the table below. The accepted value for this quantity is 9.8.

| A | B | C |
|---|---|---|
| Reliable but not valid | Not reliable and not valid | Reliable and valid |
| 10.5, 10.7, 10.6, 10.4 | 8.3, 7.5, 6.0, 5.5 | 9.7, 9.8, 9.7, 9.9 |

In the set of data in column A, each measurement is only slightly different from the others but the results are not close to the accepted value, so the measurements are reliable but not valid. This set of data suggests that the experimental method was good since the results are reliable but their lack of validity would imply that there is a problem with the measuring equipment. Calibration of the equipment would possibly eliminate this problem. A systematic error would be a likely cause of data with this type of characteristic.

In column B the measurements are very scattered and the values are not close to the accepted value, so the measurements are not reliable and not valid. This indicates poor experimental procedure as well as a problem with the equipment.

In column C the results are repeatable, meaning that each time a measurement is taken it has approximately the same value, so the measurements are reliable and valid. Clearly the experimental procedure was good and the equipment correctly set up.

## Uncertainties from graphs

The slope or gradient of a graph provides a means of determining an average value for a physical quantity. The intercept on either the $x$- or $y$-axis is dependent on the slope. A small change in the slope can produce a large change in the value of the intercept.

The points plotted may not all lie on a straight line. It may be necessary to judge the best fit line. The slope of the best fit line will give you the best value for a physical quantity and the intercept on the appropriate will give you the best value for this quantity. The placing of this line of best fit can be aided by calculating the average $x$ value and average $y$ value, and plotting this point. This is known as the **centroid** and the line of best fit is drawn so that it passes through this point.

To estimate the uncertainty in the slope and the intercept, follow the procedure outlined below:

1   Draw the line of best fit as outlined above.

2   Now draw two more lines, one of maximum slope and one of minimum slope through the plotted points. The gradients of these two lines will give you a maximum and minimum value for the slope. The difference between these two values gives you a range and the uncertainty can be taken as half the value of the range.

3   Similarly the line of best fit will give best value for the intercept. The range of the intercept values can be found from where the lines of maximum and minimum slope cut the appropriate axis. The uncertainty in the intercept value is again half the range.

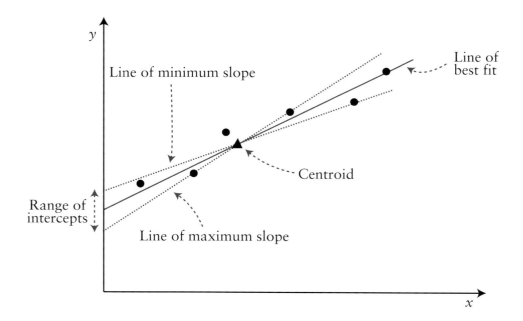

### Analysis
Record your measurements in the table below.

| Force / N | Volume of air / cm³ | |
|---|---|---|
| 1 | | |
| 2 | | |
| 3 | | |
| 4 | | |
| 5 | | |

(a) Using your measurements plot a linear graph to show the relationship between the volume and the force applied to the plunger of the syringe. To plot this graph you will need to re-arrange the equation above. Write down the re-arranged equation you plan to use.

(b) You will also need to calculate additional values that should be added to the table above with appropriate units.

(c) Plot the graph and use it to find the values of $k$ and $A$.

## 2 Introduction
In this experiment you will investigate the discharge of a capacitor.

### Aims
The aims of the experiment are:
- To obtain values for the current from a capacitor as it discharges.
- To analyse the results and obtain a linear relationship between the current and time.
- To use the data to find the value of the capacitance.

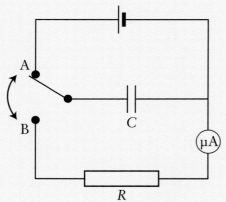

### Apparatus
You are provided with the circuit shown on the right.

### Procedure
Move the switch to position A for a few seconds. Now move the switch to position B and leave it closed. When the current reaches 100 µA start the stop clock. Record the current every 10 seconds for a total of 120 seconds.

### Theory
The relationship between the discharge current, $I$, and the time, $t$, is given by:

$$\ln I = \ln I_0 - \frac{t}{CR}$$ where $I_0$ = the initial current, in this case 100 µA
$C$ = capacitance in farads
$R$ = resistance in ohms = 100 kΩ

### Results
Record your measurements in the table below.

| $t$ / s | 0 | 10 | 20 | 30 | 40 | 50 | 60 | 70 | 80 | 90 | 100 | 110 | 120 |
|---|---|---|---|---|---|---|---|---|---|---|---|---|---|
| $I$ / µA | 100 | | | | | | | | | | | | |
| | | | | | | | | | | | | | |

**Analysis**

You are to plot a linear graph using the equation above which will allow you to calculate the capacitance, C.

(a) State the quantities to be plotted on each axis of the graph.
   Vertical (y) axis _____     Horizontal (x) axis _____

(b) Describe how you will use the linear graph to calculate C.

(c) The resistor R has a value of 100 kΩ. Calculate the value of C in μF.

3 **Introduction**

A diode is a component that conducts electricity in only one direction.

**Aim**

The purpose of this experiment is to obtain the voltage current characteristic for a diode.

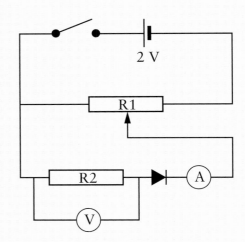

**Apparatus**

The circuit shown on the right is already set up. Resistor R2 is fixed and limits the current that can pass through the diode to prevent it overheating. Resistor R1 is variable and is used to adjust the voltage applied across the diode.

**Procedure**

Increase the voltage in steps of 0.1 V to 1.0 V. Record the current at each voltage. Design a suitable table to record your measurements. Ensure you add appropriate column headings and units to your table.

**Analysis**

(a) Plot the voltage current characteristic graph, with I on the y-axis and V on the x-axis.

(b) Determine the voltage at which the diode starts to conduct.

(c) Calculate the resistance when the voltage is 0.7 V and 0.9 V.

(d) Calculate the percentage change in the resistance between these two voltages.

4 **Introduction**

A metre rule is clamped at one so that fixed length overhangs the bench.
A mass is attached at one end and when the metre rule is displaced slightly it oscillates.

**Aim**

In this experiment you will investigate the relationship between the periodic time T of the oscillations and the M attached to the metre rule.

**Apparatus**

The apparatus is set up for you as shown on the right. You are also provided with a range of masses from 50 g to 300 g.

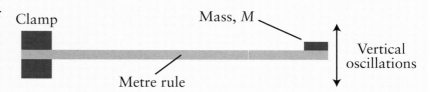

**Procedure**

You will find a 50 g mass already attached to the metre rule. Set the metre rule oscillation and record sufficient oscillation so that a more accurate value for the period, T, can be obtained. Repeat this procedure in steps of 50 g up to a maximum of 300 g. Record your measurements in a suitable table with column headings and units. Make sure you record the mass attached to the metre rule in kg.

### Analysis

The relationship between the mass, $M$, and the period, $T$, is of the form $T = kM^n$. By taking logarithms of each side plot a suitable linear graph and use it to find the value of $n$.

## Assessment Unit A2 3B

In A2 3B, you will be assessed on the analysis of experimental results. This is a separate exam paper from A2 3A and is worth a total of 50 marks. A2 3B is externally assessed.

Exercise 6.3C provides a number of sample tasks, similar to those that you will encounter in the exam.

## Exercise 6.3C

1 To investigate the cooling of water, a test tube was partially filled with hot water and a temperature sensor used to measure the temperature, $\theta_t$, of the water at regular intervals. Before the experiment began room temperature, $\theta_R$ was measured and found to be 18.0 °C. The initial temperature $\theta_I$ was 87.0 °C.

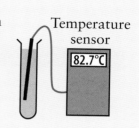

The results are shown below.

| Time / minutes | 0 | 1 | 2 | 3 | 4 | 5 | 6 | 7 | 8 |
|---|---|---|---|---|---|---|---|---|---|
| $\theta$ / °C | 86.0 | 82.7 | 77.1 | 74.3 | 71.0 | 67.9 | 65.0 | 62.3 | 58.9 |
| | | | | | | | | | |
| | | | | | | | | | |

The theory of cooling suggest that:

$\theta_t = \theta_R + Ae^{-kt}$ where $\quad t$ = time in minutes
$\quad k$ = constant
$\quad A$ = constant

(a) Using the data in the table produce a linear graph to show the relationship between the temperature difference between the liquid temperature and room temperature and the time in minutes. Additional spaces have been provided in the table for calculations.

(b) Determine the value of $k$ and state its units.

(c) Determine the value of $A$, state its unit and explain its significance.

2 The number of counts per second detected from a gamma ($\gamma$) ray source was measured with the detector placed at increasing distance from the source. The background count per second was 2.

The results are shown in the table.

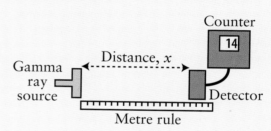

| x / cm | 2 | 3 | 4 | 5 |
|---|---|---|---|---|
| Count rate / s⁻¹ | 152 | 69 | 40 | 26 |
| | | | | |

Theory predicts that the count rate $C$ is inversely proportional to the square of the distance $x$:

$C = \dfrac{k}{x^2}$    where    $k$ = constant

(a) Use the data above to plot a suitable graph to verify this relationship.
(b) Determine the value of $k$ and use it to estimate the corrected count rate when the detector is 1 cm from the gamma ray source.

3  The diagram shows a uniform wooden rod allowed to oscillate from a pivot. This arrangement is known as a compound pendulum. The period of oscillation was determined when the rod was pivoted from different points. The distance from the end of the rod to the pivot $H$ was measured. The time for 10 oscillations was recorded. The results are shown in the table below.

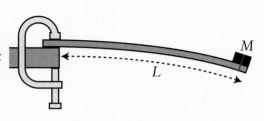

| H / m | 10T / s | | | | |
|---|---|---|---|---|---|
| 0.10 | 45.1 | | | | |
| 0.15 | 37.0 | | | | |
| 0.20 | 32.5 | | | | |
| 0.25 | 29.2 | | | | |
| 0.30 | 27.0 | | | | |

Theory suggests that the period, $T$, and distance, $H$, are related by the equation below.

$T = 2\pi\sqrt{\dfrac{k^2 + H^2}{gH}}$    where    $g$ = acceleration of free fall
$k$ = constant

(a) Rearrange the equation so that a linear graph can be obtained.
(b) Additional columns are provided for further calculations. Ensure column heading are added with the appropriate units.
(c) Using the data plot the linear graph and use it to obtain a value for $g$.

4  The Young's modulus of the material of a beam can be found by timing its oscillations when it is allowed to vibrate as shown in the diagram. A mass, $M$, is attached to the beam at measured distances from the clamped end. The time for 10 oscillations is measured. The mass is then moved to a different distance from the clamped end and the process repeated.

The results are shown in the table.

| L / m | 0.5 | 0.6 | 0.7 | 0.8 | 0.9 |
|---|---|---|---|---|---|
| **Time for 10 oscillations / s** | 5.5 | 8.8 | 10.1 | 12.8 | 14.5 |
| | | | | | |
| | | | | | |

The value of Young's modulus is given by the equation below:

$$E = \frac{16\pi^2 M}{bd^3} \bullet \frac{L^3}{T^2}$$

(a) Plot a graph of $L^3$ ($x$-axis) and $T^2$ ($y$-axis) and draw the line of best fit through the points.

(b) Determine the gradient of the line of best fit.

  (Remember this gives an average value for $\frac{L^3}{T^2}$.)

It is also possible to drawn two more lines representing the maximum and minimum gradients.

(c) Draw these two lines and determine their gradient.

Other measurements that were made are shown below along with their uncertainties.
- Mass attached to the beam = 0.5 kg $\pm$ 1%
- $b$ = width of the beam = 3.0 $\pm$ 0.01 cm
- $d$ = thickness of the beam = 5.0 $\pm$ 0.1 mm

(d) Calculate a value for the Young's modulus, $E$, stating its unit.

(e) Using the maximum and minimum values of the gradient of the graph and the uncertainties calculate the overall uncertainty in the value of Young's modulus, $E$.

# Unit 7

## Further Data Analysis and Synoptic Assessment

# 7.1 Working With Numbers

This section contains additional information on skills necessary for effective analysis of data at A2, particularly how to write numbers in scientific notation and dealing with significant figures in various situations.

## Scientific notation

This is sometimes known as **standard form**. It provides us with a way of writing numbers that are too large or small to be conveniently written in standard decimal notation. In scientific notation, numbers are written in the form:

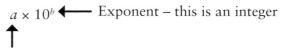

$$a \times 10^b \longleftarrow \text{Exponent – this is an integer}$$

Coefficient – this is a real number

In the **normalised** form, $a$, the coefficient has a value between 1 and 10. For example, 1,250,000 would be written as $1.25 \times 10^6$.

For numbers less than 1, the exponent has a negative value. For example, 0.00035 would be written as $3.5 \times 10^{-4}$.

## Significant figures

If an experiment provides a numerical value for a physical quantity then it is good practice when reporting your measurement to give:
- the measured value for the quantity,
- the uncertainty in your measurement,
- the appropriate unit.

The numerical value for the quantity and the uncertainty should be quoted to an appropriate number of significant figures. The number of significant figures in a number is found by counting all the digits from the first non-zero digit on the left. A zero between two non-zero digits is significant. For example:

- 845.470 has six significant figures. You start counting from the 8 which is the first non-zero digit on the left. The last, or trailing, zero has been considered significant otherwise it would not have been necessary to include it.

- 0.0516 has three significant figures, counting from the 5 which is the first non-zero digit on the left. The leading zeroes are essential to give the magnitude of the number.

### Rounding

Rounding is the process of reducing the number of significant digits in a number. The result of rounding is a number having fewer non-zero digits yet similar in magnitude. The result is less precise but easier to use. For example:

- 23 rounded to the nearest ten is 20, because 23 is closer to 20 than to 30.

The procedure for rounding is as follows:
- Decide how many significant figures you want.
- Decide which is the last digit to keep.
- Increase it by 1 if the next digit is 5 or more (this is called rounding up).
- Leave it the same if the next digit is 4 or less (this is called rounding down).

---

**Worked Examples**

1  Write 8.143 to 3 significant figures.

   **Solution**

   8.143 ◄——— This is less than 5 so 3rd significant figure is not changed.

   3rd significant figure

   Answer = 8.14. This is an example of **rounding down**.

2  Write 6.245 to 3 significant figures.

   **Solution**

   6.245 ◄——— This is equal to 5 so 3rd significant figure is changed.

   ↑

   3rd significant figure

   Answer = 6.25. This is an example of **rounding up**.

---

**Note:** When you have to perform calculations on a set of measurements then the result should be given to the same number of significant figures as the initial values. For example, $3.25^2 = 10.5625$, but this should be quoted as 10.6.

### Significant figures and scientific notation

The same rules for significant figures apply to numbers expressed in scientific notation. Remember that in the normalised form of scientific notation, leading and trailing digits do not occur, so all digits are significant. For example:
- 0.00011 (two significant figures) becomes $1.1 \times 10^{-4}$, and 0.000111500 (six significant figures) becomes $1.11500 \times 10^{-4}$.
- If we quote 1600 to four significant figures it is written as $1.600 \times 10^3$.
- If we quote 1600 to three significant figures it is written as $1.60 \times 10^3$.

### Orders of magnitude

The order of magnitude of a physical quantity is the nearest power of ten to the value of the quantity. For example, the order of magnitude of $8.85 \times 10^5$ is $10^6$.

### Significant figures and uncertainties

When reporting the value of some physical quantity, obtained through experimental work, you should be aware of the uncertainties associated with any measurements used. This has already been discussed in section 6.2. However, it is important to understand that these uncertainties will, in turn, determine the number of significant figures to which you should quote your final value. For example, say you have measured a block of metal (shown on the right) and used the values to calculate its volume.

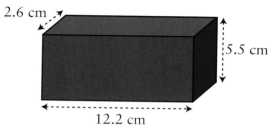

The calculated volume of the block = 12.2 × 5.5 × 2.6 = 174.46 cm³. However, this ignores the uncertainty in each measurement of length. A ruler was used, so the uncertainty in each measurement could be 0.1 cm. This uncertainty is due the scale of the ruler and the skill of the person taking the measurement. The smallest division on the ruler is 1 mm and the person taking the measurements judges that they can read the scale to ± ½ the smallest division. Since two readings are taken and then subtracted to find the length the uncertainty becomes ± 1 mm.

Taking this into account the volume of the block would have the range of values shown below:

- Minimum volume = 12.1 × 5.4 × 2.5 = 163.35 cm³
- Measured volume = 12.2 × 5.5 × 2.6 = 174.46 cm³
- Maximum volume = 12.3 × 5.6 × 2.7 = 185.98 cm³
- The actual volume of the block is between 163 cm³ and 186 cm³.

Considering the uncertainties in this simple measurement it is inappropriate to quote the volume of the block to five significant figures. It is much more appropriate to quote the result to three significant figures, since the measurements of length are given to 3 significant figures, ie 174 cm³.

Considering the difference between the maximum and minimum values for the volume, the measurement of the block's volume should be given as (174 ± 12) cm³.

## Exercise 7.1

1  To how many significant figures are each of the following numbers quoted to?
   (a) 273.16   (b) 9.81   (c) 3.1412   (d) 0.003450   (e) 0.1001

2  Re-write each of the following values to the number of significant figures given in brackets alongside each.
   (a) 645.5701   [4]      (b) 0.0125   [1]
   (c) 1678       [2]      (d) 1.245    [2]

3  Write each of the following in normalized scientific notation. The number in brackets is the number of significant figures you should quote the value to.
   (a) Density of mercury 13552 kg m⁻³ [3]
   (b) Speed of light 299 792 458 m s⁻¹ [2]
   (c) Expansion coefficient of brass 0.0000193 K⁻¹ [2]

4  Give the order of magnitude of the following quantities.
   (a) The mass of the earth = $6.0 \times 10^{24}$ kg
   (b) The universal gravitation constant G = $6.67 \times 10^{-11}$ m³ kg⁻¹ s⁻²
   (c) The speed of sound in air = 333 m s⁻¹

5 A capacitor is fully changed and then allowed to discharge through a resistor. The current is measured as the capacitor discharges. The results are shown below.

| Current / µA | 100 | 60.7 | 36.8 | 22.3 |
|---|---|---|---|---|
| Time / s | 0.0 | 10.0 | 20.0 | 30.0 |

State the number of significant figures to which the current readings are stated.

6 The energy, E, of an electron accelerated though a high voltage is often given in keV. The table below gives some of the values obtained in an experiment. Copy and complete the table by calculating $\sqrt{E}$ to three significant figures. Add the appropriate heading with unit to the blank row.

| E / keV | 30.0 | 35.0 | 40.0 |
|---|---|---|---|
|  |  |  |  |

7 The wavelength, λ, of the spectral lines in the Lyman series of hydrogen can be calculated using the equation below.

$$\frac{1}{\lambda} = 1.097 \times 10^7 (1 - \frac{1}{n^2})$$

n has integer values staring from 2. Calculate the wavelength of the first three of the spectral lines, stating your values in nm to 4 significant figures.

# 7.2 Obtaining Straight Line Graphs

In many of the experiments you undertake, a graph of one of the variables you measured against the other measured variable will not give a straight line. Instead, the graph obtained will often be a curve. Obtaining a straight line graph will require some manipulation of the measured quantities. If we have an equation relating the quantities the task is simpler. Let us begin with the example below.

The viscosity, $\eta$, of a liquid is a measure of the fluid friction an object experiences when moving through the liquid. The viscosity of a clear, thick liquid such as glycerin can be found by dropping ball bearings through a tall cylinder full of the liquid. The ball bearings quickly reach their constant terminal velocity which can be measured. The radius of the ball bearing also affects this terminal velocity. The viscosity of the liquid, $\eta$, is given by:

$$\eta = \frac{kr^2}{v}$$

where $r$ = radius of the ball bearing (m)
$v$ = terminal velocity (m s$^{-1}$)
$k$ = a constant of known value

The value of $\eta$ can be found by plotting a suitable linear graph. The equation for a straight line is $y = mx + c$ or, if it passes through the origin, $y = mx$.

To decide what graph to plot, the first step is to re-arrange the viscosity relationship so that $v$ is the subject of the equation and compare this to the equation for a straight line. So:

$$v = \frac{kr^2}{\eta}$$
$$y = mx$$

This tells us that plotting a graph of $v$ on the $y$-axis and $r^2$ on the $x$-axis will give a straight line, the gradient of which equals $k/\eta$ as shown on the right.

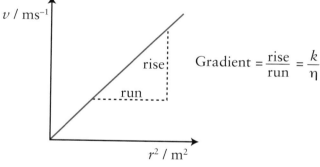

$$\text{Gradient} = \frac{\text{rise}}{\text{run}} = \frac{k}{\eta}$$

---

**Worked Example**

1 An obstructed pendulum is one where the swing is obstructed by an object in the path of the swing. The arrangement is shown in the diagram on the right. In this experiment the length $h$ is altered and the period time $T$ for different values of $h$ is measured. The acceleration due to gravity $g$ can be determined from this experiment. The relationship between $g$, $T$ and $h$ is:

$$g = \frac{\pi^2 h}{(T - A)^2}$$

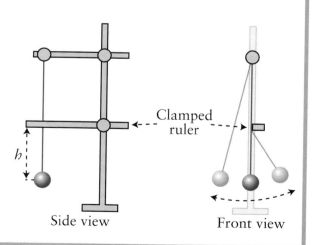

Side view

Front view

$A$ is a constant. Determine what graph must be drawn to give a straight line and hence allow the value of $g$ to be determined.

**Solution**

This relationship needs to be re-arranged so that $T$ becomes the subject of the equation. In other words, we need to have it in a form that satisfies the general equation for a straight line $y = mx + c$. So firstly:

$g(T - A)^2 = \pi^2 h$

Next, take the square root of each side and rearrange:

$T - A = \dfrac{\pi\sqrt{h}}{\sqrt{g}}$

Finally, we have:

$T = \pi\sqrt{\dfrac{h}{g}} + A$

This also has the form $y = mx + c$. Hence a graph of $T$ ($y$-axis) against $\sqrt{h}$ ($x$-axis) will give a straight line.

The gradient gives $\dfrac{\pi}{\sqrt{g}}$ and the intercept on the $y$-axis gives the constant $A$.

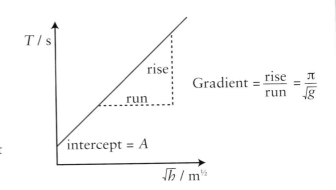

$$\text{Gradient} = \frac{\text{rise}}{\text{run}} = \frac{\pi}{\sqrt{g}}$$

## Use of logarithms

A logarithm is defined as the power to which a base must be raised to produce a given number. Two bases are common: base 10 and base $e$ (2.71828). The notation **lg** or **lg$_{10}$** is taken to mean logarithm to the base 10, and the notation **ln** is taken to mean the base $e$. For example:

- $\lg 1000 = 3.0$ since $10^3 = 1000$
- $\lg 0.01 = -2.0$ since $10^{-2} = 0.01$
- $\ln 5 = 1.6094$ since $2.71828^{1.6094} = 5$

If the relationship under investigation involves a power then the use of logarithms becomes an essential tool in the analysis of the data.

The diagram on the right shows a loaded cantilever: a metre rule clamped at one end with a mass, $M$, attached at the other end. When the free end is displaced and released the metre rule oscillates. The periodic time, $T$, of these oscillations is given by a relationship of the form $T = kM^n$, where $k$ and $n$ are constants.

Since the only variables in this expression are the mass, $M$, and the period, $T$, clearly the investigation involves varying the mass, $M$, and measuring the corresponding period, $T$.

To process the data to determine the value of the power $n$ we must take the logarithms ($\log_{10}$) of each side of the expression:

$$T = k \quad M^n$$
$$\lg T = \lg k + n \lg M$$
$$\uparrow \qquad \uparrow \qquad \uparrow \ \uparrow$$
$$y = c + m \ x$$

Comparing this with the general equation for a straight line you can see that $\lg T$ plotted on the $y$-axis against $\lg M$ on the $x$-axis will give a straight line. The intercept of the $y$-axis will give $\lg k$ and the gradient will give the power, $n$.

---

**Worked Example**

1  The aerodynamic drag force experienced by motorcycles is an important factor when considering their design. The factors affecting the amount of drag on a motorcycle can be investigated by carrying out experiments in the controlled environment of a wind tunnel. Wind tunnel experiments have shown that the aerodynamic drag force, $F_D$, on an object depends on a number of variables, according to the equation below:

$$F_D = \frac{\rho A C_D}{2} v^n \quad \text{where} \qquad \begin{aligned} &C_D = \text{the drag coefficient} \\ &A = \text{the frontal area of the motorcycle} \\ &\rho = \text{the density of the air in the wind tunnel} \\ &v = \text{the speed of the air relative to the object} \\ &n = \text{a constant} \end{aligned}$$

In a wind tunnel experiment, the variation in drag force with speed was investigated. The results of the wind tunnel experiment are shown below.

| $v \,/\, \mathrm{ms^{-1}}$ | $F_D \,/\, \mathrm{N}$ | | |
|---|---|---|---|
| 10 | 17.0 | | |
| 15 | 38.50 | | |
| 20 | 68.3 | | |
| 25 | 106 | | |
| 30 | 154 | | |
| 35 | 209 | | |

(a) One of the values in the column headed $F_D$ has been quoted to an inconsistent number of significant figures. How should this value have been recorded?

(b) Process the expression for the drag force $F_D$ so that a linear graph can be obtained from which the value of $n$ can be determined. State what should be plotted on the $y$-axis and on the $x$-axis. Describe how the value of n can be found from this graph.

(c) Copy and complete the table, inserting suitable column headings in the blank columns of the table. Complete the columns, quoting the data to three significant figures.

(d) Plot the appropriate graph and use it to find the value of $n$ in the above expression for the drag force $F_D$.

**Solution**

(a) All the velocity values have been recorded to two significant figures. All but one of the drag force values have been recorded to three significant figures, ie apart from 38.50. This should be recorded as **38.5**.

(b) Taking logarithms to the base 10 of each side of the above expression and comparing the result with the general equation for a straight line graph gives:

$$\lg_{10} F_{D} \quad = \quad \lg_{10}\left(\frac{\rho A C_{D}}{2}\right) + n\,\lg_{10} v$$

$$y \quad = \quad c \quad\; + m \;\; x$$

So $\lg_{10} F_{D}$ should be plotted on the $y$-axis and $\lg_{10} v$ plotted on the $x$-axis. The gradient of the straight line gives the value of $n$.

(c) Remember to write the log values down to three significant figures.

| $v$ / m s$^{-1}$ | $F_{D}$ / N | $\lg_{10} v$ | $\lg_{10} F_{D}$ |
|---|---|---|---|
| 10 | 17.0 | 1.00 | 1.23 |
| 15 | 38.5 | 1.18 | 1.59 |
| 20 | 68.3 | 1.30 | 1.83 |
| 25 | 106 | 1.40 | 2.03 |
| 30 | 154 | 1.48 | 2.19 |
| 35 | 209 | 1.54 | 2.32 |

(d)

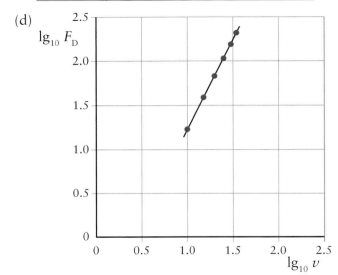

The gradient of the line = 2. The value of $n$ in the expression for the drag force is therefore 2.

**Note:** When plotting a log quantity it is simply a number; it does not have a unit. Notice that in the graph above units are **not** shown for the $x$ and the $y$-axis.

### Exponential or natural logarithms

As stated earlier, exponential or natural logarithms (ln) are to the base $e$. The quantity $e$ is associated with systems that grow or decay exponentially and continuously. Examples are radioactive decay, capacitor charge and discharge.

The value of $e$ is approximately 2.71828. Note that $\ln e = 1$.

## Worked Example

1 When a large number of identical particles are suspended in a liquid, they tend to settle in the way shown in the diagram. There are many particles at the bottom of the liquid column, but progressively fewer towards the top of the column. The number density, $n$, of particles at a height, $h$, above the bottom of the liquid column is given by:

$$n = n_0 e^{-\frac{Wh}{kT}} \qquad \text{where} \qquad$$

$n_0$ = a constant
$W$ = the weight of the particle
$k$ = Boltzmann's constant
$T$ = the Kelvin temperature

(a) What name is given to the mathematical function represented by the equation above?

(b) The quantity $n$ is the number density of the particles. Explain what this means.

(c) What is the physical interpretation of the constant $n_0$ in the above equation?

(d) Using exponential (natural) logarithms arrange the above equation so that a linear graph can be drawn.

(e) Sketch the graph, labelling each axis.

(f) What will the gradient of this graph provide?

### Solution

(a) An exponential function.

(b) The number of particles per m³.

(c) $n = n_0$ when $h = 0$. Therefore $n_0$ is the number density if all the particles were at the base of the column.

(d) $\ln(e^{-\frac{Wh}{kT}}) = -\frac{Wh}{kT} \times \ln e$. But since $\ln e = 1$, we can write that $\ln(e^{-\frac{Wh}{kT}}) = -\frac{Wh}{kT}$

Therefore taking natural logs of both sides gives:

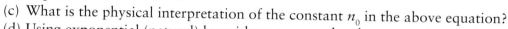

$$\ln n \quad = \quad \ln n_0 - \frac{W}{kT} h$$

$$y \quad = \quad c \quad + \quad m \quad x$$

(e)

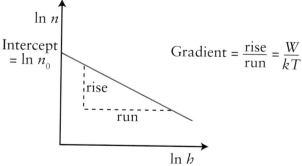

Gradient $= \dfrac{\text{rise}}{\text{run}} = \dfrac{W}{kT}$

(f) The gradient gives $\dfrac{W}{kT}$

### Exercise 7.2

1  The refractive index of a material changes with the wavelength of light. The relationship between the refractive index $n$ and the wavelength $\lambda$ is given by the equation below. $A$ and $B$ are constants.

$$n = A + \frac{B}{\lambda^2}$$

(a) What quantity would you plot on the $x$-axis and what quantity would you plot on the $y$-axis to provide a straight line graph?

(b) Sketch the graph.

(c) Describe how the values of $A$ and $B$ could be obtained from such a linear graph.

2  The resonance of sound waves in a tube closed at one end can be used to determine the speed of sound in air. The diagram on the right shows the apparatus. The frequency, $f$, of the sound emitted by the loudspeaker is set at a particular value and the length, $L$, of the air column varied until resonance occurs. This is detected when the sound increases considerably. This process is repeated for a range of frequencies. The velocity of sound is given by the relationship:

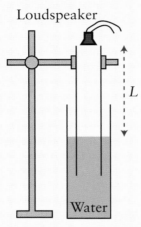

$v = 4Lf$   where $L$ = the length of air column at which
resonance is detected (m)
$f$ = the frequency of the sound (Hz)

(a) Re-arrange the equation into the form of a straight line with $L$ and $f$ as the variables.

(b) What graph should be plotted? State what should be plotted on the $x$ and $y$-axes.

(c) Describe how you would use the graph to find the velocity of sound in air.

3  The the relationship between the resistance of a metal, $R$, in $\Omega$ and its temperature, $\theta$, in °C is given by the expression:

$R = R_0(1 + \alpha\theta)$   where   $R_0$ = the resistance of the metal at 0°C
$\alpha$ = a constant known as the temperature coefficient of resistance

(a) Re-arrange the expression so that a linear graph can be obtained from the measured values of $R$ and $\theta$.

(b) Sketch the graph that would be obtained, labelling each axis.

(c) Explain how $R_0$ and $\alpha$ can be obtained from the graph, giving the units of each.

4  As an X-ray beam passes through a material it is attenuated, ie its intensity decreases. The beam intensity, $I$, after the X-rays have passed a distance $x$ into a material can be expressed in the form of an equation as shown below.

$I = I_0\, e^{-\mu x}$        where    $I_0$ = initial intensity of the X-ray beam
$x$ = distance travelled into the material
$\mu$ = attenuation coefficient of the material

(a) What linear graph would be drawn to obtain a value for the attenuation coefficient of the material $\mu$?

(b) Sketch the graph, labelling each axis.

(c) Explain how $\mu$ is obtained from the graph.

# 7.3 Synoptic Assessment

The A2 assessment units include some synoptic assessment, which encourages candidates to develop their understanding of the subject as a whole. Synoptic assessment involves:

• building on material from the AS units;

• bringing together and making connections between areas of knowledge and skills that they have explored throughout the course; and

• applying knowledge and understanding of more than one area to a particular situation or context.

## About synoptic assessment

The A-level Physics assessment expects students to show that they have an overall understanding of the Physics they are studying. Synoptic assessment will test your grasp of the connections between the different topics at AS and A2. Synoptic assessment will be assessed in modules A2 1 and A2 2. The questions in these two modules will have elements of synoptic assessment, drawing together different strands of the specification. The two questions in the exercise below refer to elements from different parts of the specification in this way.

**Exercise 7.3**

1  (a) State Newton's second law of motion.

(b) The first diagram shows two masses attached by a string that passes over a frictionless pulley. Mass $m_2$ is greater than mass $m_1$. Derive an expression for the downwards acceleration of $m_2$.

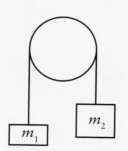

(c) (i) State Newton's first law of motion.

The second diagram shows a positive ion of charge $q$ moving with velocity $v$ through a region between two metal plates in which an electric field and a magnetic field are present. The electric field has a strength $E$ and the strength of the magnetic field is $B$. The ion passes through without deflection.

(ii) Copy the diagram and mark the polarity of the metal plates and the direction of the electric field and magnetic field which allow the ion to pass without deflection.

(iii) Write down expressions for the electric and magnetic forces acting on the ion.

(iv) This arrangement is known as velocity selector. The ions that enter the region between the plates can have a range of velocities. However using this arrangement it is possible to ensure that only ions of a certain velocity

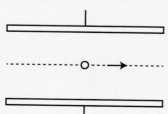

pass through without being deflected. Derive a value for this velocity is terms of the electric field strength $E$ and magnetic field strength (flux density) $B$.

2 A projectile is fired from a horizontal surface at an angle $\theta$ with an initial velocity $u$ as shown below.

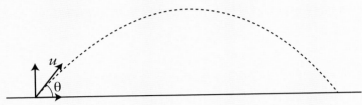

(a) Write down the initial vertical and horizontal components of the projectile's velocity. Label each component.

(c) Write your own expressions for the vertical distance $y$ and horizontal distance $x$ travelled by the projectile after it has been moving for a time $t$.

(c) The general equation for a parabola is: $y = Ax^2 + Bx + C$. A, B and C are constants. Show that the path of the projectile is a parabola.

(d) Electrons with an energy of 300 eV are projected into an electric field midway between two parallel plates as shown below. With appropriate calculations determine whether the electrons pass out of the electric field or collide with one of the metal plates. Mass of the electron $m_e = 9.1 \times 10^{-31}$ kg.

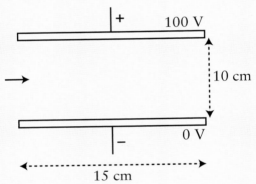

# Answers

**Exercise 4.1**

1 (a) Both springs experience the same force, ie 36 N. Using $F = kx$ for each spring gives two extensions, one of 2 cm and the other 3 cm. Total extension = 5 cm.

(b) Hooke's Law gives $F = kx$, for the combined springs $36 = k \times 5$, so $k = 7.2$ N cm$^{-1}$.

(c) $F = k_{comb} \, x$, so $x = \dfrac{F}{k_{comb}}$, $x_1 = \dfrac{F}{k_1}$, $x_2 = \dfrac{F}{k_2}$, $x = x_1 + x_2$, $\dfrac{F}{k_{comb}} = \dfrac{F}{k_1} + \dfrac{F}{k_2}$

The $F$s cancel, leaving: $1 \div k_{comb} = \dfrac{1}{k_{comb}} = \dfrac{1}{k_1} + \dfrac{1}{k_2}$. Re-arranging gives $k_{comb} = \dfrac{k_1 k_2}{k_1 + k_2}$.

2 The total upward force = 100 N so $F_1 + F_2 = 100$. The two springs have the same length so the two extensions must be equal if the iron bar is to remain horizontal. $F_1 = k_1 x$ and $F_2 = k_2 x$. $15x + 25x = 100$, giving $x = 2.5$ cm. $F_1 = 15 \times 2.5 = 37.5$ N. $F_2 = 25 \times 2.5 = 62.5$ N.

3 (a) 10 turns equals an extension of 400 mm. The force required is 32 N. Using $F = kx$, gives $32 = k \times 400$, so $k = 0.08$ N mm$^{-1}$ or 80 N m$^{-1}$.

(b) Total length = 850 + 400 = 1250 mm or 1.25 m.

4 ¼ of a turn gives a compression of 0.125 mm. Using $F = kx$: $600 \times 10^3 = k \times 0.125 \times 10^{-3}$ giving $k = 4.8 \times 10^9$ N m$^{-1}$.

5 (a) Safety spectacles – a wire under tension can snap and the end can damage eyes.

(b) Good experimental practice – to ensure that the wire has not been stretched beyond its limit of proportionality. If it has, the two measurements of length will be different.

6 Maximum upward force = $mg + ma = 2500 (9.81 + 0.5) = 25775$ N.
Maximum stress = $100 \times 10^6$ Pa = $25775 \div$ area of cross section.
Area of cross section = $\pi d^2 \div 4 = 25775 \div 100 \times 10^6$, giving d = 0.018 m (1.8 cm).

7 Area of cross section = $\pi d^2 \div 4 = 3.14 \times 10^{-6}$ m$^2$.

(a) Stress = force ÷ area of cross section = $(11 \times 9.81) \div 3.14 \times 10^{-6} = 3.44 \times 10^7$ Pa.

(b) Young Modulus = stress ÷ strain. $70 \times 10^9 = 3.44 \times 10^7 \div$ strain, giving strain = $4.91 \times 10^{-4}$ (no unit).

(c) Strain = extension ÷ original length. $4.91 \times 10^{-4} = x \div 2.0$, giving $x = 9.83 \times 10^{-4}$ m.

8 (a) Copper: length = 0.900 m. Area of cross-section = $9.0 \times 10^{-7}$ m$^2$.
Iron: length = 1.400 m. Area of cross-section = $1.3 \times 10^{-6}$ m$^2$.

(b) Young modulus $E$ = stress ÷ strain = $(F \div A) \div (\Delta L \div L_o)$, where $\Delta L$ = extension and $L_o$ = original length. Re=arranging gives $\Delta L = (FL_o) \div (AE)$

(c) $\Delta L_{copper} = (F \times 0.9) \times (9.0 \times 10^{-7} \times 130 \times 10^9)$. $\Delta L_{iron} = (F \times 1.4) \div (1.3 \times 10^{-6} \times 210 \times 10^9)$. The ratio $\Delta L_{copper} \div \Delta L_{iron} = 3 \div 2$, the extension for copper = 1.5 × extension for iron. $\Delta L_{copper} + \Delta L_{iron} = 10$ mm, so $\Delta L_{copper} = 6.0$ mm and $\Delta L_{iron} = 4.0$ mm. Since the two wires are joined the tension in each wire is the same. Substitution of these values into $F = EA\Delta L \div L_o$ = $(130 \times 10^9 \times 1.3 \times 10^{-6} \times 6 \times 10^{-3}) \div 1.4$ gives $F = 780$ N.

9 (a) Strain = extension ÷ original length = $25 \times 10^{-3} \div 10.0 = 2.5 \times 10^{-3}$ (no unit).

(b) Young modulus = stress ÷ strain, $3.0 \times 10^9 =$ stress $\div 2.5 \times 10^{-3}$ giving stress = $7.5 \times 10^6$ Pa.

(c) Stress = force ÷ area of cross section. Area of cross section = $\pi d^2 \div 4 = 7.85 \times 10^{-5}$ m$^2$. Force = $7.5 \times 10^6 \times 7.85 \times 10^{-5} = 589$ N.

(d) Opposing forces are equal to the towing force since the car is moving with constant velocity. Sum of the opposing forces = 589 N.

(e) The same pulling force is required so a larger area of cross section has no effect on the tension in the rope. However, since strain = stress ÷ young modulus, the extension would decrease, since the length and Young modulus have not changed.

(f) The ultimate or maximum stress = 21.8 MPa, using the area of cross section $7.85 \times 10^{-5}$ m$^2$ gives a maximum force of 1711 N. Resultant force = 1711 − 589 = 1122. Using $F = ma$ gives $a = 1.5$ m s$^{-2}$.

## Exercise 4.2A

1  $PV = nRT$ where $n$ = no of moles, no units, $R$ = molar gas constant = 8.3 J mol$^{-1}$ K$^{-1}$, $T$ = temperature in K. When combined we have J K$^{-1}$ K = J (mol is a number and has no unit). An alternative method is $P = F \div A = N \div$ m$^2$ and V = m$^3$. Combining we have = N m$^{-2}$ m$^3$ = Nm = J.

2  (a) Using Boyle's Law (i) $p_1V_1 = p_2V_2$, $100 \times 24 = 50 \times V_2$ giving $V_2$ = 48 litres. (ii) $100 \times 24 = 150 \times V_2$, giving $V_2$ = 16 litres.
   (b) Using Boyle's Law (i) $100 \times 24 = p_2 \times 4.8$, giving $p_2$ = 500 kPa. (ii) $100 \times 24 = p_2 \times 8$, giving $p_2$ = 300 kPa (iii) $100 \times 24 = p_2 \times 12$, giving $p_2$ = 200 kPa.

3

| Pressure, $V$ / MPa | 0.25 | 0.4 | 0.6 | 0.75 | 1.0 | 1.5 |
|---|---|---|---|---|---|---|
| Volume, $V$ / cm$^3$ | 45.0 | 28.0 | 19.0 | 15.0 | 11.3 | 7.5 |
| 1/pressure / MPa$^{-1}$ | 4.0 | 2.5 | 1.6 | 1.3 | 1.0 | 0.67 |

   (a) Graph of $V$ against $P^{-1}$ is a straight line of positive slope through (0,0) origin. At higher temperatures the slope is greater.
   (b) Gradient = $8.8 \times 10^{-8}$ MPa$^{-1}$ cm$^{-3}$.

4  If the volume of a gas was proportional to the temperature in °C then at 0°C air would have no volume. Clearly this does not happen.

5  Using Charles' Law: $V_1 \div T_1 = V_2 \div T_2$. Temperatures must be in kelvins. $12 \div 300 = V_2 \div 400$, giving $V_2$ = 16 litres.

6  Using Charles' Law: $25 \div 350 = 40 \div T_2$, giving $T_2$ = 560 K = 287 °C.

7  Using Charles' Law: $12 \div 373 = 1.2 \div T_2$, giving $T_2$ = 37.3 K = −235.7 °C.

8  Using Boyle Law: The pressure at depth = 3 atmospheres + 1 atmosphere. $(4 + 1) \times 2 = 1 \times V$, giving V = 8 cm$^3$.

9  Using the ideal gas equation: $p_1V_1 \div T_1 = p_2V_2 \div T_2$. Temperatures must be in kelvins. $1.0 \times 70 \div 280 = p_2 \times 30 \div 300$, giving $p_2$ = 2.5 atmospheres.

10 (a) No of molecules in 10 g = $10 \times 10^{-3} \div 5.35 \times 10^{-26} = 1.87 \times 10^{23}$ molecules. 1 mole = $6.02 \times 10^{23}$ molecules. No of moles = $1.87 \times 10^{23} \div 6.02 \times 10^{23}$ = 0.31 moles.
   (b) $pV = nRT$, $p = 0.31 \times 8.31 \times 323 \div 1.0 \times 10^{-4} = 8.32 \times 10^6$ Pa.
   (c) $\frac{1}{2}m<c^2> = 3 \div 2$ kT = $3 \times 1.38 \times 10^{-23} \times 323 \div 2 = 6.69 \times 10^{-21}$ J.

11 (a) The pressure is **inversely** proportional to the volume.
   (b) For an ideal gas the pressure and kelvin temperature are proportional. The graph is a straight line passing through 0 pressure and 0 temperature.
   (c) Values on the graph are pressure = 0, temperature = 0 and temperature = 353 K. Pressure = $1.5 \times 10^5$ Pa.
   (d) Gradient = $1.5 \times 10^5 \div 353 = 4.25 \times 10^2$ Pa K$^{-1}$.

12 $p = \frac{1}{3}\rho<c^2>$, $150 \times 10^3 = \frac{1}{3} \times 2.0<c^2>$, giving $<c^2> = 2.25 \times 10^5$ and rms speed = 474.3 m s$^{-1}$.

13 The additional air produces a pressure of 200 kPa. $pV = nRT$, $200 \times 10^3 \times 0.015 = n \times 8.31 \times 300$, giving $n$ = 1.2 moles.

14 (a) 1 mole of Helium has a mass of 4g. $PV = nRT$, $101 \times 10^3 \times V = 1 \times 8.31 \times 273$, giving $V = 0.0225$ m$^3$. Density = mass ÷ volume = $4 \times 10^{-3} \div 0.0225 = 0.18$ kg m$^{-3}$.

(b) 1300 m s$^{-1}$

15 $<c^2> = (c_1^2 + c_2^2 + c_3^2 + \ldots\ldots c_N^2) \div N$. $306^2 = (301^2 + 301^2 + 305^2 + 310^2 + x^2) \div 5$, giving the speed of the 5th molecule $x = 313$ m s$^{-1}$.

16 (a) ½ m$<c^2>$ = 3 ÷ $2kT$, ½ × $7.3 \times 10^{-26}$ $<c^2>$ = 3 ÷ 2 × $1.38 \times 10^{-23}$ × 303. $\sqrt{<c^2>}$ = 415 m s$^{-1}$.

(b) ½ m$<c^2>$ = 3 ÷ $2kT$, so $<c^2>$ is proportional to $T$. The graph of $<c^2>$ against $T$ would be a straight line passing through the origin.

17 See pages 19 and 20, the kinetic theory and the ideal gases.

18 (a) Charles' Law states that the volume of a fixed mass of gas at constant pressure is directly proportional to its Kelvin temperature.

(b) The acid absorbs any moisture in the trapped gas.

(c) It is difficult to measure the small volume of gas directly. However, the volume is equal to the product of the cross-section area and the length of the air thread. Since the cross-section area is constant, the length is directly proportional to the volume.

(d) Absolute zero is the theoretical temperature at which all substances have zero thermal energy. Charles thought of it as the temperature at which a gas at constant pressure would contract to zero volume. Today we think of it as the temperature at which all translational motion ceases and the gas molecules have almost no vibrational motion.

19 (a) Pressure decreases as the temperature decreases; the speed of the molecules decreases as the temperature falls; there are fewer collisions per second with the container walls and each collision is less violent than at the higher temperature; there is a smaller momentum change in each collision; each collision produces a smaller force on the walls; so the pressure on the walls decreases. See page 20.

(b) (i) $n = PV \div RT = (1.2 \times 10^5 \times 500 \times 10^{-6}) \div (8.31 \times 300) = 0.0241$ moles.

(ii) $N = nN_A = 0.0241 \times 6.02 \times 10^{23} = 1.45 \times 10^{22}$ molecules (iii) No change (the pressure, volume and temperature all change, but the ratio $PV/T$ is constant.)

## Exercise 4.2B

1  $Q = mc\Delta\theta$, so $c = Q \div m\Delta\theta$ = J kg$^{-1}$ K$^{-1}$ = N m kg$^{-1}$ K$^{-1}$ = kg m s$^{-2}$ m kg$^{-1}$ K$^{-1}$. Collecting the terms we get m$^2$ s$^{-2}$ K$^{-1}$.

2  $Q = mc\Delta\theta = 4 \times 385 \times 55 = 84\ 700$ J.

3  Energy = power × time = $I \times V \times t$ = 2 × 12 × (12 × 60) = 17 280 J. $Q = mc\Delta\theta$, so: 17280 = 3 × 500 × $\Delta\theta$, giving $\Delta\theta$ = 11.5 °C. Final temperature = 20 + 11.5 = 31.5 °C.

4  The kinetic energy is converted to heat. $E_k = \frac{1}{2}mv^2 = \frac{1}{2} \times 1400 \times 30^2 = 630\ 000$ J. $Q = mc\Delta\theta$, so 630 000 = 104 × 600 × $\Delta\theta$, giving $\Delta\theta$ = 10.1 K.

5  Energy per minute = mass per minute × c × $\Delta\theta$ = 35 × 4200 × (375 − 285) = $1.32 \times 10^7$ J/min.

6  Heat lost by copper block = heat gained by (the alcohol + aluminium can). If $T$ = final temperature then: 0.25 × 400 × (100 − $T$) = 0.15 × 2400 × ($T$ − 15) + 0.02 × 900 × ($T$ − 15) giving $T$ = 32.8 °C.

7  (a) Potential energy changed to heat = 150 × $mg\Delta h$ = 150 × 0.1 × 9.81 × 0.5 = 73.6 J. $Q = mc\Delta\theta$, so 73.6 = 0.1 × c × (15 − 12) giving c = 245 J kg$^{-1}$ K$^{-1}$.

(b) Not all the change in potential energy is changed to heat. Some is converted to sound and some also heats the glass. This results in a smaller temperature change and therefore a higher value for the specific heat capacity.

8. (a) 12 V power supply, stop clock, ammeter, voltmeter, lagging and lid.

   (b) (i) Electrical energy supplied in 800 s = $IVt$ = 5.0 × 12 × 800 = 48 000 J = Heat supplied. Heat supplied = heat absorbed by liquid + heat absorbed by calorimeter. So: 48 000 = (0.35 × $C_{liq}$ × 25) + (0.05 × 400 × 25), giving: 48 000 − 500 = 8.75 × $C_{liq}$. Therefore $C_{liq}$ = 47 500 ÷ 8.75 = 5430 J kg$^{-1}$ °C$^{-1}$. (ii) Much of the heat is lost to the environment and is not supplied to the liquid. The figure used as the heat supplied is therefore too big, so the calculated SHC is an overestimate. (iii) Wrap insulation around the calorimeter, or cool the liquid to below room temperature before beginnings.

## Exercise 4.3

1 The vertical component of the tension supports the weight. $T \sin 20$ = $W$ = 0.5 × 9.81 giving $T$ = 14.34 N. The horizontal component of the tension provides the centripetal force. $T \cos 20 = m\omega^2 r$ = 0.5 × $\omega^2$ × 0.8 cos 20, giving $\omega^2$ = 36.85 so $\omega$ = 5.99 rad s$^{-1}$. $T$ = 2π ÷ $\omega$ = 0.95 s. Therefore $f$ = $\omega$ ÷ 2π = 1.05 Hz.

2 (a) All parts of the wheel rotate with the same angular velocity of 59.6 rad s$^{-1}$.

   (b) The resultant force of the reaction force $R$ and the weight $mg$ provide the centripetal force. $R - mg = mv^2 \div r$, giving $v$ = 72 km hr$^{-1}$ = 20 m s$^{-1}$. On the point of losing contact with the road $R$ = 0, giving $mg = mv^2 \div r$. The value of the radius $r$ = 40.8 m.

3 (a) Horizontal component = $T \cos(90 - \theta)$. Vertical component = $T \sin(90 - \theta)$.

   (b) $T \cos(90 - \theta)$ provides the centripetal force. $T \sin(90 - \theta)$ supports the weight W. $T \sin(90 - \theta) = mg$. $\sin(90 - \theta)$ = 1.2 ÷ 1.5 = 0.8, so $T$ × 0.8 = 1.35 × 9.81 giving $T$ = 16.55 N.

   (c) $T \cos(90 - \theta) = mv^2 \div r$. $\cos(90 - \theta)$ = 0.9 ÷ 1.5 = 0.6, so 16.55 × 0.6 = 1.35 × $v^2$ ÷ 0.9 giving $v$ = 2.57 ms$^{-1}$.

   (d) $T$ = 2π ÷ $\omega$. $m\omega^2 r = T \cos(90 - \theta)$. So $\omega^2$ = 16.55 × 0.6 × 0.9 ÷ 1.35 giving $\omega$ = 2.57 rad s$^{-1}$ and $T$ = 2.44 s.

4 (a) 720 rpm = 720 ÷ 60 = 12 rps

   (b) $\omega$ = 2π ÷ $T$, and $T$ = 1/12 s so $\omega$ = 24π rad s$^{-1}$.

5 (a) Resultant force at B = $mg - R = mv^2 \div r$. When $R$ = 0 passengers are no longer in contact with the seat, so $mg = mv^2 \div r$ and hence $v^2 = rg$. 92 = $r$ × 9.81 giving $r$ = 8.26 m.

   (b) First calculate the velocity at the lower part using $\frac{1}{2}mv^2 = mg\Delta h$, giving $v$ = 19.8 m s$^{-1}$. Resultant force at the lower part is $R - mg = mv^2 \div r$, so $R = mg + (mv^2 \div r)$. The passenger weight appears to be the reaction force $R$. $R$ = 50 × 9.81 + (50 × 19.8$^2$ ÷ 8) = 2940 N.

## Exercise 4.4

1 (a) A particle moves with SHM if its acceleration is directly proportional to its distance from a fixed point and is always directed towards that fixed point.

   (b) (i) In both cases the acceleration is always directed towards a fixed point. (ii) For the particle moving in a circle at a constant speed, the magnitude of the acceleration is constant. For a particle moving with SHM, the magnitude of the acceleration is always changing.

2 (a) Since $a = (-)\omega^2 x$ we have: 2π = $\omega^2 A$, and since $v_{max} = \omega A$ we have: 4π = $\omega A$. Dividing $a$ by $v_{max}$ gives: $\omega$ = 0.5 s$^{-1}$. $T$ = 2π ÷ $\omega$ = 2π ÷ 0.5 = 4π s.

   (b) Since 2π = $\omega^2 A$ we have: 2π = $(0.5)^2 A$ = 0.25$A$ giving $A$ = 8π m.

3 (a) (i) Amplitude

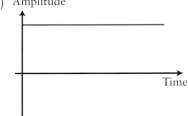

(ii) Displacement

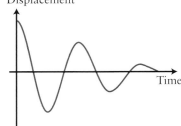

(b) (i) See Barton's pendulums on pages 55-56. (ii) Resonance occurs when a periodic driving force is of such a frequency that the amplitude of the driven system is a maximum. Condition: Resonance occurs when the frequency of the driving force is just less than the system's natural frequency.

4 (a)(i) $a = \omega^2 A = (2\pi f)^2 A = (2\pi \times 0.25)^2 \times 0.7 = 1.73$ m s$^{-2}$. $F = ma = 0.06 \times 1.73 = 0.10$ N.
(ii) $v_{max} = \omega A = (2\pi f)A = (2\pi \times 0.25) \times 0.7 = 1.10$ m s$^{-1}$.
$KE_{max} = \frac{1}{2} mv^2 = 0.5 \times 0.06 \times 1.10^2 = 0.036$ J.
(b) The comment is true. The energy of the oscillating system is decreasing because it is doing work against air resistance.

5 (a) Frequency = $1 \div$ period $= 1 \div 0.75 = 1.33$ Hz
(b) $\omega = 2\pi \div T = 8.37$ rad s$^{-1}$. $A = 2.0 \times 10^{-2}$ m. $a_{max} = \omega^2 A = 8.37^2 \times 4 \times 10^{-2} = 2.80$ m s$^{-2}$.

6 (a) Initial frequency = $1 \div T = 1 \div 0.500 = 2.00$ Hz.
(b) $\omega = 2\pi \div T = 4\pi$ rad s$^{-1}$. $a_{max} = \omega^2 A = 3.16$ ms$^{-2}$. Maximum acceleration occurs at the extremities of the motion, ie at maximum displacement.
(c) Velocity and displacement are linked by the equation $v = \pm\omega\sqrt{a^2 - x^2}$ (see pages 45 and 46). The velocity is a maximum when $x = 0$, ie at the centre of the oscillation.
$v_{max} = \omega A = 4\pi \times 2 \times 10^{-2} = 0.25$ m s$^{-1}$.
(d) $a = \omega^2 x = (4\pi)^2 \times 1.0 \times 10^{-2} = 1.58$ m s$^{-2}$.
(e) Using the equation $v = \pm\omega\sqrt{a^2 - x^2}$ gives a velocity = 0.22 m s$^{-1}$.
(f) At the lowest point the resultant upward force is $F = ma_{max} = 1.5 \times 3.16 = 4.74$ N.

7 The period of a simple pendulum is $T = 2\pi\sqrt{l \div g}$. A frequency of 0.7 Hz gives a period of 1.43 s. $1.43 = 2\pi \times \sqrt{0.35 \div g}$, giving $g = 6.76$ m s$^{-2}$.

8 (a) 500 oscillations per minute = $500 \div 60$ oscillations per second, ie frequency = 8.33 Hz.
(b)(i) At top of motion the acceleration is a maximum. $a = \omega^2 A$, $\omega = 2\pi \times$ frequency = 52.3.
$a = (52.3)^2 \times 0.1 = 273.7$ m s$^{-2}$. (ii) At the centre of he motion the displacement $x = 0$ and the acceleration = 0. (iii) At the bottom the acceleration is again a maximum = 273.7 m s$^{-2}$ but in the opposite direction to that at the top of the motion.

9 (a) $T = 2\pi\sqrt{l \div g}$. The unit of $T$ is seconds. $2\pi$ has no unit. The unit of $l$ is m$^{\frac{1}{2}}$. The unit of $2\pi\sqrt{l \div g}$ is m$^{-\frac{1}{2}}$ s$^1$. Combining the units on the right hand side gives seconds.
(b) Squaring the equation gives $T^2 = (4\pi^2 l) \div g$. Plotting $l$ on the $x$-axis with $T^2$ on the $y$-axis gives a straight line through the origin.
(c) The gradient of the line is $4\pi^2 \div g$ from which $g$ can be calculated.

10 (a) The definition of SHM is that its acceleration is proportional to its displacement from a fixed point, and the direction of the acceleration is always towards that fixed point. Hence the force is positive when the displacement is negative. Positive and negative here mean opposite directions.
(b) Amplitude = 15 mm $(1.5 \times 10^{-2}$ m).
(c) $F_{max} = 0.048 = 0.2 \times \omega^2 \times 1.5 \times 10^{-2}$ giving $\omega = 4$ rad s$^{-1}$. Period $T = 2\pi \div \omega = 1.57$ s.

11 The object will lose contact at the top of the motion at a certain frequency. The forces acting on the object are $mg - R = ma$. Loss of contact means $R = 0$. $mg = ma$, or $g = a$, so $a = 9.81$ m s$^{-2}$. $a = \omega^2 A$, $9.81 = \omega^2 \times 0.1$ giving $\omega = 9.9$ rad s$^{-1}$. Frequency $f = \omega \div 2\pi = 1.58$ Hz.

12 (a) Amplitude = 1.2 m

   (b) The period = 10.00 am to 10.25 pm = 12 hours 25 minutes = 12.42 hours.

   (c) Use $x = A \cos \omega t$, where $\omega = 2\pi \div T = 0.51$ rad s$^{-1}$. So $x = 1.2 \times \cos (0.51 \times 3) = 0.04$ m, ie 0.04 m above the centre of oscillation (remember the $\omega$ is in radians). Height above the sea bed = 0.8 + 1.2 + 0.04 = 2.04 m.

13 (a) Undamped tells us that friction is not present in a vibrating system. Damping means that friction is present in the vibrating system.

   (b) The presence of damping forces means that the total energy of the vibrating system decreases.

   (c) See pages 54 and 55.

14 See pages 55 and 56.

15 The maximum amplitude decreases as the amount of damping increases. The value of the resonant frequency decreases as the amount of damping increases.

16 See page 55.

## Exercise 4.5

1  (a) A = metal foil, B = fluorescent screen, C = microscope, D = alpha particle source.

   (b) Move microscope to a certain position, measure the angle, count the number of flashes (scintillations) in a certain time (each flash is an alpha particle), move to a new angle and repeat the observation.

   (c) Most passed through so the atom is mostly empty space. Alpha particles are positively charged so being deflected means the nucleus is also positively charged. Some are back scattered (deflected more than 90°) so the nucleus is more much more massive than the alpha particle. For example in the case of using gold as the metal the ratio of masses is approximately 200 to 4, a factor of 50.

   (d) To avoid collision with the molecules of oxygen, nitrogen and carbon dioxide in the air.

2  (a) fm = femtometre = $1.0 \times 10^{-15}$ m.

   (b) $r = kA^n$. Taking logs of both sides gives $\lg r = \lg k + n \lg A$. This is the equation of a straight line, with $\lg k$ = the intercept on the $y$-axis and $n$ = the gradient.

3  (a) $r = r_0 A^{\frac{1}{3}} = 1.2 \times 10^{-15} \times 16^{\frac{1}{3}} = 3.02 \times 10^{-15}$ m, $V = \frac{4}{3}\pi r^3 = 2.75 \times 10^{-44}$ m$^3$. $D = M \div V = (16 \times 1.66 \times 10^{-27}) \div 2.75 \times 10^{-44} = 9.66 \times 10^{17}$ kg m$^{-3}$.

   (b) Atoms are mostly empty space. The diameter of a an atom is approximately $10^{-10}$ m, giving a volume of approximately $10^{-30}$ m$^3$. The diameter of a nucleus is approximately $10^{-15}$ m, giving a volume of approximately $10^{-45}$ m$^3$, a ratio of $10^{15}$.

4  (a) $r = r_0 A^{\frac{1}{3}} = 1.2 \times 10^{-15} \times 40^{\frac{1}{3}} = 3.42 \times 10^{-15}$ m, $V = \frac{4}{3}\pi r^3 = 4.0 \times 10^{-44}$ m$^3$.

   (b) Mass – $40 \times 1.66 \times 10^{-27}$ kg, $D = M \div V = 6.64 \times 10^{-26} \div 4 \times 10^{-44} = 1.66 \times 10^{18}$ kg m$^{-3}$.

   (c) $1.66 \times 10^{18} \div 1.6 \times 10^3 \cong 10^{15}$, ie fifteen orders of magnitude (one order of magnitude means a factor of ten).

5  $r = r_0 A^{\frac{1}{3}} = 1.2 \times 10^{-15} \times 107^{\frac{1}{3}} = 5.7 \times 10^{-15}$ m. $V = \frac{4}{3}\pi (5.7 \times 10^{-17})^3 = 1.85 \times 10^{-43}$ m$^3$. Mass = mass number × mass of a nucleon = $107 \times 1.66 \times 10^{-27} = 1.78 \times 10^{-25}$ kg. $D = M \div V = 9.62 \times 10^{17}$ kg m$^{-3}$.

6  (a) Volume = $^4/_3\pi r^3$ and $r^3 = r_o^3 A$. Volume = $^4/_3\pi r_o^3 A$

   (b) Mass = mass number × mass of a nucleon = $Am$

   (c) Density = mass ÷ volume = $Am ÷ ^4/_3\pi r_o^3 A = 3m ÷ 4\pi r_o^3$. These are all constant, so the density is independent of $A$, the mass number.

7  (a) $V = ^4/_3\pi r^3$ giving $r = 6.75 \times 10^{-15}$ m. $r = r_o A^{1/3}$, giving $A = 178$.

## Exercise 4.6

1  (a) (i) In α-decay, mass number decreases by 4 and atomic number decreases by 2. (ii) In β-decay, mass number is unchanged and atomic number increases by 1.

   (b)

| Element (symbol) | Atomic number | Mass number | Decays by emitting | Leaving element |
|---|---|---|---|---|
| U | 92 | 238 | α | Th |
| Th | 90 | 234 | β | Pa |
| Pa | 91 | 234 | β | U |
| U | 92 | 234 | α | Th |
| Th | 90 | 230 | α | Ra |
| Ra | 88 | 226 | α | Rn |
| Rn | 86 | 222 | α | Po |
| Po | 84 | 218 | α | Pb |
| Pb | 82 | 214 | β | Bi |
| Bi | 83 | 214 | β | Po |

   (d) γ-ray emission changes neither atomic number nor mass number so it cannot be shown on a graph of mass number against atomic number.

   (e) (i) Uranium-238 and Uranium-234 (ii) Thorium-234 and Thorium-230

2  (a) $^{226}_{88}\text{Ra} \longrightarrow ^{222}_{86}\text{Rn} + ^4_2\text{He}$

   (b) $^{238}_{94}\text{U} \longrightarrow ^{234}_{92}\text{Th} + \alpha$

   (c) $^{87}_{37}\text{Rb} \longrightarrow ^{87}_{38}\text{Sr} + \text{e}$

3  (a) $t_{1/2} = 8.5$ minutes = 510 s. Decay constant $\lambda = 0.693 ÷ 510 = 1.36 \times 10^{-3}$ s$^{-1}$.

   (b) $A = \lambda N$, so $200 = 1.36 \times 10^{-3} \times N$ giving $N = 1.47 \times 10^5$ nuclei.

4  (a) The half-life of a radioactive material is the time taken for the activity of that material to fall to half of its original value. The decay constant is the fraction of unstable nuclei that decay per second.

   (b) $A = A_0 e^{-\lambda t}$, but from the definition of half-life, $t = T_{1/2}$.
   $A_0 ÷ 2 = A_0 e^{-\lambda T_{1/2}}$. Dividing both sides by $A_0$ and taking natural logs gives:
   $\ln 1 - \ln 2 = -\lambda T_{1/2}$. But since $\ln 1 = 0$, this gives:
   $\ln 2 = \lambda T_{1/2}$ or $T_{1/2} = \ln 2 ÷ \lambda$ (or $0.693 ÷ \lambda$ as required).

5  The half-life $t_{1/2} = 49$ days giving a decay constant = 0.014 days$^{-1}$. After 50 days the piston ring would have an activity $A = A_0 e^{-\lambda t} = 274$ Bq. The activity is proportional to the mass. An activity of 50 Bq means $50 ÷ 274 \times 0.2 = 0.04$ kg. This is the mass removed from the piston ring and deposited in the oil.

6  The half-life $t_{1/2} = 38$ days giving a decay constant $\lambda = 0.693 ÷ 38 = 0.018$ days$^{-1}$. Using $A = A_0 e^{-\lambda t}$ we have $4000 = A_0 e^{-0.018 \times 1}$ (24 hours = 1 day). This gives $A_0 = 4082$ Bq. Note that you could have converted the half-life to hours or even seconds and this would give the decay constant in hours or seconds.

7 Calculate the decay constants for each source using $\lambda = 0.693 \div t_{1/2}$. This gives $\lambda_x = 2.31 \times 10^{-2}$ s$^{-1}$ and $\lambda_y = 1.1550 \times 10^{-2}$ s$^{-1}$. Activity, $A = \lambda N$ so $A_x = 2.31 \times 10^{-2} \times N_x$ and $A_y = 1.155 \times 10^{-2} \times N_y$. Both sources have equal number of nuclei at time = 0 call this $N_0$. $N = N_0 e^{-\lambda t}$. $A_x \div A_y = N_x \div N_y$ $= (N_0 e^{-120\lambda x}) \div (N_0 e^{-120\lambda y}) = 0.25$.

8 $t_{1/2} = 1.81 \times 10^{11}$ s giving $\lambda = 3.83 \times 10^{-12}$ s$^{-1}$. $A = \lambda N$, so $5.00 \times 10^6 = 3.83 \times 10^{-12} \times N$ giving $N = 1.31 \times 10^{18}$ atoms.

9 $t_{1/2} = 5730$ years. $\lambda = 0.693 \div t_{1/2} = 1.21 \times 10^{-4}$ yr$^{-1}$. Activity is proportional to the number of nuclei, ie the mass. If the 0.2 kg sample was 1.0 kg then its activity would be $5 \times 1.5 = 7.5$ Bq. $A = A_0 e^{-\lambda t}$, so $7.5 = 20 \times e^{-1.21 \times 10^{-4} \times t}$ and $0.375 = e^{-1.21 \times 10^{-4} \times t}$. Taking natural logs of both sides we have $\ln(0.375) = -1.21 \times 10^{-4} \times t$. This gives $t = 8106$ years.

10 (a) The arrow X indicates alpha decay, the mass number decreases by 4 and the atomic number by 2. The arrow Y indicates beta decay, the mass number is unchanged and the atomic number increases by 1.

(b) The decay from Th to Z involves 4 alpha decays and 2 beta decays. 4 alpha decays means the mass number decreases by 16 and the atomic number by 8. The two beta decays have no effect on the mass number but the atomic number increases by 2. Overall A is 16 less and X is 6 less ie $^{216}_{84}$X. X is in fact an isotope of polonium (Po).

11 $t_{1/2} = 11.4$ days, $\lambda = 0.693 \div t_{1/2} = 0.061$ day$^{-1}$. Required activity = mass of patient $\times 80 \times 10^3$ $= 4.8 \times 10^6$ Bq. $A = A_0 e^{-\lambda t}$, so $4.8 \times 10^6 = A_0 e^{-0.0601 \times 1}$ giving $A_0 = 5.1 \times 10^6$ Bq.

12 $t_{1/2} = 6.0$ hr, $\lambda = 0.693 \div t_{1/2} = 0.107$ hr$^{-1}$. 140 keV $= 140 \times 1.6 \times 10^{-16} = 2.24 \times 10^{-14}$ J. $4 \times 10^6$ Bq = an energy of $8.96 \times 10^{-8}$ J. Using $A = A_0 e^{-\lambda t}$ but replacing activity with energy we have $1.0 \times 10^{-8} = 8.96 \times 10^{-8} \times e^{-0.107t}$, so $(1.0 \times 10^{-8}) \div (8.96 \times 10^8) = 0.111$. $\ln(0.111) = -0.107t$, so $-2.19 = -0.107t$ giving $t = 20.5$ hours.

13 (a) The number of decayed nuclei in a given period.
(b) The graph is a straight line of negative slope.
(c) The decay constant is approximately 0.18.
(d) The half-life is around 3.8 throws.

## Exercise 4.7

1 (a) Mass defect is the difference between the total mass of the nucleons that make up a nucleus and the mass of the nucleus when the nucleons are combined.

(b) The binding energy is the energy that must be supplied to separate the nucleons to an infinite distance.

(c) Mass defect = $(8 \times \text{mass}_{\text{proton}} + 8 \times \text{mass}_{\text{neutron}}) - \text{mass}_{\text{oxygen nucleus}}$
$= (8 \times 1.0078 \text{ u} + 8 \times 1.0087 \text{ u}) - 15.9905 \text{ u}, = 0.1415 \text{ u}$
Binding energy = $\Delta mc^2 = 0.1415 \times 1.66 \times 10^{-27} \times (3 \times 10^8)^2 = 2.11401 \times 10^{-11}$ J.
Convert to MeV: $2.11401 \times 10^{-11}$ J $\div 1.6 \times 10^{-13}$ MeV $\approx 132.13$ MeV.

(d) Average BE per nucleon = $132.13 \div 16 = 8.26$ MeV / nucleon

2 (a) Mass difference = $227.97929 - 223.97189 - 4.00151 = 0.00589$ u
(b) Mass difference = $0.00589 \times 1.66 \times 10^{-27}$ kg $= 9.7774 \times 10^{-30}$ kg.
(c) (i) Using $E = \Delta mc^2 = 9.7774 \times 10^{-30} \times (3 \times 10^8)^2 = 8.79966 \times 10^{-13}$ J.
(ii) $E = 8.79966 \times 10^{-13} \div 1.6 \times 10^{-13}$ MeV $\approx 5.5$ MeV.

(d) The energy appears mainly as the kinetic energy of the $\alpha$-particle and, to a lesser extent, the kinetic energy of the radium nucleus.

3 Mass difference = $28.97330 - (28.96880 + 0.000549) = 3.951 \times 10^{-3}$ u
$= 3.951 \times 10^{-3} \times 1.66 \times 10^{-27}$ kg $= 6.55866 \times 10^{-30}$ kg.
Energy released $= \Delta mc^2 = 6.55866 \times 10^{-30} \times (3 \times 10^8)^2 = 5.90279 \times 10^{-13}$ J.
Convert to MeV: $5.90279 \times 10^{-13}$ J $\div 1.6 \times 10^{-13}$ MeV $\approx 3.69$ MeV.

4 BE of lanthanum $= 146 \times 8.41 = 1227.86$ MeV. BE of bromine $= 87 \times 8.59 = 747.33$ MeV.
Total BE after fission $= 1227.86 + 747.33 = 1975.19$ MeV. BE of uranium-236 $= 236 \times 7.59$
$= 1791.24$ MeV. Energy released = increase in BE $= 1975.19 - 1791.24 = 183.95$ MeV
$\approx 184$ MeV.

5 (a) 1 kg of fuel contains 30 grams of uranium-235, which contains $30 N_A \div 235$ uranium-235
atoms. So, 1 kg of fuel contains $(30 \times 6.02 \times 10^{23}) \div 235 = 7.69 \times 10^{22}$ uranium-235 atoms.
(b) Energy released by fission of all uranium-235 nuclei is $7.69 \times 10^{22} \times 3 \times 10^{-11}$ J $= 2.307 \times 10^{12}$ J.
Time = energy $\div$ power $= 2.307 \times 10^{12} \div 500\,000 = 4\,614\,000$ s $= 53.4$ days.

6 Combined mass of 3 protons and 4 neutrons $= 3 \times 1.008 + 4 \times 1.009 = 7.060$ u. Mass defect
= mass of separate nucleons – mass of lithium nucleus $= 7.060 - 7.018 = 0.042$ u.
Binding energy $= 0.042 \times 932$ MeV $= 39.1$ MeV.

7 (a) $^6_3\text{Li} + {}^2_1\text{H} \longrightarrow 2\,{}^4_2\text{He}$
(b)(i) 3.6 pJ $= 3.6 \times 10^{-12}$ J $= (3.6 \times 10^{-12} \div 1.6 \times 10^{-13})$ MeV $= 22.5$ MeV. (ii) There are 8 fuel
nucleons (6 from lithium and 2 from deuterium), so energy released per nucleon $= 22.5 \div 8$
$= 2.8$ MeV per nucleon. (iii) 32 pJ $= 32 \times 10^{-12}$ J $= (32 \times 10^{-12} \div 1.6 \times 10^{-13})$ MeV $= 200$ MeV.
Energy released per nucleon in fission $= 200 \div 235 = 0.85$ MeV per nucleon. So more than 3
times as much energy is released per nucleon in fusion than in fission.
(c) There are no very long-lived radioactive waste products in fusion, unlike fission. There is an
almost inexhaustible supply of fuel for fusion, unlike fission.

8 Mass difference $= (6.0151 + 1.0087) - (4.0026 + 3.0160) = 0.0052$ u.
$\Delta m = 0.0052 \times 1.66 \times 10^{-27}$ kg. $E = \Delta mc^2 = 7.7 \times 10^{-13}$ J.

9 (a)(i) Mass of 2 protons $= 2.01456$ u; mass of 2 neutrons $= 2.01734$ u; mass of electrons
$= 0.00110$ u. So total mass of constituents $= 4.03300$ u. Mass difference $=$
$4.03300 - 4.00260 = 0.0304$ u $= 0.0304 \times 1.66 \times 10^{-27}$ kg $= 5.0464 \times 10^{-29}$ kg. (ii) Mass defect.
(b) Energy required $= mc^2 = 5.0464 \times 10^{-29} \times (3 \times 10^8)^2 = 4.54176 \times 10^{-12}$ J = KE of neutron. Speed
of neutron $= (2 \times \text{KE} \div m)^{1/2} = (2 \times 4.54176 \times 10^{-12} \div 1.00867 \times 1.66 \times 10^{-27})^{1/2} = 7.37 \times 10^7$ m s$^{-1}$.

10 You re-write the equation as a mass / energy equation. $^2_1\text{H} + {}^2_1\text{H} \longrightarrow {}^4_2\text{He} + \text{energy} + {}^1_0\text{n}$.
Energy release $= 3.28$ MeV $= 5.25 \times 10^{-13}$ J. Using $E = \Delta mc^2$ gives $\Delta m = 5.83 \times 10^{-30}$ kg
$= 0.0035120$ u. So: mass of neutron $= 2.014102 + 2.014102 - 3.016030 - 0.0035120$
$= 1.0086620$ u. Convert to kg: $1.0086620 \times 1.66 \times 10^{-27} = 1.6743 \times 10^{-27}$ kg.

11 W = 4, X = 56, Y = 90

12 (a) $^{235}_{92}\text{U} + {}^1_0\text{n} \longrightarrow {}^{236}_{92}\text{U} \longrightarrow {}^{141}_{56}\text{Ba} + {}^{92}_{36}\text{Kr} + 3\,{}^1_0\text{n}$
(b) Kinetic energy of the fission fragments, ie the Ba and Kr nuclei plus the fission neutrons
emitted.
(c) Similar to the solution to question 10 above, write down a mass / energy equation.
$3\,{}^1_0\text{n} - {}^1_0\text{n} = 2\,{}^1_0\text{n} = (235.0439 - 91.9265 - 140.9143)$ u $+ 173.2$ MeV
173.2 MeV $= 173.2 \times 1.6 \times 10^{-13}$ J. Using $E = \Delta mc^2$ this is equivalent to 0.184 u.
So $2\,{}^1_0\text{n} = 2.024$ u. The mass of $^1_0\text{n} = 2.024 \div 2 = 1.012$ u $= 1.69 \times 10^{-27}$ kg.

13 6.0438 u $+$ 8.0696 u $= 14.1134$. Mass defect $= 0.1102$ u, giving energy $= 102.7$ MeV.

14 (a) Energy radiated in 1 year = $3.8 \times 10^{26} \times 3.16 \times 10^7 = 1.20 \times 10^{34}$ J. Mass lost in 1 year = $E \div c^2$
= $1.20 \times 10^{34} \div (3 \times 10^8)^2 = 1.33 \times 10^{17}$ kg. 0.5% of star's mass = $0.005 \times 2 \times 10^{30} = 1 \times 10^{28}$ kg.
So time to lose $1 \times 10^{28}$ kg = $1 \times 10^{28} \div 1.33 \times 10^{17} = 7.5 \times 10^{10}$ years.

(b) Kinetic energy of a hydrogen atom $\frac{1}{2}m<c^2> = 1.5\,kT$, so:
$<c^2> = 3kT \div m = (3 \times 1.38 \times 10^{-23} \times 6000) \div (1.67 \times 10^{-27})$ and hence $\sqrt{<c^2>} = 12\,000$ m s$^{-1}$.

15 Sum of masses on LHS = $235.0439 + 1.0087 = 236.0526$ u.
Sum of masses on RHS = $91.8976 + 140.9136 + 3 \times 1.0087 = 235.8373$ u.
Reduction in mass = $236.0526 - 235.8373 = 0.2153$ u = $(0.2153 \times 1.66 \times 10^{-27})$ kg
= $3.57398 \times 10^{-28}$ kg.
Energy released = $mc^2 = 3.57398 \times 10^{-28} \times 9 \times 10^{16}$ J = $3.21658 \times 10^{-11}$ J
= $3.21658 \times 10^{-11} \div 1.6 \times 10^{-13}$ MeV = 201 MeV.

## Exercise 4.8

1 The **critical size** is the minimum size of a nuclear reactor core so that sufficient numbers of neutrons are retained within the reactor core to sustain the chain reaction. The critical size must at least include enough fissionable material to reach a critical mass. If the size of the reactor core is less than a certain minimum, too many neutrons escape the chain reaction stops. A **chain reaction** refers to a process in which neutrons released in the fission of a nucleus go on to cause further fissions with the release of even more neutrons. The process may be controlled as in a nuclear power station, or uncontrolled in the case of a nuclear bomb. The **moderator** is a material that reduces the speed of fast neutrons. Uranium-235 undergoes fission with the slower neutrons sometimes termed thermal neutrons. **Control rods** are used to change the fission rate of uranium and plutonium. They are composed of elements such as boron or cadmium that are capable of absorbing many neutrons without themselves undergoing fission. **Coolants** are used to capture and transfer the heat released by fission. This heat then used to produce steam which in turn drives turbines to generate electricity.

2 KE after a collision = 0.7 KE before collision.
Consider the 1$^{st}$ collision KE$_{after}$ = 0.7 KE$_{before}$ = $0.7 \times 1.0 \times 10^6$ eV.
Consider the 2$^{nd}$ collision KE$_{after}$ = $0.7 \times 0.7 \times 1.0 \times 10^6$ eV.
Consider the $n$th collision KE$_{after}$ = $0.7^n \times 1.0 \times 10^6$ eV.
We know that after the $n$th collision the energy has to be less than 1 eV. Therefore:
$1.0 = 0.7^n \times 1.0 \times 10^6$, giving $n = 39$ collisions.

3 (a) Environmental **Advantages** of nuclear power: • Emits low amounts of carbon dioxide so no contribution to global warming. • Less carbon dioxide than that of fossil fuels. • Emits little or no sulphur dioxide so no contribution to acid rain. Environmental **Disadvantages** of nuclear power: • Like fossil fuels, nuclear fuels are non-renewable energy resources. • If an accident should happen large amounts of radioactive material could be released into the environment. • Nuclear waste remains radioactive and is hazardous to health for thousands of years.

(b) Concerns of society: • Storage of radioactive waste. • Dangers associated with a nuclear accident. • Issues associated with a possible terrorist attack on a power station.

4 (a) The high temperature gives the hydrogen nuclei enough energy to overcome the electrical repulsion between the protons. At these temperatures, hydrogen is a plasma, a collection of protons and electrons. Atoms do not exist at these high temperatures.

(b) In ITER, different types of magnetic fields combine to shape the plasma into the form of a ring, or torus. This is meant to isolate the very hot plasma from vessel walls in order to retain the energy for as long as possible.

(c) Gravitational forces confine the plasma. This requires a very large mass, eg the mass of the Sun is around $1.9 \times 10^{30}$ kg and the mass of the Earth $6 \times 10^{24}$ kg.

5  (a) A nuclear reaction in which atomic nuclei of low atomic number fuse to form a heavier nucleus with the release of energy.

(b) This a reaction you should be able to recall in an exam. A nucleus of deuterium (D) fuses with a nucleus of tritium (T) to form a helium nucleus (He) and a neutron together with the release of energy: $^{2}_{1}D + ^{3}_{1}T \rightarrow ^{4}_{2}He + ^{1}_{0}n$.

(c) Any two from these three: 1. This produces a greater energy release than other similar reactions. 2. There is plentiful supply of deuterium from sea water and tritium from lithium. 3. Limited waste products (neutron irradiated materials) so no long term storage required.

6  (a) A tokamak is today's best investigated fusion device design. It is a torus-shaped (donut) vacuum chamber surrounded by magnetic coils, which create a toroidal magnetic field.

(b) Plasma heating in the ITER tokamak consists of: 1. Induced current by electromagnetic induction, allowing the electrons and ions to gain energy. However as the plasma heats up its resistance increases and so the heating effect of the current is reduced. 2. Deuterium ions are accelerated into the plasma and on the way they gain electrons so become neutral. They collide with the particles in the plasma and transfer energy to them. 3. High energy microwaves transfer energy directly to the particles in the plasma.

(c) High-energy neutrons produced by the fusion reactions are slowed in the blanket. Their kinetic energy is transformed into heat energy and collected by the water coolant. In a fusion power plant, this energy would be used for electrical power production.

## Exercise 5.2

1  $F = Gm_1m_2 \div r^2$, so: $G = Fr^2 \div m_1m_2$. So the unit for $G$ is N m$^2$ kg$^{-2}$. The base unit of N is kg m s$^{-2}$. So in base units $G$ is measured in kg m s$^{-2}$ m$^2$ kg$^{-2}$. This simplifies to give $G$ kg$^{-1}$ m$^3$ s$^{-2}$.

2  (a) Centripetal force $= mv^2 \div r = 9.11 \times 10^{-31} \times (2.2 \times 10^6)^2 \div 50 \times 10^{-12} = 8.82 \times 10^{-8}$ N

(b) Gravitational force $= Gm_1m_2 \div r^2 = 6.67 \times 10^{-11} \times 9.11 \times 10^{-31} \times 1.66 \times 10^{-27} \div (50 \times 10^{-12})^2$
$= 4.03 \times 10^{-47}$ N. Comment: The gravitational force is very much smaller than the centripetal force; the gravitational force can be ignored when considering the force causing the electron to circle the proton in hydrogen.

3  $g = F \div m = 180$ N $\div 5$ kg $= 36$ N kg$^{-1}$.

4  (a) Halving the distance quadruples the force, so $F = 36 \times 4 = 144$ N.
(b) Trebling the distance reduces the force to 1/9th of its former value. So $F = 144 \div 9 = 16$ N.

5

| Force / N | 4.0 | 2.6 | 1.8 | 1.3 | 1.0 | 0.79 |
|---|---|---|---|---|---|---|
| $1/r^2$ / m$^{-2}$ $\times 10^{-13}$ | 2.5 | 1.6 | 1.1 | 0.8 | 0.6 | 0.5 |

(a) See row for $1/r^2$ above. Graph of force $F$ (vertical axis) against $1/r^2$ is a straight line through the origin of gradient $1.6 \times 10^{13}$ N m$^2$, showing that $F$ is inversely proportional to $r^2$.

(b) The gradient of the graph ($1.6 \times 10^{13}$ N m$^2$) is equal to $GM_p$, where $M_p$ is the mass of the planet. At the surface, force on 1 kg $= GM_p \div R_p^2 = g = 5$. So gradient $= 5 R_p^2$.
So, $R_p = \sqrt{(1.6 \times 10^{13} \div 5)} = 1.8 \times 10^6$ m.

6  $F = GM_s M_E \div r^2 = M_E r\omega^2$ where $\omega$ is the angular velocity of the Earth's orbit so $GM_s = r^3\omega^2$.
   $G = (4\pi^2 r^3) \div (M_s T^2)$ where $T$ is the period of the Earth's orbit.
   $G = (4\pi^2\{1.5\times10^{11}\}^3) \div \{2\times10^{30} \times (365.25 \times 24 \times 3600)^2\} = (1.332\times10^{35}) \div (1.992\times10^{45})$
   $= 6.69\times10^{-11}$ N m$^2$ kg$^{-2}$.

7  $F = GM_1 M_2 \div r^2 = 6.67\times10^{-11} \times 2 \times 3 \div 2^2 = 1.0005\times10^{-10}$ N. If friction can be ignored,
   then $a = F \div m$. This gives acceleration of the 2 kg mass $= 5.00\times10^{-11}$ m s$^{-2}$ and the acceleration
   of 3 kg mass $= 3.33\times10^{-11}$ m s$^{-2}$.

8  Let the distance from the Sun to the neutral point be $d$. Then the distance from Jupiter to
   neutral point is $(7.8\times10^{11} - d)$. At the neutral point the gravitational field due to the Sun is
   equal to that due to Jupiter. So: $GM_s \div d^2 = GM_j \div (7.8\times10^{11} - d)^2$. Cancelling $G$, substituting,
   and taking the square root of both sides and simplifying gives:
   $\sqrt{(1.9\times10^{27})}\, d = \sqrt{(2\times10^{30})} \times (7.8\times10^{11} - d)$. So: $4.3589\times10^{13}\, d = 1.1031\times10^{27} - 1.4142\times10^{15}\, d$.
   This gives $d = (1.1031\times10^{27}) \div (4.3589\times10^{13} + 1.4142\times10^{15}) = 7.57\times10^{11}$ m.

9  From Kepler's third law, $T_p = \sqrt{(T_E^2 \times r_p^3 \div r_E^3)} = \sqrt{(1^2 \times 630^3 \div 1^3)} = 15\ 813$ years.

10 (a) According to Kepler's third law, the relationship between $T$ and $r$ is: $T^2 = kr^3$. Taking logs
   gives: $\log T = 0.5 \log k + 1.5 \log r$. So a graph of $\log T$ ($y$-axis) against $\log r$ is a straight line
   of gradient 1.5 and with an intercept on the vertical axis. Figures as below:

| Planet | A | B | C | D | E |
|---|---|---|---|---|---|
| Log (r / m) | 12.00 | 12.18 | 12.35 | 12.54 | 12.70 |
| Log (T / s) | 9.00 | 9.26 | 9.53 | 9.82 | 10.05 |

   Using these data the gradient is approximately 1.5, depending on the line of best fit. This
   gradient confirms Kepler's third law. The intercept on the vertical axis is approximately –9.
   (b) $T^2 = (4\pi^2 \div GM_s) \times r^3$ (see page 107). The intercept is therefore $0.5 \times \log (4\pi^2 \div GM_s) = -9$.
   Hence $(4\pi^2 \div GM_s) = 10^{-18}$, so $M_s = (4\pi^2 \div G \times 10^{-18}) = 5.9\times10^{29}$ kg (approx).

## Exercise 5.3

1  $F = \dfrac{mv^2}{r} = \dfrac{Q_1 Q_2}{4\pi\varepsilon_0 r^2}$. Rearranging gives: $r = \dfrac{Q_1 Q_2}{4\pi\varepsilon_0 mv^2} = \dfrac{1.6\times10^{-19} \times 1.6\times10^{-19}}{4\pi \times 8.85\times10^{-12} \times 9.11\times10^{-31} \times (2.2\times10^6)^2}$
   $= 5.22\times10^{-11}$ m

2  $E = \dfrac{Q}{4\pi\varepsilon_0 r^2}$. Rearranging and substituting gives: $Q = 4\pi \times (8.85\times10^{-12}) \times 1^2 \times 1 = 1.11\times10^{-10}$ C.

3  Suppose the distance from the smaller charge to the neutral point is $d$. The distance from the
   neutral point to the larger charge is therefore $(1 - d)$. At this point the field due to the +5 C is
   equal to the field due to +3 C.
   Using $E = \dfrac{Q}{4\pi\varepsilon_0 r^2}$ we have: $\dfrac{3}{4\pi\varepsilon_0 d^2} = \dfrac{5}{4\pi\varepsilon_0 (1 - d)^2}$.
   Cancelling the $4\pi\varepsilon_0$ and taking square roots of both sides gives: $\dfrac{\sqrt{3}}{d} = \dfrac{\sqrt{5}}{1 - d}$
   Rearranging gives: $(\sqrt{5} + \sqrt{3})d = \sqrt{3}$, so $d = 0.44$ m (from the +3 C charge).

4  (a) The electric field between the plates $= V \div d = 200 \div 0.04 = 5000$ V m$^{-1}$. The force on a
   proton *anywhere* in this field is $E_q = 5000 \times 1.6\times10^{-19} = 8\times10^{-16}$ N. The direction of the force
   is the same as that of the field (away from the positive plate and towards the negative plate).
   (b) The size and direction of the force would remain unchanged.

5  The acceleration is uniform since the force is constant in size and direction. From Newton's
   equations of motion, $a = -u^2 \div 2s = -(1\times10^{12}) \div 0.8 = -1.25\times10^{12}$ m s$^{-2}$. The minus sign only
   indicates the direction of the acceleration and will be ignored from this point onwards. The

force on the electron = $ma = 9.11 \times 10^{-31} \times 1.25 \times 10^{12} = 1.14 \times 10^{-18}$ N. From the definition of electric field, $E = F \div q = 1.14 \times 10^{-18} \div 1.6 \times 10^{-19} = 7.12$ N C$^{-1}$.

6  Assume that C, the apex of the triangle, is above AB. Since the charges are of the same sign and equal in magnitude, the horizontal components of the field produced by each charge at C will cancel out. Each charge will produce an electric field at C of:

$$E = \frac{Q}{4\pi\varepsilon_0 r^2} = \frac{5 \times 10^{-9}}{4\pi \times 8.85 \times 10^{-12} \times (0.01)^2} = 4495.9 \text{ N C}^{-1}.$$

The upwards vertical component of this field is $E \sin 60° = 3893.6$ N C$^{-1}$. The two vertical components therefore produce a combined field of 7787 N C$^{-1}$ or approximately 7790 N C$^{-1}$.

7  (a) $F$ = horizontal component of tension in string = $3 \times 10^{-4} \times \sin 30° = 1.5 \times 10^{-4}$ N.

   (b) Since repulsion between the two spheres with the same charge provides this force:

   $F = \dfrac{Q^2}{4\pi\varepsilon_0 r^2}$. Substituting and re-arranging gives:

   $Q^2 = 4\pi\varepsilon_0 r^2 F = 4\pi \times 8.85 \times 10^{-12} \times 0.04^2 \times 1.5 \times 10^{-4} = 2.669 \times 10^{-17}$, giving $Q = 5.17$ nC.

   (c) Zero.

8  (a) $E = (-) V \div d = 1.6$ kV $\div 0.04 = 40$ kV m$^{-1}$.

   (b) Upper plate is at a positive potential and the electric field is vertically downwards.

   (c) Since the vertical forces are in equilibrium, $Eq = mg$, so:

   $q = mg \div E = 3.84 \times 10^{-14} \div 40 \times 10^3 = 9.6 \times 10^{-19}$ C.

   Number of electrons = charge on oil drop ÷ charge on 1 electron

   $= 9.6 \times 10^{-19}$ C $\div 1.6 \times 10^{-19}$ C = 6 excess electrons.

## Exercise 5.4

1  (a) Connect the three 4 μF capacitors in series. $\dfrac{1}{C} = \dfrac{1}{C_1} + \dfrac{1}{C_2} + \dfrac{1}{C_3} = \dfrac{3}{4}$. So $C = \dfrac{4}{3} = 1.33$ μF.

   (b) Connect two 4 μF capacitors in series and across that combination place a 4 μF capacitor in parallel. The two 4 μF capacitors in series have a combined capacitance of 2 μF. Connecting 4 μF in parallel with this gives a combined capacitance C where C = 2 + 4 = 6 μF.

2  Between X and Y the combined capacitance is 1.5 μF. ($\dfrac{1}{C} = \dfrac{1}{2} + \dfrac{1}{6} = \dfrac{4}{6}$ giving C = 1.5 μF.)

   Between Y and Z the combined capacitance is 2.4 μF. ($\dfrac{1}{C} = \dfrac{1}{6} + \dfrac{1}{4} = \dfrac{5}{12}$ giving C = 2.4 μF.

   Between X and Z the combined capacitance is 1.33 μF. ($\dfrac{1}{C} = \dfrac{1}{2} + \dfrac{1}{4} = \dfrac{4}{6}$ giving C = 1.33 μF.)

   So there is maximum capacitance between Y and Z.

3  (a) Two 10 μF capacitors in series have a combined capacitance of 5 μF. Two 5 μF capacitors in parallel have a combined capacitance of 10 μF. So between X and P the capacitance is 10 μF. Between P and Y the capacitance is also 10 μF. So between X and Y the total capacitance is 5 μF.

   (b) Each pathway from X to Y has four 10 μF capacitors in series, of total capacitance 2.5 μF. The two pathways are identical and are in parallel. So their combined capacitance is 5 μF.

4  Suppose the capacitance of each capacitor is C. Then the capacitance of each pathway from X to Y is $C \div 2$ (two capacitors in series). There are three pathways in parallel, each of capacitance $C \div 2$. So the total capacitance of the network is $3C \div 2$. So $3C \div 2 = 33$ μF, giving $C = 22$ μF.

5  (a) 1 μF capacitor: $V = Q \div C = 1.5 \times 10^{-9} \div 1 \times 10^{-6} = 1.5 \times 10^{-3}$ V = 1.5 mV.

   100 pF capacitor: $V = Q \div C = 1.5 \times 10^{-9} \div 100 \times 10^{-12} = 15$ V.

(b) 1 µF capacitor: $E = \frac{1}{2}CV^2 = 0.5 \times 1\times10^{-6} \times 0.0015^2 = 1.125\times10^{-12}$ J.
100 pF capacitor: $E = \frac{1}{2}CV^2 = 0.5\times100\times10^{-12} \times 15^2 = 1.125\times10^{-8}$ J.

6  (a) Charge initially on $C_1 = CV = 12\times10^{-6} \times 400 = 4.8\times10^{-3}$ C = 4.8 mC. Combined capacitance of $C_1$ and $C_2$ in parallel = 12 + 4 = 16 µF. The p.d. across each capacitor is therefore $V = Q \div C = 4.8\times10^{-3} \div 16\times10^{-6} = 300$ V. So charge remaining on $C_1 = CV = 12\times10^{-6} \times 300 = 3.6\times10^{-3}$ C = 3.6 mC

(b) When capacitors are connected in parallel the p.d. across each is the same, so the charge stored in each is proportional to the capacitance of each capacitor. Since this is in the ratio of 3:1, the charge removed each time $C_2$ is disconnected is 25% of the combined charge which is stored. After $n$ connections and disconnections, the total charge remaining on $C_1$ (in mC) is $4.8 \times (0.75)^n$. The table shows how the charge in $C_1$ changes with the number of discharges.

| Charge stored in mC | 4.80 | 3.60 | 2.70 | 2.03 |
|---|---|---|---|---|
| Number of discharges, $n$ | 0 | 1 | 2 | 3 |

It therefore requires 3 discharges to bring the charge stored in $C_1$ to below 50% of its initial value of 4.8 mC.

7  (a) The 5 µF and 25 µF capacitors are in parallel.

(b) The parallel arrangement adds to 30 µF. So there are 10 µF and 30 µF in series.
$\frac{1}{C} = \frac{1}{C_1} + \frac{1}{C_2} = \frac{1}{10} + \frac{1}{30} = \frac{4}{30}$, giving C = 7.5 µF.

(c) $E = \frac{1}{2}CV^2 = 0.5 \times 7.5\times10^{-6} \times 12^2 = 5.4\times10^{-4}$ J.

8  (a) $V = Q \div C = 4.8\times10^{-3} \div 300\times10^{-6} = 16$ V. $E = \frac{1}{2}CV^2 = 0.5 \times 300\times10^{-6} \times 16^2 = 0.0384$ J.

(b) Total capacitance when S is closed is 800 µF. Total charge stored = $4.8\times10^{-3}$ C.
So p.d., $V = Q \div C = 4.8\times10^{-3} \div 800\times10^{-6} = 6$ V.

9  (a) See graph on right.

(b) The time constant, $\tau$, is the product of resistance and capacitance and is the time taken for the voltage across the capacitor to fall to 37% of the original value ($V_0 \div e$).

(c) Time constant $\tau = RC = 22\times10^6 \times 47\times10^{-9} = 1.034$ s
Since $V = V_0 e^{-t/\tau}$, $\ln V = \ln V_0 - t \div \tau$, so
$t = \tau \times \ln(V_0 \div V) = 1.034 \times \ln(1 \div 0.14) = 2.03$ s approximately. (Readers will also see from page 129 that the approximate time to decay to 14% of the original value is 2 time constants.)

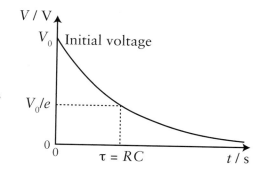

10 (a)

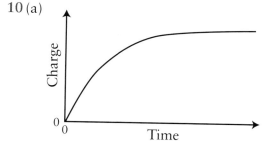

(b)

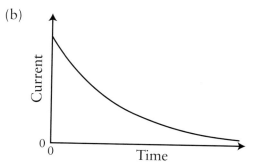

11 (a) See diagram on right.

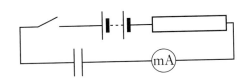

   (b) $I = V \div R = 20 \div 10\,000 = 2 \times 10^{-3}$ A = 2 mA.

   (c) $\tau = RC = 10\,000 \times 470 \times 10^{-6} = 4.7$ s.

   (d) When discharging, $I = I_o e^{-t/\tau}$, $\ln I = \ln I_o - t \div \tau$, so:

     $t = \tau \times \ln(I_o \div I) = 4.7 \times \ln(4) = 6.5$ s approximately.

12 (a) The straight line graph is $\ln (I / \text{mA})$ ($y$-axis) against $t / s$ ($x$-axis).

| Time / s | 0 | 5 | 10 | 15 | 20 | 25 | 30 | 35 |
|---|---|---|---|---|---|---|---|---|
| $I$ / mA | 72 | 54 | 41 | 31 | 23 | 17 | 13 | 10 |
| $\ln (I / \text{mA})$ | 4.28 | 3.99 | 3.71 | 3.43 | 3.14 | 2.83 | 2.56 | 2.30 |

   The graph has an intercept of 4.28 on the vertical axis and a gradient of $-1/\tau$. The gradient of the graph is approximately $-5.66 \times 10^{-2}$ s$^{-1}$.

   (b) $R = -1 \div (C \times \text{gradient}) = -1 \div \{8 \times 10^{-6} \times (-5.66 \times 10^{-2})\} = 2.2$ MΩ approximately.

13 (a) $E = \frac{1}{2}CV^2$, so $100 = 0.5 \times 50 \times 10^{-6} \times V^2$. So $V^2 = 4 \times 10^6$, giving $V = 2000$ V.

   (b) Charge supplied $Q = VC = 2000 \times 50 \times 10^{-6} = 0.1$ C.

     Average current = charge supplied ÷ time = $0.1 \div 3 = 0.033$ A = 33 mA.

   (c) Power = $IV = 0.033 \times 2000 = 66$ W.

   (d) Consider three 50 μF capacitors in series with each other with 1500 V across the combination. The p.d. across each capacitor would be 500 V and the capacitance of the combination would be 50/3 μF. Now, three such series combinations in parallel with each other would have a combined capacitance of 50 μF with 500 V across each individual capacitor.

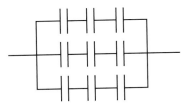

14 Energy = average power × time = $1.5 \times 10^4 \times 20 \times 10^{-6} = 0.3$ J.

   $E = \frac{1}{2}CV^2$, so $0.3 = 0.5 \times 47 \times 10^{-6} \times V^2$. So $V^2 = 1.277 \times 10^4$, giving $V = 113$ V.

15 (a) $I = V \div R = 1.5 \div 500\,000 = 3$ μA.

   (b) $Q = VC = 1.5 \times 250 \times 10^{-6} = 3.75 \times 10^{-4}$ C.

   (c) $E = \frac{1}{2}CV^2 = 0.5 \times 250 \times 10^{-6} \times 1.5^2 = 2.81 \times 10^{-4}$ J.

16 (a) The 47 μF marking means that in normal use the ratio of the charge stored in coulombs to the potential difference across the capacitor in volts is $47 \times 10^{-6}$ CV$^{-1}$. The 12 V marking means that the capacitor is designed to be used at 12 V and below. Above 12 V the insulator (dielectric) between the metal plates starts to break down and charge will leak from one side of the capacitor to the other.

   (b) Connect 3 of the capacitors in series with each other. Do this three times in total. Now connect the three series combinations in parallel with each other. The total capacitance is 2 mF and the maximum voltage across each is 200 V.

17 Since $Q = CV$, the charge stored in the combination of capacitors in parallel is 6C. The combined capacitance of the capacitors in parallel is $(C + 47 \times 10^{-6})$. Since the combined voltage is 4 V and $Q = CV$, we have $6C = (C + 47 \times 10^{-6}) \times 4$. Dividing by 4 gives: $1.5C = C + 47 \times 10^{-6}$. Hence, $C = 94 \times 10^{-6}$ F = 94 μF.

18 First connect the 3 mF and the 6 mF capacitors in series with each other. This gives a total of 2 mF. Now connect the 9 mF capacitor in parallel with the series combination. This gives a total of 11 mF.

19 Charge which leaks away is $CV = 30 \times 10^{-6} \times 4 = 120$ μC.

   Average leakage current = charge ÷ time = 120 μC ÷ 60 s = 2 μA.

20 (a) The time constant, $\tau = RC = 100 \times 10^6 \times 1 \times 10^{-6} = 100$ s. Since $V = V_o e^{-t/\tau}$:
$\ln V = \ln V_o - t \div \tau$, so $t = \tau \times \ln(V_o \div V) = 100 \times \ln(200 \div 100) = 69.3$ s (approximately).

(b) Additional time, $t = \tau \times \ln(V_o \div V) = 100 \times \ln(100 \div 50) = 69.3$ s. The time taken for the voltage to fall from 200 V to 100 V (ie by 50%) is the same as the time taken to fall from 100 V to 50 V (also 50%). It is a characteristic of an exponential decal that the time taken for the voltage to fall by the same ratio is constant. Readers should recall that this is used in radioactive decay, where the time taken for the activity to fall by 50% is constant and known as the half-life.

(c) Since 200 s represents 2 time constants, the voltage after 200 s is $V_o \div e^2 = 200 \div e^2$ = approximately 27.1 V.

## Exercise 5.5

1 (a) Current is in direction X to Y (Fleming's left hand rule).
(b) $I = F \div BL = (0.8 \times 10^{-3} \times 9.81) \div (2 \times 10^{-5} \times 1.2) = 327$ A.

2 (a) Force on conductor is upwards in plane of page, perpendicular to horizontal line between the magnet's poles.
(b) $B = F \div IL = (1.44 \times 10^{-3}) \div (2.40 \times 0.04) = 0.015$ T = 15 mT.

3 The induced e.m.f. is equal to the negative of the rate of change of magnetic flux linkage, this is the negative of the gradient of the graph shown.
Time 0 s to 2 s, e.m.f.. = $-2 \div 2 = -1$ V.     Time 2 s to 3 s, e.m.f. = 0 V.
Time 3 s to 4 s, e.m.f.. = $-(-4 \div 1) = +4$ V.    Time 4 s to 7 s, e.m.f. = 0 V.
Time 7 s to 8 s, e.m.f.. = $-6 \div 1 = -6$ V.     Time 8 s to 9 s, e.m.f. = 0 V.
Time 9 s to 13 s, e.m.f.. = $-(-4 \div 4) = +1$ V.

4 $E = BA \div t = BLv$. Speed of blood = $E \div BL = 0.0003 \div (0.060 \times 0.01) = 0.5$ ms$^{-1}$. Note that there is considerable uncertainty in this method as the speed of the blood is different across the artery.

5 (a) $\omega = 2\pi f = 2 \times \pi \times 50 = 314$ radians s$^{-1}$.
(b) Maximum flux = $BAN$. Maximum e.m.f. = $BAN\omega = 325$ V.
Maximum flux = maximum emf $\div \omega = 325 \div 314 = 1.04$ Wb-turns.

6 (a) Change in flux in 5 seconds = $\Delta B \times A \times N = -0.9 \times (25 \times 10^{-4}) \times 1000 = -2.25$ Wb-turns.
Induced e.m.f. = $-$rate of change of flux linkage = $-(-2.25 \div 5) = 0.45$ V.
Current = $V \div R = 0.45 \div 9 = 0.05$ A.

(b) Current does not change direction because rate of change of flux linkage is constant throughout.

7 (a) A sinusoidal input voltage to the primary coil causes a magnetic field around that coil which varies sinusoidally. The iron core links the primary and secondary coils magnetically, resulting in a magnetic field around the secondary coil which also varies sinusoidally. This means there is a changing magnetic flux linked with the secondary coil. This changing magnetic flux causes an e.m.f. to be induced across the terminals of the secondary coil.

(b) Step-down. $N_P \div N_S = V_P \div V_S$, where $V_P$ and $V_S$ are the voltages at the primary and secondary coils respectively.

8 (a) Using the turns ratio $N_P \div N_S = V_P \div V_S = 11$ kV $\div 275$ kV = 0.04.
(b) Assuming a 100% efficiency means input power = output power.
Input power = $176 \times 10^6$ W = $11 \times 10^3 \times I_P$ giving $I_P = 16\,000$ A.
Output power = $176 \times 10^6$ W = $275 \times 10^3 \times I_S$ giving $I_S = 640$ A.

(c) 2% of the power generated = $3.52\times10^6$ W. Power loss = $I^2R$, where $R$ is the resistance of the transmission lines. So: $3.52\times10^6 = 640^2 \times R$, giving $R = 8.6\ \Omega$.

(d) Power losses result from: • Resistance of the windings of both coils. • Not all the magnetic flux from the primary coil passes through the secondary coil. • Repeatedly reversing the direction of magnetisation of the core generates heat as large currents (eddy currents) are induced in the core, which heats up the coils and increase their resistance so causing even more energy loss.

## Exercise 5.6

1  (a) The time spent in the field is $L \div v$ where $L$ is the horizontal length of the plate and $v$ is the horizontal component of the particle's velocity. Neither of these change as the particle moves through the field.

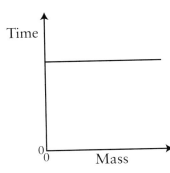

(b) Since vertical velocity $v = at = qVt \div dm$:
Increase in KE = $\frac{1}{2}mv^2 = \frac{1}{2}q^2V^2t^2 \div d^2m = k't^2$ where $k'$ is a constant.
KE = initial KE + $k't^2$ (for further information and identification of symbol meanings, see page 162).

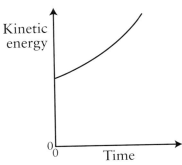

2  (a) $F = ma = 6.40\times10^{-25} \times 1.60\times10^{11} = 1.02\times10^{-13}$ N.
(b) $E = F \div q = 1.02\times10^{-13} \div 3.20\times10^{-19} = 3.20\times10^5$ N C$^{-1}$.

3  (a) P.d. between plates = $Ed = 2500 \times 20\times10^{-3} = 50$ V. Since $\frac{1}{2}mv^2 = eV$:
$v^2 = 2eV \div m = (2 \times 1.60\times10^{-19} \times 50) \div 9.11\times10^{-31}$, giving $v = 4.19\times10^6$ ms$^{-1}$.
(b) Average speed = $\frac{1}{2}(0 + 4.19\times10^6) = 2.095\times10^6$ m s$^{-1}$.
Time = distance $\div$ average speed = $20\times10^{-3} \div 2.095\times10^6 = 9.55\times10^{-9}$ s.
(c) At all points the accelerating force on the electron is the same.

4  Accelerating force in the field = $qE = 1.6\times10^{-19} \times 500 = 8\times10^{-17}$ N.
Acceleration = $F \div m = 8\times10^{-17} \div 3.32\times10^{-27} = 2.41\times10^{10}$ m s$^{-2}$.
If the deuterium ion just clips the extreme edge of the plate, in a time $t$, then
$s = \frac{1}{2}at^2$ (since $u = 0$), so $20\times10^{-3} = \frac{1}{2}\times 2.41\times10^{10} \times t^2$, $t^2 = 1.66\times10^{-12}$ s$^2$ , giving $t = 1.29\times10^{-6}$ s.
Horizontal length $L$ = constant horizontal velocity × time in field
= $7.76\times10^4 \times 1.29\times10^{-6} = 0.10$ m = 10 cm.

5  (a) $Bqv = mv^2 \div r$, so $r = mv \div Bq = (v \div B) \div (q \div m) =( 4\times10^5 \div 0.0025) \div (4.5\times10^8) = 0.36$ m.
(b) The radius is directly proportional to speed. With a smaller speed, the ions will travel in a semicircle of smaller radius and strike the plate further to the left.

6. (a) $F = Bqv = 150\times10^{-3} \times 1.6\times10^{-19} \times 2.5\times10^6 = 6\times10^{-14}$ N.
(b) By Fleming's left hand rule, force is into the plane of the paper.

7 (a) By Fleming's left hand rule the beam direction is into the field at the top and out of the field at the bottom.

(b) Magnitude of mass and velocity remain the same, so magnitude of momentum is unchanged. Direction of velocity is continually changing, so direction of momentum is also continually changing.

(c) Centripetal force = magnetic force, so $Bqv = mv^2 \div r$ which rearranges to give Momentum, $mv = Bqr$.

## Exercise 5.7

1 Synchrotrons are accelerators which keep particles moving in a circle of constant radius. As speed increases the magnetic force must increase to provide the centripetal force. This is done by increasing the magnetic field strength.

2 Protons are charged, so moving protons will experience a magnetic force in a magnetic field. Neutrons are not charged and cannot experience a magnetic force in this way.

3 $m \div m_o = 1 \div \sqrt{(1 - 0.99^2)} = 7.09$. So increase in mass is by a factor of 7.09 or 609%.

4 2 antiprotons and 1 antineutron.

5 Scientists don't really know. Antimatter in our universe is quickly annihilated when it comes into contact with ordinary matter. However, why there are not equal amounts of matter and antimatter in the first place is still a mystery.

6 $_{-1}^{0}e + {}_{1}^{0}p \longrightarrow \gamma + \gamma$

7 $_{19}^{40}K \longrightarrow {}_{18}^{40}Ar + {}_{1}^{0}p$

8 Total mass annihilated = 0.500 + 0.500 = 1 gram = $1 \times 10^{-3}$ kg.
$E = mc^2 = 0.001 \times (3 \times 10^8)^2 = 9 \times 10^{13}$ J.

## Exercise 5.8A

1 (a) A particle that is not made up of smaller particles.

(b) Neutron, pi-meson, proton

(c) Leptons are fundamental particles, hadrons are not (hadrons have structure). Leptons are not affected by the strong nuclear force, hadrons are affected by the strong nuclear force.

(d)(i) Mesons consist of a quark-antiquark doublet. (iii) Baryons are made up of 3 quarks.

2 (a) Leptons – these are the 3 electrons which orbit the nucleus. Baryons – there are 7 of them, they are the 3 protons and 4 neutrons in the nucleus. Mesons – there are none in this atom.

(b) The process is β+ decay. Conservation of charge – the LHS has a total charge of +1. So to conserve charge X must have zero charge. Lepton number – the LHS has a lepton number of zero. On the RHS, the lepton number of the neutron is zero and the lepton number of the positron is −1. So to conserve lepton number, X must have a lepton number of 1. Therefore X is an electron-neutrino.

3 (a)(i) Proton – uud (ii) Neutron – udd.

(b) Proton charge is $+\frac{2}{3}e + \frac{2}{3}e + (-\frac{1}{3}e) = +1e$.
Neutron charge is $+\frac{2}{3}e + (-\frac{1}{3}e) + (-\frac{1}{3}e) = 0$.

(c)(i) According to Quantum Field Theory, all the four fundamental forces can be treated as the exchange of particles. These particles are called gauge bosons and are said to 'mediate' or carry the force involved.

(ii) d → u + W⁻, followed by: W⁻ → e⁻ + $\bar{v}_e$

(iii) Weak nuclear force.

4 (a) (i) A boson is a particle which mediates the force between fundamental particles. (ii) Strong nuclear force: gluons. Weak force: W⁺, W⁰ and W⁻ particles.

(b) Antiproton: anti-up, anti-up, anti-down. Antineutron: anti-up, anti-down, anti-down.

(c) Electrons, unlike protons and neutrons, are not affected by the strong nuclear force.

5

| Particle | Quark structure | Quark charges | | Particle charge | Particle Baryon number |
|---|---|---|---|---|---|
| Proton | uud | u<br>u<br>d | $+\frac{2}{3}e$<br>$+\frac{2}{3}e$<br>$-\frac{1}{3}e$ | +1e | 1 |
| Neutron | udd | u<br>d<br>d | $+\frac{2}{3}e$<br>$-\frac{1}{3}e$<br>$-\frac{1}{3}e$ | 0 | 1 |

6  u $\bar{u}$   charge = 0
   d $\bar{d}$   charge = 0
   u $\bar{d}$   charge = +1 e
   d $\bar{u}$   charge = −1 e

## Exercise 6.1A

1  7.27 cm        2  4.03 cm        3  9.18 cm

## Exercise 6.1B

1  3.56 cm        2  5.80 cm        3  7.72 cm

## Exercise 6.3A

1  Uncertainty in voltage is ± 0.2 V, which is ± 4.1% of 4.9 V.
   Uncertainty in ammeter = 0.1 A, which is ± 33.3% of 0.3 A.
   $R = V \div I$, so total uncertainty = 4.1 + 33.3 = 37.4% of 16.3 Ω, so value = 16.3 ± 6 Ω.

## Exercise 6.3B

1  The re-arranged equation is $1/V = A + kF$. A typical set of results is shown in the table.

| Force / N | Volume of air / cm³ | 1/V / cm⁻³ |
|---|---|---|
| 0 | 5 | 0.2 |
| 1 | 4.44 | 0.23 |
| 2 | 3.98 | 0.25 |
| 3 | 3.62 | 0.28 |
| 4 | 3.31 | 0.30 |
| 5 | 3.05 | 0.33 |

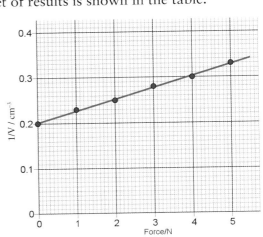

See graph on the right of $1/V$ ($y$-axis) against force. The gradient gives $k \approx 0.025$. The intercept on the $y$-axis gives $A \approx 0.2$.

2

| t / s | I / μA | ln (I / μA) |
|-------|--------|-------------|
| 0 | 100 | 4.6 |
| 10 | 81 | 4.4 |
| 20 | 67 | 4.2 |
| 30 | 55 | 4.0 |
| 40 | 45 | 3.8 |
| 50 | 33 | 3.5 |
| 60 | 27 | 3.3 |
| 70 | 22 | 3.1 |
| 80 | 18 | 2.9 |
| 90 | 15 | 2.7 |
| 100 | 12 | 2.5 |
| 110 | 10 | 2.3 |
| 120 | 8 | 2.1 |

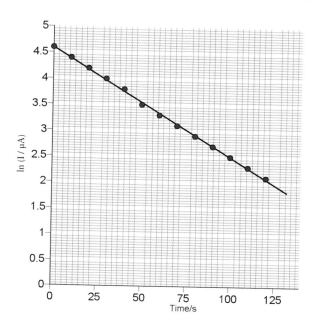

(a) Vertical axis: natural log (base $e$) current, ie ln $I$. Horizontal axis: time, $t$ in seconds.

(b)(c) Gradient = $-1/CR$ = $-0.021$ (from graph) so $CR$ = 47.6 s.
    $C \times 1.0 \times 10^5$ = 47.6, giving $C$ = 476 μF.

3  Results table similar to that shown below:

| Voltage / V | 0 | 0.1 | 0.2 | 0.3 | 0.4 | 0.5 | 0.6 | 0.7 | 0.8 | 0.9 | 1.0 |
|-------------|---|-----|-----|-----|-----|-----|-----|-----|-----|-----|-----|
| Current / mA | 0 | 0 | 0 | 0 | 0 | 2 | 5 | 10 | 30 | 80 | 140 |

(a)

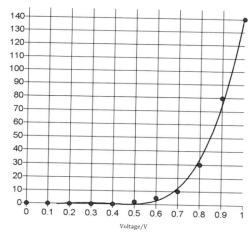

(b) Conduction starts at around 0.5 V (from graph).

(c) To find the resistance:
    at 0.7 V = 0.7 ÷ 0.01 = 70 Ω
    at 0.9 V = 0.9 ÷ 0.08 = 11.2 Ω

(d) Percentage change
    = (70 − 11.2) ÷ 70 = 0.84
    = 84% decrease

4  $T = kM^n$: Taking logarithms we get $\log T = \log k + n \log M$
Compare this to the equation of a straight line, $y = c + mx$. So a graph of $\log M$ ($x$-axis) and $\log T$ ($y$-axis) gives a straight line. The gradient gives $n$. The graph below shows a typical set of results. In this case the gradient (and hence $n$) $\approx 0.5$.

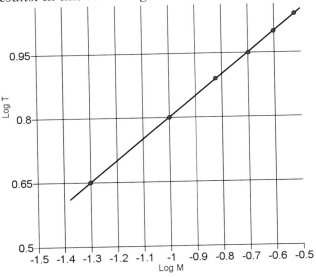

## Exercise 6.3C

1  (a)

| Time / minutes | 0 | 1 | 2 | 3 | 4 | 5 | 6 | 7 | 8 |
|---|---|---|---|---|---|---|---|---|---|
| $\theta$ /°C | 86.0 | 82.7 | 77.1 | 74.3 | 71.0 | 67.9 | 65.0 | 62.3 | 58.9 |
| $(\theta_t - \theta_r)$ /°C | 68.0 | 64.7 | 59.1 | 56.3 | 53.0 | 49.9 | 47.0 | 44.3 | 40.9 |
| $\ln(\theta_t - \theta_r)$ | 4.22 | 4.17 | 4.08 | 4.03 | 3.97 | 3.91 | 3.85 | 3.79 | 3.71 |

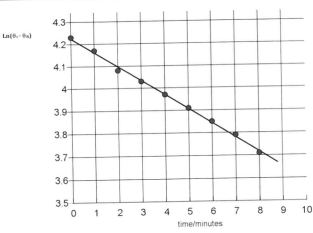

(b) $k = 0.06$ °C min$^{-1}$

(c) $\ln A = 4.22$, so $A = 68$ °C. Within the limits of uncertainty it is difference between the staring temperature of the liquid and room temperature.

2  (a) The count rate is corrected for background by subtracting 2 counts per second from measured count rate.

| $x$ / cm | 2 | 3 | 4 | 5 |
|---|---|---|---|---|
| $1/x^2$ / cm² | 0.25 | 0.11 | 0.06 | 0.04 |
| Corrected count rate / s⁻¹ | 150 | 67 | 38 | 24 |

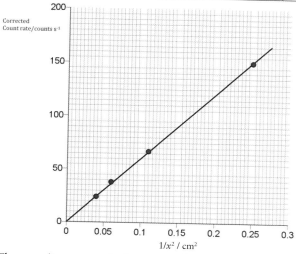

(b) The gradient equals $k = 603$ (from graph).

(c) The estimated count rate $C$ at 1 cm $= k \div x^2 = 603 \div 1^2 = 603$ counts s⁻¹.

3  (a) Rearranged equation is $T^2H = \dfrac{2\pi^2 k^2}{g} + \dfrac{2\pi^2 H^2}{g}$  ($y = c + mx$)

(b) Completed table as below:

| $H$ / m | $10T$ / s | $H^2$ / m² | $T$ / s | $T^2$ / s² | $T^2H$ / ms² |
|---|---|---|---|---|---|
| 0.10 | 45.1 | 0.010 | 4.51 | 20.34 | 2.03 |
| 0.15 | 37.0 | 0.023 | 3.70 | 13.69 | 2.05 |
| 0.20 | 32.5 | 0.040 | 3.23 | 10.43 | 2.09 |
| 0.25 | 29.2 | 0.063 | 2.92 | 8.53 | 2.13 |
| 0.30 | 27.0 | 0.090 | 2.70 | 7.29 | 2.19 |

(c)

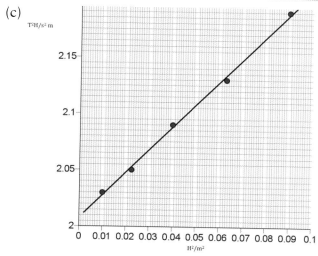

From graph, gradient $= \dfrac{2\pi^2}{g} = 2.0$, giving $g = \dfrac{2\pi^2}{2} = 9.86$ m s⁻²

4 (a)

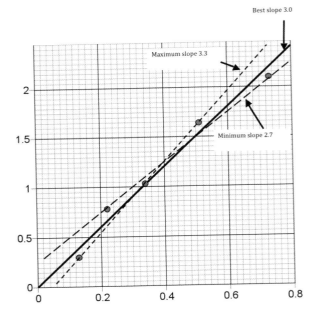

(b) Best value for the gradient = 3.0.

(c) The maximum gradient line and minimum gradient are shown on the graph above. Maximum value for the gradient = 3.3, and minimum value for the gradient = 2.7.

(d) $E = \dfrac{16\pi^2 \times 0.5}{3\times 10^{-2} \times (0.5\times 10^{-3})^2} \times \dfrac{1}{\text{gradient}} = 3.51\times 10^9$ Pa.

(e) To find the overall uncertainty determine the percentage uncertainty for each quantity and add them. The gradient = 3.0 ±0.3, equal to an uncertainty of 10%. The uncertainty in the mass, $M$, is 1%. The uncertainty in $b$ is 0.3%. The uncertainty in $d$ is 2%, but since $d$ is squared the uncertainty is 4%. So the overall uncertainty is 10 + 1 + 0.3 + 4 = 15.3%. The absolute uncertainty is 15.3% of $3.51\times 10^9$ = $0.54\times 10^9$. So the final value for Young's modulus $E$ is written as $E = (3.51 \pm 0.54)\times 10^9$ Pa.

## Exercise 7.1

1  (a) 5          (b) 3          (c) 5          (d) 4          (e) 4

2  (a) 645.6    (b) 0          (c) 1700      (d) 1.2

3  (a) $1.36\times 10^4$          (b) $3.0\times 10^8$          (c) $1.9\times 10^{-5}$

4  (a) 25        (b) –10        (c) 2

5  3 significant figures

6  $\sqrt{E}$ or $E^{½}$ / keV$^{½}$

7  n = 2 gives 1/λ = $1.097\times 10^7$ (1 – 1/22) gives λ = $1.2154\times 10^{-7}$ m = 121.5 nm
   n = 3  gives 1/λ = $1.097\times 10^7$ (1 – 1/32) gives λ = $1.0255\times 10^{-7}$ m = 102.5 nm
   n = 4 gives 1/λ = $1.097\times 10^7$ (1 – 1/42) gives λ = $0.9723\times 10^{-7}$ m = 97.23 nm

## Exercise 7.2

1  (a) y-axis: $n$ the refractive index.
        x-axis: $1/\lambda^2$

(b)
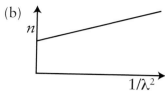

(c) $A$ = intercept on $y$-axis and $B$ is the gradient of the straight line.

2  (a) $L = v/4f$

   (b) $L$ ($y$-axis) against $1/f$ ($x$-axis)

   (c) Gradient equals $v/4$

3  (a) $R = R_0 + R_0\alpha\theta$

   (b)
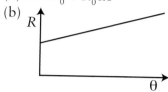

   (c) $R_o$ is the intercept on the $y$-axis and $\alpha$ is equal to the gradient ÷ intercept.

4  (a) Take natural logs of each side to give $\ln I = \ln I_0 - \mu x$. Plot $\ln I$ on the $y$-axis and $x$ on the $x$-axis.

   (b)
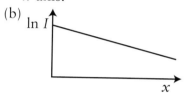

   (c) $\mu$ = negative of the gradient

## Exercise 7.3

1  (a) Newton's second law: The acceleration of an object is inversely proportional to its mass, directly proportional to the resultant force and takes place in the same direction as the unbalanced force.

   (b) Take the up direction as positive. The tension in the string connecting the two masses is $T$. The mass $m_1$ will accelerate upwards with an acceleration $+a$ and the mass $m_2$ will have a downwards acceleration $-a$. Applying Newton's second law to each mass we have: $T - m_1g = + m_1a$ and $T - m_2g = -m_2a$ Therefore: $T = m_1g = + m_1a$ Substituting for $T$ we have $m_1a + m_1g - m_2g = -m_2a$. This finally gives: $a = g(m_2 - m_1) \div (m_1 + m_2)$

   (c) (i) Newton's first law: If a body is at rest, it will remain at rest unless a resultant force acts on the object. If the body is moving in a straight line with constant speed, it will continue to move in this way unless a resultant force acts on it.

   (ii) If the upper plate is positive then the electric force $F_{el}$ is upwards. To balance the this the magnetic force $F_{mag}$ must be downwards. The direction of the magnetic field is obtained using Fleming's left hand rule. The direction is into the page.

   (iii) $F_{el} = qE$ ($E$ is the electric force per unit charge), $F_{mag} = Bqv$ ($v$ is the velocity of the ion so therefore: $qE = Bqv$, giving $v = E \div B$.

2  (a) Horizontal component = $u \cos \theta$, vertical component = $u \sin \theta$.

(b) Horizontal distance $x = (u \cos \theta)t$.

Vertical distance (using $s = ut + \frac{1}{2} at^2$) is $y = (u \sin \theta)t + \frac{1}{2}gt^2$

(c) $t = x \div u \cos \theta$. Substituting into the expression for $y$ gives: $y = x \cdot \dfrac{u \sin \theta}{u \cos \theta} + \dfrac{gx^2}{2u^2 \cos^2 \theta}$

This can be rearranged to give: $y = \dfrac{g}{2u^2 \cos^2 \theta} \cdot x^2 + \dfrac{u \sin \theta}{u \cos \theta} \cdot x$, which is the equation of a parabola.

(d) The energy is 300 eV = $300 \times 1.6 \times 10^{-19} = 4.8 \times 10^{-17}$ J.

Using $E_k = \frac{1}{2}m_e v^2$ gives $v = 1.03 \times 10^7$ m s$^{-1}$.

Time to travel 15 cm = $0.15 \div 1.03 \times 10^7 = 1.46 \times 10^{-8}$ s.

Vertical deflection in this time is needed using $s = ut + \frac{1}{2}at^2$.

Vertical force $F = eE = 1.6 \times 10^{-19} \times E$. $E = V \div d = 100 \div 0.1 = 1.0 \times 10^3$ V m$^{-1}$.

Vertical acceleration $= F \div m = (1.0 \times 10^3 \times 1.6 \times 10^{-19}) \div 9.1 \times 10^{-31} = 1.76 \times 10^{14}$ m s$^{-2}$.

Vertical deflection $= \frac{1}{2} \times 1.76 \times 10^{14} \times (1.46 \times 10^{-8})^2 = 1.88$ cm.

This means the electrons will pass out without colliding with the metal plates.

If the deflection had been 5 cm or more they would have collided.